B

Scientific
PROGRAMMING
IN
BUSINESS
AND INDUSTRY

NEW YORK · JOHN WILEY & SONS, INC.

London

Scientific

Programming

in

Business

and Industry

Andrew Vazsonyi

Ramo-Wooldridge, a Division of the Thompson
Ramo-Wooldridge Corp.

THIRD PRINTING, JUNE, 1963

Library of Congress Catalog Card Number: 58-10813

Printed in the United States of America

PREFACE

A short while ago one of the leading business magazines wrote that "a manager might be defined as a man who wants to navigate his course of business as effectively and predictably as he can. He maneuvers not so much by feel as by instruments which become more numerous and more complex year after year. The device of *linear programming* materialized only a few years ago. . . ."

We can visualize Mr. Smith, Executive Vice President of a large corporation, raising his eyebrows at this last sentence. Later, in other business magazines, he runs across statements that business decisions are being made by mathematics, or that long-haired Ph.D's are taking part in business management. Mr. Smith is exposed repeatedly to such irritating remarks, and finally he calls in his bright young assistant, George, and consults him. It so happens that George has recently attended a number of conferences where such subjects as linear programming, statistical decision theory, and operations research were discussed. In fact, he is sold on them and suggests to Mr. Smith that they should do something about them. So Mr. Smith directs George to take a few months off and develop a strategy for the corporation to capitalize on these new scientific managerial methods.

However, George feels that he is not a scientist and that his mathematics is not up to dealing with these new methods. He suggests that Paul (who is quite a mathematician), from Quality Control, should help him. What we have now is a two-man committee with the assignment of charting a course of action for the corporation. George and Paul concur that one of the things they must do is to really educate themselves in the new methods. Both of them attend some meetings and read a few selected papers, but they feel that this is not enough. What they need is a book which treats some of these scientific methods from the point of view of the businessman. What book should they study?

I suggest to George and Paul that they study my book; it is written for them. It is written for the businessman, manager, and controller, for the marketing, production, and financial executive, and for the student of business who is willing to spend the time to assimilate the meaning and potentialities of these new scientific business tools. Specifically, this book is written for management personnel without advanced academic training in mathematics or science.

Some years ago when I started work in this field, I made the assumption that linear programming and, more generally, scientific programming are not something for an initiated few, but are subjects that can be made accessible to all. Let the condition be added that they are accessible only to those who are willing to spend a considerable amount of time on the subject, because scientific programming cannot be grasped in a three-page memorandum, or cannot be understood during an after-dinner discussion.

Today, I do not consider it an assumption any more that scientific programming can be explained to the typical businessman. I feel that this has been proven. There are dozens of businessmen in this country commanding a good knowledge of the subject. I have been fortunate in receiving numerous helpful comments and criticism from businessmen on the various lectures and articles I had prepared on the subject. These comments were not only gratifying but enabled me to sharpen considerably the method of presentation I have used heretofore. That is the reason that I decided to write this book. I intend to demonstrate to the business world that scientific programming is not only useful but that it is also understandable.

The method of presentation in this book is different from that of other mathematical books you might have come across. The reason is simple: This is not a book on mathematics; it is a book on business management. There are a lot of equations in the book, but this should not mislead the reader; the equations are there because they are the best way to describe the particular business problem.

Mathematics is a subject that is supposed to be rigorous; everything is supposed to be proven. Here is a warning for the purist: there is not a single "proof" in this book, at least no "proof" that a mathematician would accept as such. For those who are interested in rigor and proof, other works in the field are recommended. Instead of "proving" theorems, a great deal of effort is spent in presenting arguments so that they make sense. In some instances, it is explained how *not* to solve a problem. It is explained why the problem is solved as it is presented, and why in a certain sense the solution is an inevitable outcome of extending "common sense."

This sort of presentation takes many pages, and no attempt is made to abbreviate. This book could have been written to take up, say, only half as many pages, but it would not have been the same book. In a "popularizing" type of work, it is false economy to save on length and put the burden on the reader. The author should balance the effort the readers need to expend to understand the subject against the effort of developing the material.

The book opens with Part I, The Fundamentals. Chapter 1 starts with a description of what mathematical programming is. Three major business areas follow, describing applications of mathematical programming. The last part of the chapter describes certain business fields where mathematical methods other than mathematical programming have been used. This is done so that the reader will understand that there are mathematical methods other than programming to be used in business. Chapter 1 ends with a brief description of the all-important concept of the mathematical model.

Chapter 2 describes transportation allocation by linear programming, perhaps the most successful application of this technique yet. The main presentation does not use mathematical equations It is possible to avoid equations in the transportation problem because the mathematics of the problem does not necessarily require equations. This is the reason why I selected the transportation problem as a case study in mathematical reasoning. The chapter aims to build up confidence in mathematical reasoning, and to show that mathematics is an extension of common sense and not a mysterious luxury. As far as our friends George and Paul are concerned, I suspect that Paul will find the going a little bit slow as he knows quite a bit of mathematics. On the other hand, George will probably be happy because he will be able to see what mathematical programming can do.

Chapter 3 goes through a series of further illustrations of what scientific programming can do. It also goes one step beyond, as it shows how to formulate these problems in the form of mathematical equations. George might get a little bit unhappy here as he might feel that the illustrations are not quite realistic. On the other hand, Paul will be delighted as he will see how mathematics can be useful in solving business problems.

Part II, Mathematical Programming, is more difficult than Part I. This is the part that described how to compute solutions to mathematical programming problems. Chapter 4 describes the simplex method, which is the principal computational technique of linear programming. Paul will be in his element here; things are getting quite involved. In fact, he will probably help George at some of the more subtle points.

Chapter 5 describes the dual theorem, the important technique that gives information on pricing. Chapter 6 is a visual representation of linear programming and contains some unusual illustrations to make things easier. Chapters 7 and 8, convex and dynamic programming, refer to some subject matters that are quite new, even in this new field of mathematical programming. Chapter 9 contains the elements of the theory of games—a field that has received considerable publicity during the last few years.

A note of caution here: Chapters 5–9 are not easy to study. I expect that George will have to rely on some of the advice given by Paul. In fact, George might feel that he should skip some of the text. I will not be offended as long as he concentrates on the business aspects of the text.

Part III discusses production and inventory control. This is a field where methods are still tentative, and therefore the presentation is to be considered more as a progress report than as an account of accomplishments. Chapter 10 describes some statistical methods that can be, and have been, applied to the control of inventories. This topic usually would not be called programming, though perhaps it could be called programming under uncertainty. I have made a special effort here to develop the necessary background in statistics with the aid of some illustrative inventory control problems, instead of assuming a knowledge of statistics. Chapter 10 ends with a reference to the statistical theory of decisions, a field of science that offers some important possibilities for managerial decision making.

The beginning of Chapter 10 is quite easy. Paul might even be bored. Later, the going gets tough and some of the mathematics gets so involved that George should not try to follow details. I trust, though, that with the aid of Paul it will be possible for him to follow the business aspects of the theory.

Chapter 11 is a short one. It deals with the problem of scheduling production on assembly lines. Another short chapter, Chapter 12, deals with the problem of scheduling job-shop-type production. Finally Chapter 13 concludes the book by presenting a general mathematical model of production scheduling.

The various scheduling models presented in Part III are new and only partially tested in actual industrial operations. Here, we are dealing primarily with an unverified theory. However, I believe George and Paul will benefit by working through this material. If they feel a certain amount of critical skepticism in connection with the theory, I will not be unduly disturbed. The text here is again not easy to assimilate. I expect that they will both have to work pretty hard to get through these last few chapters.

A few words now on what to expect from studying this book: The reader cannot expect to become an expert in the field of scientific programming; in fact, he will not be very efficient even in the computational techniques. This book is neither a treatise on the subject, covering all the fine points, nor a series of recipes that tell him exactly how to make the computations. What he *can* expect to get is a thorough understanding of what scientific programming is and what it means to the business world.

He will be able to establish an understanding with experts; he will be able to appraise whether in his own business scientific programming can help him, and, more specifically, whether it will be a good investment for him to consult an expert with whom to discuss his problems. He will be able to carry out computations for illustrative cases; he will be able to follow some of the more advanced literature. Furthermore, he will be able to study some of the other mathematical techniques that are being developed for the business world

How long will it take the reader to study this book and obtain these benefits? This depends mostly on the type of mind he has. If mathematical thinking comes easily to him, perhaps a couple of months will do. Otherwise, the going will be slower. In my course work, I cover a good part of the text in a six month period of forty five hours of lecturing.

Here is a final note: the scientific method is becoming an important instrument for the business world. It is helping, and it will help even more in the future, to solve some problems, but it will never be a complete substitute for common sense, intuition good judgment, and experience. These will always play a dominant role in human actions. Scientific methodology will not provide executives with pat answers, nor will it make their jobs easier. In fact, their jobs will be more difficult, because real talent will be more and more directed to the art of dealing effectively with the truly intangible affairs of the business world.

ANDREW VAZSONYI

Philadelphia, Pennsylvania
April 1958

Acknowledgments

I am indebted mainly to the research workers in the field of scientific programming and management sciences, without whose creative contributions this book could never have been written. I have borrowed freely from all the works I have studied, and find it hard to pinpoint the origin of these various fragments. Certainly, there are many omissions in this book. If I have missed some important contributions to the field, it was unintentional.

In the text I have used, primarily, the following four publications:

A. Charnes, W. W. Cooper, and A. Henderson, *An Introduction to Linear Programming*, John Wiley & Sons, New York, 1953.

R. Dorfman, *Application of Linear Programming to the Theory of the Firm*, University of California Press, 1951.

A. Henderson, and R. Schlaifer, "Mathematical Programming: Better Information for Better Decision Making," *Harvard Business Review*, May-June 1954.

G. H. Symonds, *Linear Programming: The Solution of Refinery Problems*, Esso Standard Oil Company, New York, 1955.

I wish to take this opportunity to express my gratitude to three of my colleagues who through their works and through many verbal discussions have greatly encouraged me in writing this book. They are George B. Dantzig of The RAND Corporation, William W. Cooper of Carnegie Institute of Technology, and Abraham Charnes of Purdue University.

I also wish to acknowledge my indebtedness to Ralph A. Tiemann of Convair, Pomona Division of General Dynamics Corporation, and Jack K. Weinstock of The Ramo-Wooldridge Corporation, who by a careful review of the complete manuscript called my attention to numerous errors and also gave me valuable advice in improving the readability of the text.   Credit is also due to the other reviewers whose comments have been welcome.   Finally I wish to acknowledge my indebtedness to Ramo-Wooldridge for providing me with an environment that made it possible to write this book.

CONTENTS

PART I. THE FUNDAMENTALS

Chapter 1   The Use of Mathematical Models in Business.   3

1 WHAT IS SCIENTIFIC PROGRAMMING? 3
2 TRANSPORTATION ALLOCATION: WHERE TO SHIP 4
3 ALLOCATION OF RAW MATERIALS AND PRODUCTION FACILITIES 5
4 SCIENTIFIC PROGRAMMING IN THE OIL INDUSTRY 6
5 METHODS OF PRODUCTION AND INVENTORY CONTROL 6
6 A SCHEDULING SYSTEM IN AGRICULTURE 8
7 EQUIPMENT REQUIREMENTS FOR DIAL TELEPHONES 8
8 TRAFFIC DELAYS AT TOLL BOOTHS 9
9 SERVICING OF AUTOMATIC MACHINES 10
10 STATISTICAL SAMPLING IN ACCOUNTING AND PRODUCTION 11
11 REGRESSION ANALYSIS IN FINANCIAL PLANNING 12
12 THE MAINTENANCE OF RAILROADS 13
13 MONTE CARLO METHOD OR THE SIMULATION OF BUSINESS ENTERPRISES 14
14 THE EFFECT OF ADVERTISING ON SALES 15
15 APPLICATIONS OF THE THEORY OF VALUE TO QUALITY CONTROL 17
16 THE CONCEPT OF MATHEMATICAL MODELS 17

xiii

Chapter 2   Transportation Allocation by Linear Programming . .   20

   1   STATEMENT OF THE PROBLEM   20
   2   TWO FACTORIES AND TWO WAREHOUSES   22
   3   TWO FACTORIES AND THREE WAREHOUSES   26
   4   METHOD OF SOLVING THE TRANSPORTATION PROBLEM   29
   5   ALTERNATE OPTIMUM SOLUTIONS   35
   6   SENSITIVITY ANALYSIS   38
   7   COMBINED TRANSPORTATION AND PRODUCTION ALLOCATION   41
   8   DEGENERACY   46
   9   MATHEMATICAL FORMULATION OF THE TRANSPORTATION PROBLEM   47

Chapter 3   Illustrations of Mathematical Programming   53

   1   ALLOCATION OF PRODUCTION FACILITIES WHEN ALTERNATE MACHINE ROUTING IS POSSIBLE   53
   2   ALLOCATION OF LAND, CAPITAL, AND LABOR FOR A FARMING ENTERPRISE   58
   3   ALLOCATION OF PRODUCTION FACILITIES WHEN PRODUCTS MAY BE MANUFACTURED ON ALTERNATE MACHINES   61
   4   ALLOCATION OF RAW MATERIALS TO MATCH MARKET REQUIREMENTS   65
   5   ALLOCATION OF TRANSPORTATION FACILITIES TO ALTERNATE ROUTING   67
   6   AN EXERCISE IN FUEL OIL BLENDING   69
   7   BLENDING OF CONSTITUENTS: WHAT AND HOW TO PRODUCE   72
   8   A STUDY OF AN OIL CORPORATION   76
   9   A PROBLEM IN PRODUCTION AND INVENTORY CONTROL   79
  10   A PROBLEM RELATED TO THE ATTRITION OF PRODUCTION FACILITIES   87
  11   WHAT TO PRODUCE IN FACE OF COMPETITION: AN APPLICATION OF THE THEORY OF GAMES   89
  12   THE GENERAL MATHEMATICAL FORMULATION OF THE PROBLEM OF LINEAR PROGRAMMING   92

PART II.   MATHEMATICAL PROGRAMMING

Chapter 4   The Simplex Method of Linear Programming   99

   1   STATEMENT OF THE PROBLEM.   HOW NOT TO SOLVE IT   99

Contents

2 THE FUNDAMENTAL THEOREM OF LINEAR PROGRAMMING
101

3 TECHNIQUE OF MODIFYING A SOLUTION   103

4 TECHNIQUE OF MODIFYING A FAMILY OF SOLUTIONS   107

5 SYMBOLIC FORMULATION OF MODIFICATION PRINCIPLE   111

6 THE SIMPLEX TRANSFORMATION   113

7 TECHNIQUE OF COMPUTING THE FIRST FAMILY OF SOLUTIONS
120

8 RECAPITULATION OF THE SIMPLEX METHOD   125

9 DEGENERACY   132

10 CONCLUDING REMARKS   144

Chapter 5   The Dual Theorem of Linear Programming   146

1 PRICE IMPUTATIONS: A NEW WAY OF LOOKING AT THE
PROBLEM   146

2 THE DUAL PROBLEM   150

3 GENERAL STATEMENT OF THE DUAL THEOREM   152

4 APPLICATION TO TRANSPORTATION ALLOCATION   154

5 THE GENERALIZED TRANSPORTATION ALLOCATION PROBLEM
161

Chapter 6   The Geometry of Linear Programming   171

1 THE REQUIREMENT SPACE   171

2 THE SOLUTION SPACE   181

3 THE GRAVITY SPACE   188

Chapter 7   Convex Programming   194

1 WHAT IS CONVEX PROGRAMMING   194

2 GENERAL STATEMENT OF THE PROBLEM OF CONVEX PRO-
GRAMMING   198

3 THE PROBLEM OF THE DISTRIBUTION OF EFFORT   202

4 THE STUDY OF AN OIL CORPORATION   206

5 A PROBLEM IN PRODUCTION AND INVENTORY CONTROL   213

Chapter 8   Dynamic Programming   219

1 DISTRIBUTION OF SALES EFFORT BETWEEN VARIOUS MAR-
KETING AREAS   219

2 A WAREHOUSING PROBLEM   227

3 A PROBLEM IN PRODUCTION AND INVENTORY CONTROL   238

4 A PROBLEM RELATED TO STABLE EMPLOYMENT   244

5 A PROBLEM RELATED TO ATTRITION OF PRODUCTION FACILI-
   TIES 250

6 GENERAL DESCRIPTION OF DYNAMIC PROGRAMMING PROB-
   LEMS 252

Chapter 9 The Elements of the Theory of Games 255

1 WHAT IS A TWO-PERSON ZERO-SUM GAME? 255
2 THE STRATEGY OF THE OPPONENT 263
3 A FOUR BY FIVE TWO-PERSON RECTANGULAR GAME 270
4 THE m BY n RECTANGULAR GAME 279
5 COMPUTATION OF OPTIMUM STRATEGIES 281
6 "PROOF" OF THE MINIMAX THEOREM 283

PART III. PROGRAMMING IN PRODUCTION AND INVENTORY CONTROL

Chapter 10 Statistical Inventory Control 287

1   PROTECTION AGAINST UNCERTAINTY 287
2   THE NORMAL DISTRIBUTION 294
3   THE POISSON DISTRIBUTION 300
4   THE RECTANGULAR DISTRIBUTION 302
5   PROTECTION AGAINST LOSS OF BUSINESS 304
6   THE IMPUTED COST OF A SHORTAGE; LOSS FUNCTIONS 307
7   OPTIMUM INVENTORY RULE FOR A NAVAL PROBLEM 315
8   OPTIMUM INVENTORY RULES FOR SINGLE-STAGE PROBLEMS
    320
9   OPTIMUM INVENTORY RULES FOR MANY-STAGE PROBLEMS
    328
10 THE TWO-BIN SYSTEM OF INVENTORY CONTROL 330
11 CYCLIC INVENTORY CONTROL SYSTEMS 338
12 INVENTORY ORDERING FUNCTIONS; PREDICTORS; RETRO-
    SPECTIVE SIMULATION 345
13 THE S-s RULE OF INVENTORY CONTROL 353
14 ORDERING RULES FOR THE CONTROL OF LARGE NUMBERS OF
    PARTS 360
15 EMPLOYMENT AND PRODUCTION STABILIZATION THROUGH
    INVENTORY CONTROL 362
16 PRODUCTION SMOOTHING THROUGH INVENTORY CONTROL
    368
17 STATISTICAL DECISION THEORY AND METHODS OF INVENTORY
    CONTROL 372

Contents

Chapter 11   Assembly Line Flow Scheduling 376

     1   THE CONCEPT OF SCHEDULING FUNCTIONS   376
     2   MANPOWER REQUIREMENTS FOR A SINGLE ASSEMBLY LINE 386
     3   MULTIPLE ASSEMBLY LINE PRODUCTION   395
     4   MATHEMATICAL MODEL OF ASSEMBLY LINE PRODUCTION 403

Chapter 12   Machine Shop Scheduling 410

     1   A TWO-STAGE PROBLEM   410
     2   MORE GENERAL FORMULATION OF THE PROBLEM   415
     3   THE PROBLEM OF SHOP LOADING   418

Chapter 13   A Mathematical Model of Production Scheduling . . 429

     1   THE PROBLEM OF PARTS LISTING; THE GOZINTO THEOREM 429
     2   PRODUCTION ON MANY ASSEMBLY LINES   439
     3   SCHEDULING FROM THE POINT OF VIEW OF DECISION THEORY 452
     4   SCHEDULING LABOR, INVENTORIES, COSTS, AND RECEIPTS 464

Contents

Chapter 11 Assembly Line Flow Scheduling 379

Chapter 12 Machine Shop Scheduling

MATHEMATICAL SYMBOLS

$a = b$	a is equal to b	
$a < b$	a is less than b	
$a \leq b$	a is equal to or less than b	
$a > b$	a is greater than b	
$a \geq b$	a is equal to or greater than b	
$+$	plus (or positive)	
$-$	minus (or negative)	
$\pm$	plus or minus	
$\times$ or $\cdot$	multiplied by	
$=$	equals	
$\neq$	does not equal	
$\cong$	approximately equal to	
$\sim$	similar to	
x_1	x sub one	
x_n	x sub n	
$\left.\begin{matrix} f(x) \\ g(x) \end{matrix}\right\}$	functions of x	
Σ	summation of	
$\displaystyle\sum_1^n$	summation of terms $1 + 2 + \cdots + n$	
$x_{2,5}$	double index denotes the fifth number in the second row	
$x_{i,j}$	double index denotes the jth number in the ith row	

A	α	alpha
B	β	beta
Γ	γ	gamma
Δ	δ	delta
E	ϵ	epsilon
Z	ζ	zeta
H	η	eta
Θ	θ	theta
I	ι	iota
K	κ	kappa
Λ	λ	lambda
M	μ	mu
N	ν	nu
Ξ	ξ	xi
O	o	omicron
Π	π	pi
P	ρ	rho
Σ	σ	sigma
T	τ	tau
Υ	υ	upsilon
Φ	φ	phi
X	χ	chi
Ψ	ψ	psi
Ω	ω	omega

PART I

THE FUNDAMENTALS

CHAPTER 1

THE USE
OF MATHEMATICAL MODELS
IN BUSINESS

1. WHAT IS SCIENTIFIC PROGRAMMING?

Scientific programming is a particular technique for making business decisions. We have to make decisions only when we have various alternate courses of action available and would like to know which is the best of these alternate possible actions; the necessity of selecting the best action constitutes a decision problem.

Let us consider three examples.

(a) The traffic manager of a large manufacturing firm would have no problem if each group of the firm's customers were close to a particular production plant, and if these customers could be supplied best from these nearby factories. However, this would be a most unusual circumstance. Variations in production costs and customer demands compel the traffic manager to ship from various factories to various consumer areas without regard to distance. The problem he is faced with is how to allocate the production capacity of the various factories to the various consumer areas.

(b) If a production manager had a large surplus of machines and labor, he would have no trouble deciding what machine to use to produce what part. In practice, however, he seldom has a surplus and must decide how to assign his production facilities to the products to be manufactured.

(c) If the manager of an oil refinery had unlimited supplies of crudes, production facilities, storage tanks, etc., he would have to do very little planning. However, how often does a situation like this occur?

In all these examples the managers have something in common: they must decide how to allocate limited resources to reach certain goals, and how to do this in the best possible way. The "best" way may be the cheapest way or the way that yields the highest profit. *The allocation of limited means in order to reach specific goals in the best fashion* is roughly the definition of scientific programming.

It is, of course, impossible to get too much information out of such a broad definition as the one given. The fact of the matter is that the concept of scientific programming is not sufficiently crystallized to give a precise definition. Different workers in the field classify techniques in different ways. We can explain our concept of scientific programming best by surveying the most important areas where scientific programming can be used. On the other hand, the concept of linear programming is quite precise, and after the required mathematics is developed we will give the definition of linear programming (Chapter 3).

2. TRANSPORTATION ALLOCATION: WHERE TO SHIP

The problem of the traffic manager, where to ship from which factory, is one of the oldest problems that has been successfully handled by scientific programming. This problem is referred to as the transportation allocation problem.

It is reported in the paper by Henderson and Schlaifer* that the Heinz Corporation is using scientific programming extensively. The H. J. Heinz Company has half a dozen plants scattered across the United States from New Jersey to California, and it distributes catsup from about 70 warehouses located in all parts of the country. Production capacity in the west is higher than requirements, and therefore large shipments have to be made to the east. Management makes a decision every month to select the cheapest possible traffic pattern. This is a straightforward transportation problem, and the solution is being computed now with scientific programming.

This is, however, only a small part of the problem. Suppose that one of the warehouses is used only to a small extent. How would the profit structure change if this warehouse were closed down? On the other hand, suppose one of the warehouses is a bottleneck and is full most of the time. Should this warehouse be enlarged, or should another warehouse be built in a more opportune location, or should

---

* See Acknowledgments, p. xi.

a warehouse be rented? Perhaps an alternate routing policy would increase the cost of transportation, but the cost would still be below the cost of establishing a new warehouse.

Suppose there is a change in freight costs on certain routes. This might not only affect costs on particular routes, but it might also require reallocation of the overall traffic pattern. How would this affect the total transportation costs?

All these are problems of allocation and can be handled by scientific programming.

Similarly, the manager can ask other questions: Where should the factories be located? How much should each factory produce? What factory should be shut down, and which one should work overtime?

It is, of course, irrelevant whether the manager must deal with surface, water, or air transportation. The principles he uses will be the same. For example, Professor Merrill M. Flood* made a comprehensive study of the best traffic pattern for the oil tankers of the United States Navy using linear programming, and we will see later in this book similar application to air transportation.

3. ALLOCATION OF RAW MATERIALS AND PRODUCTION FACILITIES

Let us concentrate now on some of the allocation problems that might possibly face the manager of a manufacturing plant. He may have the problem that his raw materials are limited in quantity; he has to allocate them to products so that maximum profit results. His decision may be complicated by the fact that discounts on products change the profit margin; also, he cannot sell more than there is a market for. He might have to contend with some policy decisions, for example, certain customers may have to be supplied with products not so much for profits as for good will. Problems of this type can be handled by scientific programming.

Another problem the manager might face is determining what production facilities he should have. Does he have too many machines or too few? What is his profit loss due to inadequate facilities? Should he go on overtime or establish a night shift? Can he rearrange his machines and route the products through his factory so that he can produce more, or reroute so that his profit goes up? Maximum volume does not necessarily mean maximum profit.

* "Applications of Transportation Theory to Scheduling a Military Tanker Fleet," *Journal of the Operations Research Society of America*, Vol. 2, No. 2, May, 1954.

We have talked so far in terms of a manufacturing firm. Let us consider, however, a farmer. His production facilities such as land, machinery, and labor are limited too. He faces decisions on what crops to grow, how much land to lease, etc.

It is obvious, then, that production is a broad field, where programming can make important contributions in managerial decision making.

4. SCIENTIFIC PROGRAMMING IN THE OIL INDUSTRY

This is an industry where scientific programming is probably used more than anywhere else, as there are many refineries which need programming in one form or another. The reason for this is not hard to find. For instance, refineries face complex decisions on how to blend various constituents into different end products. There are such a vast number of possibilities that it is very difficult to determine the most profitable policy. Furthermore, changes in market requirements make it necessary to modify blending policies as time goes on. The various requirements imposed on end products, such as octane number and the Reid vapor pressure, make these decisions quite complicated.

Scientific programming can give assistance in such problems and even in more complicated ones. Such things as purchasing policies and the costs of maintaining good customer relations can be assessed. The loss of profit imposed by the limited capacities of refinery equipment can be determined, and improvement in profit expected from new facilities can be evaluated. The problem of recycling in multistage processes can be studied quantitatively; the overall design of a complete refinery can be explored in relation to the potential market.

Often it is impossible to select the best course of action on the basis of current market conditions since it is expected that competitive action will significantly change conditions. There have been some attempts to make decisions in such cases on the basis of the *theory of games*. As you will see, game theoretical problems can be solved with the aid of scientific programming and, therefore, decisions including the behavior of competitors can be made.

5. METHODS OF PRODUCTION AND INVENTORY CONTROL

This is a field where simple mathematics has been used for many years. Manufacturers or department stores must decide when to purchase an article and in what quantity. Frequent orders lead to low inventories, but ordering costs go high. On the other hand, ordering once in ten years leads to high inventory and obsolescence. The method of obtaining the "economic lot size" is well known and can be found in handbooks.

However, there are some important points ignored in the conventional analysis: it is usually assumed that the demand is known and, also, that the lead time from ordering to receipt is a fixed time delay. Now, neither of these is true in general, and, therefore, some sort of cushion to protect the buyer from runouts is required. How large should this cushion be? Should it be so large that he never runs out of stock? He can never be quite sure of this, even with very large inventories.

During the last few years, progress on this problem has been made. The buyer starts by admitting that in the long run there is always a chance of running out of stock. Maybe he allows himself to run out of stock once a year. Such a formulation of the problem permits the development of a statistical theory. When a certain dollar loss is assigned to a shortage, it is possible to compute the long-run cost of any particular policy, such as that of keeping a certain protective level of stock. It is then possible to determine the best ordering quantity, one which leads to the lowest cost.

In a manufacturing plant, the problem is even more complicated. There are cost of setup time, run time, and inventory, all leading again to the optimum lot size concept. However, the conventional optimum lot size concept, as described in the handbooks of production, is often inadequate to deal with real life situations, and special techniques must be devised.*

Another major problem of today is the maintenance of steady employment. A manager cannot hire and fire at will, even if he is willing to pay the expenses involved. Some recent studies focus on these problems of employment and develop methods of stabilizing the labor force.† In one particular study, the best policy was computed by balancing seasonal variations in demand against variations in employment.‡

* A. Vazsonyi, "Economic Lot Size Formulas in Manufacturing," *Journal of the Operations Research Society of America*, Vol. 5, No. 1, February, 1957. See also A. Vazsonyi, "Operations Research in Production Control," *Journal of the Operations Research Society of America*, Vol. 4, No. 1, February, 1956.

† W. Karush and A. Vazsonyi, "Mathematical Programming and Service Scheduling," *Management Science*, Vol. 3, No. 2, January, 1957, p. 140.

‡ C. C. Holt, F. Modigliani, and H. A. Simon, "Linear Decision Rule for Production and Employment Scheduling," *Management Science*, Vol. 2, No. 1, October, 1955.

Studies of this type will be more and more numerous as production and inventory control is a field particularly open to mathematical treatment.

6. A SCHEDULING SYSTEM IN AGRICULTURE

Seabrook Farms, New Jersey, is a large farming enterprise that faced serious labor turnover problems due to the seasonal nature of the business. At peak periods of harvest, capacities were insufficient even when maximum labor force and overtime were utilized. Crops were harvested late, and products were processed late. This resulted in insufficient capacity for storage, and the quality of the product was adversely affected.

In this case, an analysis of the time elapsed between planting and harvesting was made,* and it was found that this time lapse could be quite accurately predicted. This analysis led to a climatic calendar which makes it possible to schedule planting so that harvest occurs at predictable times. Installation of the climatic calendar led to reduction of labor cost, elimination of excess capacity, stabilization of labor force, and other advantages.

7. EQUIPMENT REQUIREMENT FOR DIAL TELEPHONES

All the examples so far relate to scientific programming, this being the subject matter of this book. However, it should be realized that scientific programming is just one of many new mathematical methods that are being introduced to the business world. These other methods are beyond the scope of this book, but still it will be useful to go through a few examples. This will also help to clarify what we mean by scientific programming.

When Bell Telephone decided to change from the manual exchange system to the automatic one, a number of questions arose.† How should management decide on the quantity of switching equipment

---

* C. W. Thornthwaite, "Operations Research in Agriculture," *Journal of the Operations Research Society of America*, Vol. 1, No. 2, February, 1953; *ibid., Operations Research for Management*, Vol. 1, edited by J. F. McCloskey and P. N. Trefethen, The Johns Hopkins Press, Baltimore, 1954, pp. 368–380.

† W. O. Turner, "Estimation of Requirements in Dial Telephone Central Offices," *Proceedings of the Conference on Operations Research in Marketing*, Case Institute of Technology, January, 1953.

to be procured? Management wanted to provide better service at less expense, but how good was the service? What is good service? Is there any way to compare an automatic system with a manual one as far as performance is concerned?

Questions of this type could perhaps be studied on a purely empirical basis. A few test cities could be set up and experiments designed to obtain guides for decisions. But such an approach would be expensive and also uncertain in its outcome.

Instead of a purely empirical approach, Bell Telephone decided to develop a theoretical framework, and to verify and extend the theory by field studies. It is obvious that the measure of good telephone service is closely tied in with the time the caller has to wait to get a connection. However, when this concept becomes a quantitative one, a lot of problems appear. Bell Telephone is not so much interested in the time one individual has to wait; rather it is interested in the "average" time waited. But what is this average? When there are frequent calls, such as, say, at noon time, people have to wait more "on the average." During the night, the waiting time is negligible. Mondays are different from Sundays, holidays from weekdays, and so on. Obviously common sense alone cannot deal with all these ramifications.

The *theory of waiting lines*, or *queuing theory*, is a vastly refined concept of "average waiting time." The theory establishes quantitative relationships between the quality of service and the equipment required, such as line finders, markers, and registers.

When this theory is coupled with cost analysis, it is possible to establish exact relationships between cost and quality of service. On the basis of such relationships, management can use its judgment in balancing costs and quality of service. The theory of waiting lines, therefore, provides an important instrument to the management of Bell Telephone for making decisions.

The same theory has been applied by the Port of New York Authority to the problem of scheduling the working hours of telephone operators who answer various inquiries. By staggering the working hours in an appropriate fashion, and by part-time employment during peak periods, it is possible to obtain better service at lower cost.

8. TRAFFIC DELAYS AT TOLL BOOTHS

The theory of waiting lines has many other industrial applications. One of the important operations of the Port of New York Authority is the operation of toll plazas at tunnels and bridges.* Decisions involving large funds have to be made as to the number of officers to be employed, the number of plazas to keep open at different times of the day and the year, and the distribution of proper relief periods for officers.

With the use of statistical methods it was possible to establish a measure of the "goodness" of the service and to define what "good service" is. Analysis was made of such parameters as the variation in traffic, hour to hour and day to day, or traffic delays as related to the number of plazas kept open.

This mathematical analysis of the traffic problem resulted not only in a reduction in cost but also in better service.

9. SERVICING OF AUTOMATIC MACHINES

Another interesting application of the theory of waiting lines is reported by a Swedish investigator.† In a certain plant there is a large number of automatic machines requiring no production operators. The machines break down from time to time and so there is need for a crew of repair men. The problem is how to make a decision on the size of the repair crew that will balance the cost of idle time of repairmen against the loss of production due to idle machines.

In this problem, a probabilistic study of machine breakdowns and the time required to repair machines was made. Quantitative relationships between idle machines and idle repair men were obtained, using the theory of waiting lines. The mathematical formulation led to various tables from which the most economical number of repairmen can be selected as required by varying conditions.

The theory of waiting lines has been applied to too many business problems to be able to describe all of them here. In one instance, the optimum number of clerks to staff tool cribs in a factory has been determined.‡ Another application is to the handling of ore in British

---

* L. C. Edie," Traffic Delays at Toll Booths," *Journal of the Operations Research Society of America*, Vol. 2, May, 1954.

† W. Feller, *An Introduction to Probability Theory and Its Applications*, Vol. 1, John Wiley & Sons, New York, 1950, p. 379.

‡ Georges Brigham, "On a Congestion Problem in an Aircraft Factory," *Journal of the Operations Research Society of America*, Vol. 3, No. 4, November, 1955.

ports.* A further application is the determination of dock facilities for trucks.†

10. STATISTICAL SAMPLING IN ACCOUNTING AND PRODUCTION

Accounting methods are supposed to be accurate. In fact, accuracy is considered to be the very essence of accounting. Of course, a lot of time and money must often be spent to get accurate records. Recently, there has been a growing realization of the fact that when executives make their decisions they pay more attention to thousands of dollars than to cents. Furthermore, executives get impatient in waiting a long time for the cents when they are in a great hurry to know the millions. This sort of a consideration is a strong indication to a statistician that methods of statistics can be used in accounting.

An interesting example of the use of statistics in accounting is the study of the interline settlements for railroads, involving less than carload shipments. Here it is obvious that it is impractical to make a detailed account for each shipment as exact settlement would require a tremendous clerical effort. In fact, the railroads have agreed to a plan of settling these accounts on a percentage basis. As time goes on, the railroads suspect that the percentages should change, and then a check is made involving a great deal of clerical expense.

At the May, 1953, meeting of the Operations Research Society of America, W. R. Van Voorhis of the Case Institute of Technology reported that sampling methods can be applied to this accounting problem. To use technical language, the so-called method of *ratio estimates on a stratified basis* was used. This method is again a greatly extended version of common sense. If we have a large urn full of white and black balls, and if we take a thousand of them out while blindfolded and find that there are 200 white ones, we would say with confidence that 20% of the balls are white. However, if we take out only 100 and find 20 white ones, we might still think that 20% are white but our "confidence" would go down. Similarly, in the case of

---

* R. T. Eddison, "Ore Handling at British Ports," in *Operations Research for Management,* Vol. 2, edited by J. F. McCloskey and J. M. Coppinger, The Johns Hopkins Press, Baltimore, 1954, pp. 134–145.

† D. H. Schiller and M. M. Lavin, "Determining Requirements of Warehouse Dock Facilities," *Proceedings of the Conference on Case Studies in Operations Research,* Case Institute of Technology, February, 1956.

railroad accounting it was shown that only 10% of the shipments need to be sampled to find the dollar value of the settlement with an accuracy of about $\frac{1}{2}$%. Being $\frac{1}{2}$% off every month is too small a thing to worry about; as time goes on, small ups and downs will even out. Even if they did not and a railroad lost this $\frac{1}{2}$%, the sampling technique would still save clerical costs amounting to more than the $\frac{1}{2}$% loss.

It can be seen, then, that when statistical methods are used substantial savings in accounting costs can be effected. Recently United Airlines has accepted this type of statistical interline accounting, and a yearly saving of $50,000 in clerical costs has resulted. It is to be expected that other airlines will follow suit, and that further substantial savings will be realized.

It is interesting to note that such techniques have been used in many other fields, though the similarity of the method applied is not always apparent. Suppose in a large factory the manager wants to know how much of the time a certain machine is operating. How long is this machine under maintenance? What fraction of the time is spent on setups? What fraction of the time is the machine idle? He could get answers to these problems by keeping accurate time records, but this would not make sense, because keeping the records may cost more than the advantages gained from the records. A statistical method called *ratio delay analysis* has been used to answer such questions. The method consists of periodically inspecting the plant and sampling what the various machines are doing. True, the answers will not be absolutely accurate, but the important thing is that information accurate enough for making decisions can be obtained at a small cost.

From the point of view of the underlying theory, the method used in interline accounting, or in the machine shop, is exactly the same.

11. REGRESSION ANALYSIS IN FINANCIAL PLANNING

Another interesting application of statistical methods in accounting has been developed in connection with the problem of budgeting and forecasting.* In a particular corporation, it took two to three months to prepare a forecast, and this was too slow for financial planning. The management first sought improvement with the aid of electronic computers, but it was found that the forecasting system was not well adapted to electronic data processing.

* A. Vazsonyi, "Statistical Techniques for Financial Planning and Forecasting," *The Controller,* Vol. 25, No. 5, May 1957.

However, a statistical study revealed that the various overhead accounts could be correlated well with some of the basic variables of the corporation. For instance, regression equations could be developed to relate the various overhead accounts to the number of workers employed. These equations were accurate enough to meet the forecasting needs of the corporation.

Application of these equations resulted in great simplification in financial calculations, and reduced sharply the clerical labor required. Furthermore, the computations based on these regression equations could be carried out automatically. Not only is it possible now to complete the forecast in a time period of two weeks, but the forecast can be prepared at a substantially lower cost.

There are, of course, many other applications of regression analysis in business and industry. For instance, the Port of New York Authority has studied the problem of the flow of traffic in tunnels and bridges.* It was found that the flow of traffic correlates well with vehicular speed and, also, with the spacing of vehicles. As an application of this regression analysis, regulations for the speed and spacing of vehicles were developed which resulted in increased flow of traffic.

Rayco Manufacturing Co.† used multiple regression analysis to predict the sales potential for seat covers in the San Francisco-Oakland area. This study was started by collecting sales data from Chicago and other areas. With the aid of correlation charts, 74 factors were initially selected as influencing sales. This number was later reduced to 37, as these 37 variables represented the most influential factors. Using regression analysis, sales contour maps were prepared which allowed Rayco to determine how many store sites they had to find in the San Francisco-Oakland area, and also where their stores should be located.

12. THE MAINTENANCE OF RAILROADS

Have you ever wondered whether you should buy a new car after keeping your car for two years, three years, or four years? There are all sorts of arguments on both sides for each, but none of them are conclusive. The reason is that there are so many intangibles

* Edward S. Olcott, "The Influence of Vehicular Speed and Spacing on Tunnel Capacity," in *Operations Research for Management*, Vol. 2, edited by J. F. McCloskey and J. M. Coppinger, The Johns Hopkins Press, 1956, p. 57.

† Eli J. Goldberg, "Other than Giants can Benefit: Planning Store Location," *Marketing's Role in Scientific Management*, edited by R. L. Clewett, American Marketing Association, 1957, p. 458.

that vary from individual to individual that no general rule can be established.

However, for the railroads the problem is a more pressing one. When should rails and ties be replaced? Should all rails be changed every twenty-five years? When a rail fails it must be replaced, but individual replacement costs are high. If the railroad waits too long, individual replacement costs will get excessive. On the other hand, if all the rails are changed every five years, there will not be much individual replacement but overall costs still will be high. What is the cheapest replacement plan?

The *theory of failures* has been applied only recently to problems of the maintenance and replacement of equipment, although the theory itself has been used for many years in other fields. This theory of failures (or the theory of replacements), deals with the problem of determining the probability that a certain piece of equipment will fail within a specified time period.

The railroads represent an industry where such a theory can make substantial contributions. Important decisions that heretofore have been made intuitively can be made on a strictly economic basis. Some of the problems whose answers can be obtained by using the theory are:*

1. The desired level of preventive maintenance.
2. Size of the budget.
3. Fraction of budget to be expended on rails, ties, etc.
4. Fraction of budget alloted to each part of the railroad system.
5. Programming of replacement and surfacing work on track.
6. Composition and size of labor forces.
7. How to schedule the work for the different forces; the cycling of replacements of ties, rails, and surfacing.
8. The weight of rail to use.
9. When to eliminate curves and grades.
10. Whether or not to use continuous welded rail.

13. MONTE CARLO METHOD, OR THE SIMULATION OF BUSINESS ENTERPRISES

Suppose Mr. Smith is in the business of manufacturing ball bearings. His manufacturing problems are quite difficult because of the very high tolerances he must keep. He could try to make the balls almost perfect in size; then it would be easy to assemble the bearings.

* R. Crane, "Analysis of Maintenance of Way Problems," Seminar on Operations Research, Railway Systems and Procedures Association, 1954.

On the other hand, he could use a lower tolerance and require the assembly man to make trials until he succeeds in assembling a bearing. Of course, if the tolerances are too poor, the assemblyman might spend days and days before he gets a single bearing assembled. Should Mr. Smith put his emphasis on tolerances or on saving assembly labor? The answer is some sort of a compromise, but what is the most economical compromise?

One way to answer this problem would be to go into pilot plant production and try things out. This would, however, defeat Mr. Smith's purpose because he would have to provide expensive machinery, capable of turning out the high-accuracy components. Is there any other way to answer this problem without building any equipment and running any trials?

The Monte Carlo method allows the manufacturer to simulate conditions that would occur under actual conditions in his plant. It is possible to set up a sort of theoretical factory and solve problems on paper or on an electronic computer. The method is rather simple and can be used without any scientific training.

The particular example discussed here is, of course, only an illustrative case—there are many real business problems, statistical in nature, that can be answered with the Monte Carlo method. One of the most interesting programs undertaken so far is the study by United Airlines, which deals with the problem of aircraft routing and maintenance.* This problem is being solved by the Monte Carlo method. The numerical computations are carried out by a large-scale electronic computer. There is every indication that the application of the Monte Carlo method results not only in better customer service but also in reduced costs.

The Monte Carlo method, or, more generally, the simulation of operations, is rapidly becoming one of the important tools of business and industry. Production and inventory control and transportation process control are some of the many fields where this method has been applied with success.†

14. THE EFFECT OF ADVERTISING ON SALES

One of the most vexing problems faced by management is how to decide on the amount of money to be spent on advertising or on other

---

* W. E. Alberts, "System Simulation," Seventh National Conference of the American Institute of Industrial Engineers, May 18, 1956.

† A. Vazsonyi, "Electronic Simulation of Business Operations (The Monte Carlo Method)," Second Annual West Coast Engineering Management Conference, May 27–28, 1957, p. 65.

promotional efforts aimed at increasing sales. What is the pulling power of a particular advertising campaign? How much plus business has been obtained? How many catalogues should be mailed out to customers, and how does management select those to whom these catalogues should be sent? Such problems do not appear, at first glance, even subject to quantitative analysis. There are, however, a number of instances where scientific analysis of problems of this nature have resulted in quantitative decision criteria.

In one particular case, a study was made for a firm giving promotional help to retailers.* Since all retailers were not included in this promotion, data could be compared between the firms promoted and those not promoted. Statistical analysis of these data, based on a mathematical model, led to criteria which indicated how much money should be spent on promotion in order to maximize the overall profit of the firm. The study also showed how effective was the selection of the retailers promoted, and also how potential gains could be obtained by improving the method of selection.

The Lamp Division of General Electric Company was the subject of a study to determine how sales depend on the number of calls that salesmen make.† It was found, for instance, that salesmen were making too many calls and, in fact, that sales would not drop even if the number of sales calls were drastically reduced. This suggested a reassignment of salesmen so that the same number of salesmen could cover more customers.

A mail order house was plagued with the problem of goods returned. A statistical study showed quantitatively the importance of the timeliness of delivery to customers, and also gave a criterion for not accepting purchases in certain cases. An overall improvement in the profit position of the firm was obtained.

A mathematical analysis of advertising pulling power in a particular department store resulted in a quantitative evaluation of advertising campaigns. As a result of this study, the relative position of the department store, as far as customer goodwill was concerned, was determined. This made it possible to evaluate the department store's performance in the community on a long-range basis.

In another department store a study was made of the effect of

* J. F. Magee, "The Effect of Promotional Effort on Sales," *Journal of the Operations Research Society of America*, Vol. 1, No. 2, February, 1953. See also *Operations Research for Management*, Vol. 1, edited by J. F. McCloskey and P. N. Trefethen, The Johns Hopkins Press, Baltimore, 1954, pp. 305–320.

† R. L. Ackoff, "Allocation of Sales Effort," *Proceedings of the Conference on "What is Operations Research Accomplishing in Industry?"*, Case Institute of Technology, April, 1955.

opening the store during certain evenings.* Dollar figures were obtained regarding the true plus business obtained. The dollar value of business transferred from day to evening was obtained; also, the change in business during the day caused by the evening opening was determined. This study resulted in important guides for management with respect the question of the "true" profits obtained from evening sales.

15. APPLICATIONS OF THE THEORY OF VALUE TO QUALITY CONTROL

Frequently it appears that certain problems are not subject to quantitative treatment. Here is an interesting illustration from a quality control study, conducted at the Commercial Solvents Corporation.† When packaging penicillin, quality control techniques were applied to uncover various types of defects. Each of these defects was considered of various seriousness, and there was no way to determine how to "add" the incidence of the various types of defects. For instance, what would be more serious: to have defects b, c, and d with incidences 5, 4, and 3, or defect a in incidence 8?

This problem was solved by using results of a recently developed theory of value.‡ The approximate measure of each defect was determined, making it possible to add numerically the defects observed. A simple decision rule was obtained: when the sum of the measures of defects was more than 8, the lot was to be rejected; when it was less than 8, the lot was to be accepted.

16. THE CONCEPT OF MATHEMATICAL MODELS

We have seen now a few business examples where scientific programming and, in general, mathematical methods can be used. In the technical literature, the system of equations that describes a business problem is referred to as the *mathematical model* of the business problem,

---

* H. C. Levinson, "Experiences in Commercial Operations Research," *Journal of the Operations Research Society of America*, Vol. 1, No. 4, August, 1953, pp. 265–288. See also *Operations Research for Management*, Vol. 1, edited by J. F. McCloskey and P. N. Trefethen, The Johns Hopkins Press, Baltimore, 1954.

† P. Stillson, "A Method for Defect Evaluation," *Industrial Quality Control*, Vol. 11, No. 1, 1954.

‡ C. W. Churchman and R. L. Ackoff, "An Approximate Measure of Value," *Journal of the Operations Research Society of America*, Vol. 2, No. 2, 1954.

and in Chapters 2 and 3 we will go into great detail in explaining how to set up such models. A mathematical model can be looked upon as an approximate description of a business problem in the language of mathematics.

The most difficult problem, when applying mathematical techniques to business situations, is to establish the mathematical model. For this reason, a thorough understanding of the concept of mathematical models, how to develop them and how to test them, is most necessary. Unfortunately, it is very difficult to explain what a mathematical model is, what it does, and how one should go about setting one up. In fact, one of the basic objectives of this book is to explain the concept of a mathematical model. It might be useful at this stage to say a few words about the advantages of using mathematical models. The following list should help:

(*a*) The mathematical model makes it possible to describe and comprehend the facts of the situation better than any verbal description can hope to do.

(*b*) The mathematical model uncovers relations between the various aspects of the problem which are not apparent in the verbal description.

(*c*) The mathematical model indicates what data should be collected to deal with the problem quantitatively.

(*d*) The mathematical model establishes measures of effectiveness.

(*e*) The mathematical model explains situations that have been left unexplained in the past by giving cause and effect relationships.

(*f*) The mathematical model makes it possible to deal with the problem in its entirety and allows a consideration of all the major variables of the problem simultaneously.

(*g*) A mathematical model is capable of being enlarged step by step to a more comprehensive model to include factors that are neglected in verbal descriptions.

(*h*) The mathematical model makes it possible to use mathematical techniques that otherwise appear to have no applicability to the problem.

(*i*) A mathematical model frequently leads to a solution that can be adequately described and justified on the basis of verbal descriptions.

(*j*) It is often the case that the factors entering into the problem are so many that only elaborate data processing procedures can yield significant answers. In such a case, a mathematical model forms an immediate bridge to the use of large-scale electronic data processors.

Let us finally say a few words about the process in which scientific programming (or mathematics in general) is applied to a business problem.

The first phase of the process is the establishment of a frame of reference. This phase of the work depends primarily on judgment; this is the time when it is necessary to get a feel for the problem and to determine the strategy to be followed.

The second phase is the establishment of a conceptual model, which usually can be best expressed in the form of a mathematical model. However, before the model can be considered pertinent, its validity must be tested to find out whether it does what it is supposed to do. This can be done by going through the list above and asking the questions: Does the model describe the situation better than the verbal description? Does it indicate what data to collect, etc.? If the answers are affirmative, the model is satisfactory; if not, the model must be revised.

The third phase of the process is obtaining acceptance of the model by operating personnel and designing the business system required to put the mathematical model into action. The fourth or final phase consists of the indoctrinating of operating personnel and the introduction of the new business system as an operational practice.

CHAPTER 2

TRANSPORTATION ALLOCATION BY LINEAR PROGRAMMING

1. STATEMENT OF THE PROBLEM

Let us consider a manufacturing firm that owns factories and warehouses in different geographical locations. We will consider a fixed time period, and assume that the output of each factory and the requirements of each warehouse are known. The problem is what quantities of goods to ship and from what factories to what warehouses (during this fixed time period) at a minimum total transportation cost. To be more specific, let us take a particular example represented in Table 1: There are 3 factories and 5 warehouses; transportation costs per unit of goods are shown in Table 1. For instance, it costs $103 per unit of goods to ship from factory 1 to

TABLE 1. Unit Shipping Costs, Requirements, and Capacities

		Warehouses					Total
		W_1	W_2	W_3	W_4	W_5	
Factories	F_1	102	101	102	103	103	100
	F_2	102	102	102	101	99	100
	F_3	103	103	102	101	102	120
Total		40	40	80	80	80	320

warehouse 4. Table 1 also shows that the total output of the factories is 100, 100, and 120 units; whereas the requirements in the warehouses are 40, 40, 80, 80, and 80 units.

Before we proceed to solve this problem, we will make a simplification. We note that a total of 320 units are to be shipped. It is easy to see that, if *all* costs are reduced by a fixed amount, the transportation allocation will be unchanged. In Table 2 every trans-

TABLE 2. Reduced Unit Shipping Costs, Requirements, and Capacities

		Warehouses					Total
		W_1	W_2	W_3	W_4	W_5	
Factories	F_1	$C_{1,1} = 2$	$C_{1,2} = 1$	$C_{1,3} = 2$	$C_{1,4} = 3$	$C_{1,5} = 3$	100
	F_2	$C_{2,1} = 2$	$C_{2,2} = 2$	$C_{2,3} = 2$	$C_{2,4} = 1$	$C_{2,5} = -1$	100
	F_3	$C_{3,1} = 3$	$C_{3,2} = 3$	$C_{3,3} = 2$	$C_{3,4} = 1$	$C_{3,5} = 2$	120
Total		40	40	80	80	80	320

portation cost is reduced by the fixed amount of $100.00. The same table also introduces a mathematical notation to describe these various transportation costs. As an example, $c_{2,3}$ denotes the transportation cost from F_2 to W_3, $c_{3,1}$ denotes the transportation cost from F_3 to W_1.[*] Notice that $c_{2,5}$ (transportation from F_2 to W_5) is minus $1. This should not disturb us, as negative numbers are permissible in the method of solution. Furthermore, this minus $1 could be interpreted as a subsidy, meaning that, when F_2 ships some goods to W_5, there is a subsidy of $1 to be received. From now on we will refer to our problem as represented in Table 2, with the reduced costs, and shall not refer to the original problem.

The problem is, then, to determine the unknown quantities to be shipped from each factory to each warehouse. In order to be able to talk about these unknowns, we introduce a mathematical notation as shown in Table 3. For instance, the quantity to be shipped from F_2 to W_3 will be denoted by $x_{2,3}$, or the quantity to be shipped from F_3 to W_1 by $x_{3,1}$, etc.

One way to determine the unknowns in Table 3 would be to use a cut and try method. In fact, in such a simple problem this might be the quickest way. However, our purpose is to determine a general method that will work in a bigger problem. Suppose we have 20 fac-

---

[*] F_3 denotes factory 3; W_1 denotes warehouse 1, etc.

tories and 50 warehouses. A cut and try method would be very tedious because the possible combinations that are to be searched are astronomical. Furthermore, in such a large problem it would be difficult to capitalize on experience or judgment.

TABLE 3. Definition of Unknowns

| | | \multicolumn{5}{c}{Warehouses} | Total |
		W_1	W_2	W_3	W_4	W_5	
	F_1	$x_{1,1}$	$x_{1,2}$	$x_{1,3}$	$x_{1,4}$	$x_{1,5}$	100
Factories	F_2	$x_{2,1}$	$x_{2,2}$	$x_{2,3}$	$x_{2,4}$	$x_{2,5}$	100
	F_3	$x_{3,1}$	$x_{3,2}$	$x_{3,3}$	$x_{3,4}$	$x_{3,5}$	120
Total		40	40	80	80	80	320

Frequently, in scientific problems, a great deal can be learned from simple examples. Here, it will be instructive to solve some very simple problems first that require no mathematical technique at all.

2. TWO FACTORIES AND TWO WAREHOUSES

To begin with, let us consider this ridiculously simple problem: There are only 2 factories and 2 warehouses; F_1 produces 8 units, F_2 produces 5 units; requirements at W_1 are 7 units, requirements at W_2 are 6 units, as shown in the table. The table also shows the transporta-

	W_1	W_2	
F_1	2	3	8
F_2	4	7	5
	7	6	

tion costs. For instance, from F_1 to W_2 it costs $3 for each unit of goods shipped. How do we determine the cheapest transportation allocation? First of all, it is easy to see that F_1 must ship to W_1 at least 2 units, but not more than 7 units. This is simply due to the fact that, if F_1 sends, say, only 1 unit to W_1, then F_1 still has 7 units to ship to W_2, but W_2 requires only a total of 6 units.

On the other hand, it is obvious that F_1 should not send to W_1 8 units, as the total requirements at W_1 are only 7 units. The problem, then, is how to select the unknown quantity x to be shipped from F_1 to W_1 that leads to the lowest total transportation cost. In order to answer this question, we make a table showing the total transportation cost associated with each value of the unknown quantity x:

x	2	3	4	5	6	7
Cost	42	44	46	48	50	52

For instance, this table shows that, if we ship from F_1 to W_1 3 units, then the transportation cost will be \$44. How did we compute this \$44? If we send 3 units from F_1 to W_1 we must send 5 units from F_1 to W_2, as F_1 produces a total of 8 units. Requirements at W_1 are 7 units. So far, we have shipped only 3, and therefore we must ship another 4 units from F_2 to W_1. Finally, we must ship 1 unit from F_2 to W_2 to balance the requirements. The cost of shipping 3 units from F_1 to W_1 will be \$6, as each unit costs \$2 to be shipped, etc. Adding up these quantities, we get $3(2) + 5(3) + 4(4) + 1(7) = 44$. This is the way the table was prepared, and it can be seen that the cheapest possible transportation cost is \$42. This is obtained when 2 units are shipped from F_1 to W_1, 6 units from F_1 to W_2, 5 units from F_2 to W_1, and nothing from F_2 to W_2 as shown in the table. This

	W_1	W_2	
F_1	2	6	8
F_2	5	0	5
	7	6	

will perhaps convince us that we have found the cheapest transportation cost. However, someone might raise the objection that we did not explore fractional shipments. What about sending 2.3 units from F_1 to W_1? In order to answer this objection, we prepare Fig. 1, where the horizontal axis shows the unknown quantities shipped from F_1 to W_1 and the vertical axis shows the dollar cost. Both the table and the figure show that, if we ship 2 units from F_1 to W_1, the cost is \$42, whereas if we ship 7 units from F_1 to W_1, the cost is \$52. However, Figure 1 also shows that, whatever number of units we ship (remember, this quantity must be between 2 and 7 units), the costs lie on a straight line.   For instance, if we ship $3\frac{1}{2}$ units from F_1 to W_1, the cost will be \$45.   This graphical representation should, then, convince us that whatever quantities we ship from F_1 to W_1, the cheapest transportation cost is obtained when we are at the lowest point of the straight line—that is, when we ship 2 units from F_1 to W_1.

There is something more that we can learn from this simple example: whatever costs, requirements, and capacities we encounter, the cost

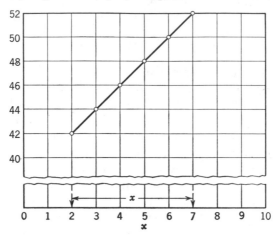

FIG. 1.   Solution of transportation problem when there are two factories and two warehouses.

line will always be straight.   This means, then, that the lowest transportation cost will be either at the left-hand-side or at the right-hand-side edge of the diagram.   In our particular case, x could not go below the quantity 2 as that would imply a negative quantity of units shipped from F_2 to W_2.   Similarly, in any case it will be impossible for x to go below a certain quantity or above a certain quantity because that would entail a negative shipment.   This means, however, that always there will be one particular route that is not used.   It might not be from F_2 to W_2 it might be from F_2 to W_1, or from F_1 to W_1, or from F_1 to W_2.   The important point is that one of the routes will always be unused.   In other words, one of the unknowns always takes the value zero.   In a certain sense, then, we can say that the 2-factory, 2-warehouse problem reduces to the problem of finding out which of the routes is not used—that is, which of the unknowns is zero.   Because if we know which of the routes is unused (or which of the unknowns is zero), then it is simple to determine the other shipments.   This sounds like a lot of fuss about a very simple matter.   Suppose, however, we consider a transportation problem where there are 20 factories and 30 warehouses. Select any 2 factories and any 2 warehouses, and focus attention on this 2-factory, 2-warehouse problem. For the moment let us assume that we are at liberty only to change the transportation between these 2 factories and 2 warehouses. Obviously, if we have the cheapest allocation of transportation for the big problem, we must have the cheapest allocation for this 2 by 2 problem. In other words, our big problem can be considered as built up of many 2 by 2 problems. However, we have just discovered that the 2 by 2 problem always implies that one of the routes is not used (i.e., one of the shipments must be zero). On the basis of this very simple reasoning, then, we conclude that in the big problem there must be a number of unused routes. In fact, when we realize that there are many ways to select 2 factories and 2 warehouses, and that each of these selections will involve a zero, we conclude that there are going to be quite a number of unused routes.

For example, suppose we have 8 factories and 8 warehouses, forming a table similar to a chessboard. Suppose now that on our chessboard we select four squares according to the pattern shown in the figure.

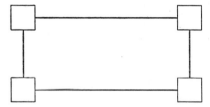

This corresponds to selecting 2 factories and 2 warehouses. According to our observation, one of the four numbers on the four squares must be zero, whichever way we select this rectangular pattern. The fact of the matter is that it can be shown that, even if we use more complicated "rectangular" patterns, such as shown in Table 11, we must have a zero at least at one of the "corners." Now, let us pose this question: how many numbers (not counting zeros) can we put on a chess board such that selection of any of these rectangular patterns will involve at least 1 zero? If we try, we will soon be convinced that we can put only 15 numbers on the board and not more. This means that, in this 8 by 8 problem, out of the 64 unknown numbers there cannot be more than 15 that are not zeros, which implies that out of the 64 numbers there must be at least 49 zeros. We make a point here that there will be *at least* 49 zeros, as there might be perhaps 50, 51, etc., zeros. The problem is to determine where these 49 zeros are located on the chess board. (Going back to our 2 by 2 example, we

have only shown that there must be at least 1 zero. However, there is a possibility that there would be 2 zeros in the 2 by 2 problem. This can happen when F_1 exactly satisfies the demand, say, at W_1, and F_2 exactly satisfies the demand at W_2, and this particular allocation happens to give the lowest possible cost. We will consider this case of *degeneracy* in Section 8 of this chapter.)

We see, then, that the 2-factory, 2-warehouse problem is quite instructive and leads to some very interesting conclusions in connection with a transportation problem of any size.

3. TWO FACTORIES AND THREE WAREHOUSES

We proceed now to a somewhat more complicated problem. Requirements, capacities, and transportation costs are given by the table shown. What is the cheapest allocation of transportation here?

	W_1	W_2	W_3	
F_1	6	4	2	10
F_2	5	4	3	8
	6	7	5	

Let us denote by x the quantity shipped from F_1 to W_1, and by y the quantity shipped from F_1 to W_2. We can compute transportation costs for any value of x and y, as shown in Table 4. For instance, it can be seen that, if we ship 3 units from F_1 to W_1 and 5 units from F_1 to W_2, that is, if we assign the value 3 to x and the value 5 to y, we get a cost of \$74. This computation is carried out by recognizing that 2 units must be shipped from F_1 to W_3, 3 units from F_2 to W_1, 2 units from F_2 to W_2, and 3 units from F_2 to W_3, as shown in the table.

	W_1	W_2	W_3	
F_1	3	5	2	10
F_2	3	2	3	8
	6	7	5	

The cost can be easily computed as $3(6) + 5(4) + 2(2) + 3(5) + 2(4) + 3(3) = 74$. This is the way all the other numbers in Table 4 are

TABLE 4. Solution of Transportation Problem When There Are Two Factories and Three Warehouses

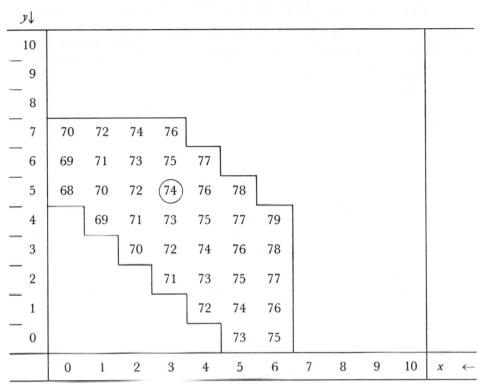

computed for the various values of x and y.   There are some empty squares on the table, and the reason is that, if you try to use a value of x and y associated with an empty square, you would get some negative number of units shipped from some factory to some warehouse.   Table 4 shows that the cheapest transportation cost is $68; this cost is associated with sending no shipments from F_1 to W_1, that is, the value of x is zero, and with sending 5 units from F_1 to W_2, which means that the unknown y must take the value 5.   This result is shown in a tabular form.

	W_1	W_2	W_3	
F_1	0	5	5	10
F_2	6	2	0	8
	6	7	5	

Someone might object that we have not considered fractional shipments.   The geometrical representation in Fig. 2 allows us to survey
fractional shipments.   The shaded area shows the values of x and y
to be considered; any point outside of the shaded area involves some
sort of a negative shipment.   The problem is to select a point in the
shaded area which has the lowest transportation cost, or the one
through which the dotted line with the lowest number passes.   It is
clear from the diagram that the corner marked with a star (associated

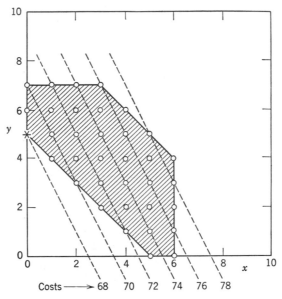

FIG. 2.   Solution of the transportation problem when there are two factories and
three warehouses.

with the values $x = 0$ and $y = 5$) is the point that has the lowest
transportation cost, the $68.   Figure 2 convinces us then that this
$68 is indeed the lowest possible transportation cost.

Let us realize at this point that it is not a coincidence that the cheapest solution is given by a corner of the shaded area.   The fact of the
matter is that whatever requirements, capacities, and costs we have,
as long as we have 2 factories and 3 warehouses the diagram will
always look something like the one in Fig. 2, and the lowest transportation cost will always be located at a corner of the shaded figure.
Furthermore, this implies that two of the routes will always be unused,
which means that out of the 6 unknowns there will always be at least
2 zeros.   (Not more than four of the routes will be utilized.)

If we recall our chessboard example you will easily recognize that we cannot possibly have more than four of the routes utilized. Otherwise, we could select 2 warehouses such that in the 2-factory, 2-warehouse problem all four routes would be utilized, which we know to be unnecessary.

Should we proceed now to the 2-factory, 4-warehouse or perhaps the 3-factory, 3-warehouse case? It is apparent that the unknowns begin to grow fast in number, that we would have to deal with 8 or 9 unknowns, and that the simple procedures we have used so far become impractical. What we need is a general method that systematically gives us answers in any transportation problem. Therefore, we proceed now to develop a general method, using the 3 by 5 case of Table 2 as an illustration, and you will see that the simple examples we discussed so far will be quite useful in the presentation.

4. METHOD OF SOLVING THE TRANSPORTATION PROBLEM

Let us return to the 3 by 5 problem shown in Table 2, and let us try to obtain some sort of a solution to the problem, even if this will not be the cheapest solution. Table 5 shows how such a first solution can be obtained. We know that F_1 produces 100 units; how much of this should be shipped to W_1? As the total requirement in W_1 is 40, we can ship 40 units; this leaves 60 units in F_1 to be shipped to some other warehouse. W_2 can take another 40 of these units, and we still have 20 units left at F_1. We ship this 20 to W_3. As W_3 requires 80 units, we still have to ship to W_3 another 60 units. We get these 60 units from F_2. Now we have W_3 full, but F_2 still has 40 units to be disposed of. This we ship to W_4. Now we have disposed of every-

TABLE 5. First Solution

(Total cost, $520)

		W_1		W_2		W_3		W_4		W_5		Total
						Warehouses						Total
Factories	F_1	40	2	40	1	20	?	0	3	0	3	100
	F_2	0	2	0	2	60	2	40	1	0	-1	100
	F_3	0	3	0	3	0	2	40	1	80	2	120
Total		40		40		80		80		80		320

thing from F_2. In order to fill up W_4 we must ship from F_3. This
leads to shipping 40 units from F_3 to W_4. Finally, the 80 units left at
F_3 must be shipped to W_5.*

What is the total cost of transportation? For convenience, in the
upper right corner of each square in Table 5 we list the individual
shipping costs. It can be easily computed that the total cost is \$520.
The question we pose now is how to change this allocation of transportation so that the total shipping cost will decrease.

It is clear that we cannot change, say, just one of the x's or even
two of them, as the sum in each row and also in each column is given.

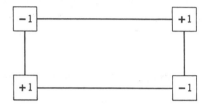

However, if we change four of them by $+1$ or -1 according to the
pattern shown in the figure, then the sum in any row or any column
does not change. This is a *permissible* way of changing the unknowns,
provided all the quantities remain positive. To make clear how this

TABLE 6.   Evaluation of a Change in $x_{1,4}$

(Unit increase in $x_{1,4}$ results in a cost increase of \$2)

		Warehouses					Total
		W_1	W_2	W_3	W_4	W_5	
	F_1	40 ²	40 ¹	20 − 1 ²	0 + 1 ³ [+2]	0 ³	100
Factories	F_2	0 ²	0 ²	60 + 1 ²	40 − 1 ¹	0 ⁻¹	100
	F_3	0 ³	0 ³	0 ²	40 ¹	80 ²	120
Total		40	40	80	80	80	320

modification is carried through, we repeat in Table 6 our first solution,
and we indicate a change of $+1$ in $x_{1,4}$ and $x_{2,3}$ and a change of -1
in $x_{1,3}$ and $x_{2,4}$. The difference between the solutions of Table 5
and Table 6 is, then, that the numbers

* **This procedure is often called the north-west rule.**

20	0
60	40

are replaced by

19	1
61	39

Obviously, both F_1 and F_2 are still shipping 100 units of goods, and both W_3 and W_4 are still receiving 80. How does the total cost of this new allocation compare with the first solution? The difference in total costs is given by

$$c_{1,4} + c_{2,3} - c_{1,3} - c_{2,4} = 3 + 2 - 2 - 1 = +2$$

So we see that the total transportation cost increases by \$2. To remember this, we list the number $+2$ on the lower right-hand corner, in the box for $x_{1,4}$. This indicates then that, by increasing $x_{1,4}$ by a unit, the total shipping cost is increased by \$2.

Therefore, changing $x_{1,4}$ is not a wise thing to do. Let us try now to change $x_{2,5}$. This is shown in Table 7. Going through the

TABLE 7. Evaluation of a Change in $x_{2,5}$

(Unit increase in $x_{2,5}$ results in cost decrease of \$3)

		Warehouses					Total
		W_1	W_2	W_3	W_4	W_5	
	F_1						100
Factories	F_2				$40 - 1$	$0 + 1$	100
	F_3				$40 + 1$	$80 - 1$	120
Total		40	40	80	80	80	320

same argument as before, we see that this change results in a decrease of \$3 in transportation costs, and so we list the number -3 at the lower right-hand corner of $x_{2,5}$. If we increase $x_{2,5}$ by 2 units, we will save \$6, so we should try to increase $x_{2,5}$ as much as possible. Inspecting $x_{2,4}$ we observe that, as $x_{2,5}$ is increased, $x_{2,4}$ decreases. We cannot make $x_{2,4}$ negative, so we can subtract not more than 40. This means that we should add 40 to $x_{2,5}$. Simultaneously, we must add 40 to $x_{3,4}$ and subtract 40 both from $x_{3,5}$ and $x_{2,4}$. In this way we get a second solution listed in Table 8. There is a decrease in cost

TABLE 8. A Second Solution
(Total cost, $400)

		Warehouses					Total
		W_1	W_2	W_3	W_4	W_5	
	F_1	40 ^{2}	40 ^{1}	20 ^{2}	0 ^{3}	0 ^{3}	100
Factories	F_2	0 ^{2}	0 ^{2}	60 ^{2}	0 ^{1}	40 $^{-1}$	100
	F_3	0 ^{3}	0 ^{3}	0 ^{2}	80 ^{1}	40 ^{2}	120
Total		40	40	80	80	80	320

of 40($3), or $120. The total cost associated with the second solution is $400.

Let us stop for a moment now and ask the question, "Why did we change $x_{2,5}$?" Maybe we should have changed $x_{3,1}$. In order to see whether we should have changed $x_{3,1}$, let us try to evaluate what an increase in $x_{3,1}$ implies in transportation cost. To do this we have to apply a pattern of change to the first solution shown in the figure.

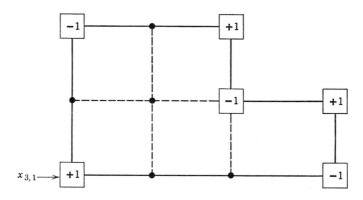

We remind ourselves here that the number in the lower left-hand corner is zero; all other numbers are not zero. When the pattern of change indicated by the figure is carried out, we are led to Table 9.

The lower right-hand number in the box for $x_{3,1}$ shows that the unit increases in $x_{3,1}$ result in \$1 increase in transportation cost.

Every x (that is, 0) can be evaluated using this method of changes. This is shown in Table 10. For instance, a unit increase in $x_{3,2}$ results in a \$2 increase in transportation cost. The various patterns used in

TABLE 9. Evaluation of a Change in $x_{3,1}$

(Unit increase in $x_{3,1}$ results in \$1 increase in cost)

		Warehouses					Total
		W_1	W_2	W_3	W_4	W_5	
Factories	F_1	$40 - 1^{2}$		$20 + 1^{2}$			
	F_2			$60 - 1^{2}$	$40 + 1^{1}$		
	F_3	$0 + 1^{3}$ $\boxed{+1}$			$40 - 1^{1}$		
Total							

TABLE 10. Evaluation of a Change in the x's from the First Solution

(For instance an increase in $x_{3,2}$ results in a \$2 increase in cost)

		Warehouses					Total
		W_1	W_2	W_3	W_4	W_5	
Factories	F_1	40^{2}	40^{1}	20^{2}	0^{3} $\boxed{1\cdot2}$	0^{3} $\boxed{+1}$	100
	F_2	0^{2} $\boxed{0}$	0^{2} $\boxed{+1}$	60^{2}	40^{1}	0^{-1} $\boxed{-3}$	100
	F_3	0^{3} $\boxed{+1}$	0^{3} $\boxed{+2}$	0^{2} $\boxed{0}$	40^{1}	80^{2}	120
Total		40	40	80	80	80	320

evaluating these potential changes are shown in Table 11. Each square, where x has the value zero, is evaluated (see the filled circles). Note that the corner of each pattern (shown by open circles) refers to an x that is not zero. It can be seen, indeed, that the best saving in transportation cost can be accomplished by changing $x_{2,5}$, which has the evaluating number of -3. We see, therefore, that the best possible move in changing our first solution is to go to the solution that we called the second solution (Table 8).

TABLE 11. Patterns Showing the Square Evaluations for the Solution Shown in Table 8

(Filled circles represent squares to be evaluated)

		Warehouses					Total
		W_1	W_2	W_3	W_4	W_5	
	F_1						
Factories	F_2						
	F_3						
Total							

Now we can repeat the procedure and apply the same technique of change to our second solution.   Table 12 shows an evaluation of the

TABLE 12.   Evaluation of a Change in the x's from the Second Solution

		Warehouses					Total
		W_1	W_2	W_3	W_4	W_5	
	F_1	40 ^{2} $*$	40 ^{1} $*$	20 ^{2} $*$	0 ^{3} $\boxed{+5}$	0 ^{3} $\boxed{+4}$	100
Factories	F_2	0 ^{2} $\boxed{0}$	0 ^{2} $\boxed{+1}$	60 ^{2} $*$	0 ^{1} $\boxed{+3}$	40 $^{-1}$ $*$	100
	F_3	0 ^{3} $\boxed{-2}$	0 ^{3} $\boxed{-1}$	0 ^{2} $\boxed{-3}$	80 ^{1} $*$	40 ^{2} $*$	120
Total		40	40	80	80	80	320

x's in the second solution.   It can be seen that the best is to change $x_{3,3}$, as this leads to a \$3 saving for each unit shipped from factory 3 to warehouse 3.   An increase in $x_{3,3}$ is obtained through the pattern shown.   We cannot increase $x_{3,3}$ more than 40, as otherwise $x_{3,5}$ would

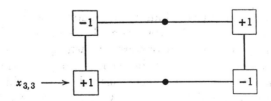

become negative.   An increase of 40 in $x_{3,3}$ leads to 0 at $x_{3,5}$, to 80 at $x_{2,5}$, and to 20 at $x_{2,3}$.

Now we have our third solution, shown in Table 13. We still do not know whether this is the cheapest. However, by repeating the previous process and evaluating the x's (that are zero), it can be seen that no change leads to a decrease in transportation cost, and therefore our third solution is the optimum solution. The transportation cost can be computed as \$280.

TABLE 13. Third or Optimum Solution

(Evaluation of changes in x's shows that the cost cannot be decreased further. Total cost, \$280. This optimum solution is a *basic* solution)

| | | \multicolumn{5}{c}{Warehouses} | Total |
		W_1	W_2	W_3	W_4	W_5	
	F_1	40 ^2 *	40 ^1 *	20 ^2 *	0 ^3 [+2]	0 ^3 [+4]	100
Factories	F_2	0 ^2 [0]	0 ^2 [+1]	20 ^2 *	0 ^1 [0]	80 ^{-1} *	100
	F_3	0 ^3 [+1]	0 ^3 [+2]	40 ^2 *	80 ^1 *	0 ^2 [+3]	120
\multicolumn{2}{c}{Total}	40	40	80	80	80	320

It is important to note that a change in $x_{2,4}$ leads to no change in transportation cost as indicated by the zero in the lower right-hand corner of the $F_2 W_4$ box in Table 13. This is an indication that there are alternative schemes of allocation which lead to a transportation cost of \$280. We proceed now to study such alternate optima.

5. ALTERNATE OPTIMUM SOLUTIONS

Let us consider Table 13 and add N to $x_{2,4}$ and $x_{3,3}$; simultaneously, subtract N from $x_{2,3}$ and $x_{3,4}$. This implies the following change:

$20 - N$	$0 + N$
$40 + N$	$80 - N$

The square evaluation at $x_{2,4}$ is zero, and, therefore, this change in the solution implies no change in the total transportation cost. One can assign to N any value not more than 20 and still have a new optimum solution. If we use the value $N = 20$, we get the solution shown in Table 14. If we use $N = 14$, we get the solution in Table 15. It is recognized, therefore, that there is an infinite variety of optimum solutions to our problem depending on the value of N, each having the same minimum total transportation cost of \$280.

TABLE 14. An Alternate Optimum Solution
(Total cost, \$280. This optimum solution is a *basic* solution)

		Warehouses					Total
		W_1	W_2	W_3	W_4	W_5	
Factories	F_1	40 ² *	40 ¹ *	20 ² *	0 ³ +2	0 ³ +4	100
	F_2	0 ² 0	0 ² +1	0 ² *	20 ¹ 0	80 ⁻¹ *	100
	F_3	0 ³ +1	0 ³ +2	60 ² *	60 ¹ *	0 ² +3	120
Total		40	40	80	80	80	320

TABLE 15. A Further Alternate Optimum Solution
(Total cost, \$280. This optimum solution is not a basic solution)

		Warehouses					Total
		W_1	W_2	W_3	W_4	W_5	
Factories	F_1	40 ² *	40 ¹ *	20 ² *	0 ³ +2	0 ³ +4	100
	F_2	0 ² 0	0 ² +1	6 ² *	14 ¹ 0	80 ⁻¹ *	100
	F_3	0 ³ +1	0 ³ +2	54 ² *	66 ¹ *	0 ² +3	120
Total		40	40	80	80	80	320

Similarly, it is possible to obtain some other alternate solutions when one realizes that the square evaluation at $x_{2,1}$ also has the value of 0. Consider the optimum solution in Table 13, and add, for instance, 20 to $x_{2,1}$ and to $x_{1,3}$, and subtract 20 from $x_{1,1}$ and $x_{2,3}$. The resulting new optimum solution is shown in Table 16.

However, this is not all, as there are still other ways to generate optimum solutions. Take the numbers in Table 13, and multiply every number by A. Then take the numbers in Table 16, and multiply each of them by B. Add the corresponding numbers in these new tables, and divide every number by $A + B$. It is easy to see that this method gives again a new optimum solution for any value of A and B. To illustrate, take the numbers from Table 13 and multiply them by 3, and take the numbers from Table 16 and multiply

TABLE 16. A Third Alternate Optimum Solution

(Total cost, \$280. This solution is a *basic* solution)

		Warehouses					Total
		W_1	W_2	W_3	W_4	W_5	
	F_1	20	40	40	0	0	100
Factories	F_2	20	0	0	0	80	100
	F_3	0	0	40	80	0	120
Total		40	40	80	80	80	320

TABLE 17. A Fourth Alternate Optimum Solution

(Total cost, \$280. This solution is not a basic solution)

		Warehouses					Total
		W_1	W_2	W_3	W_4	W_5	
	F_1	26	40	34	0	0	100
Factories	F_2	14	0	6	0	80	100
	F_3	0	0	40	80	0	120
Total		40	40	80	80	80	320

them by 7. Add the corresponding numbers, and divide by 10. The resulting numbers are shown in Table 17.

There is an important point to note in connection with these alternate optima. The solutions in Tables 13, 14, and 16 have exactly 8 zeros. Recall from our study of the chessboard problem that we expect to have 8 zeros in a 3 by 5 problem. The solutions in Tables 15 and 17 have only 7. How can this be? Have we not convinced ourselves that in the 3 by 5 problem we must have at least 8 zeros?

Let us return to Fig. 1. We said the cheapest solution must be either at the right-hand or left-hand end of the straight line. Suppose, however, that the straight line is horizontal. Then, both ends have the same transportation cost. Furthermore, any point on the straight line has the same (minimum) transportation cost. The solutions at the two end points each have one route unutilized and are called basic solutions. Combinations of these two basic solutions still have minimal costs but have no routes unutilized.

In our more complicated 3 by 5 problem, Tables 13, 14, and 16 represent basic solutions, as these have exactly 8 zeros. Tables 15 and 17 represent optimum solutions, but these are *not* basic solutions. The important property of optimum basic solutions is that any other optimum solutions can be derived as a combination of the basic optimum solutions. On the other hand, having a variety of nonbasic optimum solutions does not necessarily allow computation of all the possible optimum solutions. In the present problem there are three optimum basic solutions shown in Tables 13, 14, and 16, and all other optimum solutions are combinations of these basic solutions.

A further important property of a basic solution is the following: If all square evaluations are positive, then the basic solution is optimal, i.e., it has a minimum cost. The solutions in Tables 5 and 8 are basic solutions (there are 8 zeros) but are *not* optimal, whereas the solutions in Tables 13, 14, and 16 are basic and optimal. On the other hand, if we have a solution which is not basic (that is, it has 7 or fewer zeros) and if all the square evaluations are positive, then we have no assurance yet that the solution is an optimum one. Soon we will have an opportunity to use this property of a basic solution.

In a general case of the transportation problem, there are n rows and m columns. A basic solution is defined as one having at least $mn - m - n + 1$ zeros, and it is of interest to determine all the optimum basic solutions if there is more than one optimum solution.

6. SENSITIVITY ANALYSIS

The problem we want to investigate is the following: Suppose some of the requirements or capacities or transportation costs are changed by a small amount. How does the minimum transportation cost change?

We could answer this problem by starting anew to solve the problem. However, in many cases there are important short cuts in the computations, and it will be useful to describe some of these.

Suppose the capacity of F_2 drops from 100 units to 90 units and, simultaneously, requirements at W_3 drop to 70. By inspecting Table 13, it is natural to conclude that the shipments from F_2 to W_3 should also drop by 10. This solution is shown in Table 18. However, one asks the question whether this is the cheapest possible solution. The answer is yes. The justification lies in the fact that this new solution is still a basic solution, as it has 8 zeros and all the square evaluations are positive. According to our discussion in the last section, this new solution is an optimum solution.

TABLE 18. Optimum Solution When Capacity of F_2 Is Decreased to 90 and Requirement at W_3 Is Decreased to 70

(Total cost decreases by $20)

		Warehouses					Total
		W_1	W_2	W_3	W_4	W_5	
	F_1	40	40	20	0	0	100
Factories	F_2	0	0	10	0	80	90
	F_3	0	0	40	80	0	120
Total		40	40	70	80	80	310

Suppose now that the capacity of F_2 drops to 70 and, simultaneously, at W_3 requirements drop to 50. What do we do in this case? It is not possible to drop the shipments from F_2 to W_3 by 30, as this leads to a negative number. In this case, the short cut we used does not work and we have to either use an alternate approach or treat the problem as a new one and start anew.

Let us now consider the possibility that the capacity of F_3 increases to 130 and the requirements at W_5 increase to 90. How do we get the solution now? It would be natural to decide to ship 10 units from F_3 to W_5. This will increase the total transportation cost by $20. Is this, however, an optimum solution? This solution has only 7 zeros and, consequently, it is not a basic solution. Therefore, we cannot say that this is an optimum solution. By making a proper pattern of changes, this new solution can be turned into a basic solution. Subtract 10 from $x_{2,3}$ and $x_{3,5}$, and add 10 to $x_{3,3}$ and $x_{2,5}$. (This is the pattern used when the square at $x_{3,5}$ was evaluated.) This solution is shown in Table 19. We know that this solution is an optimum one, as it is a basic solution and all the square evaluations are positive. Notice that the total transportation cost has *decreased* by $10 in spite of the fact that 10 more units are handled. This is due to the subsidy received when shipping from F_2 to W_5. It can be seen that one has to be quite careful in evaluating cost changes when the problem changes, as the optimum solution does not necessarily vary in an obvious fashion.

Now we will consider a change in transportation costs. Suppose the cost from F_3 to W_2 increases from $3 to $5. What would be the influence of the increase on our total transportation cost? The answer is none. This is obvious when we inspect Table 13, as there

TABLE 19.   Optimum Solution When Capacity of F_3 Is Increased to 130 and Requirement at W_5 Is Increased to 90

(Total cost decreases by $10)

		Warehouses					Total
		W_1	W_2	W_3	W_4	W_5	
Factories	F_1	40	40	20	0	0	100
	F_2	0	0	10	0	90	100
	F_3	0	0	50	80	0	130
Total		40	40	80	80	90	330

are no shipments from F_3 to W_2. This transportation route is too expensive even for $3 per unit of goods, so when the cost increases to $5 per unit there is no change in total transportation cost.

Suppose now that the subsidy when shipping from F_2 to W_5 is abolished, and that a cost of $3 per unit of goods is charged. The square evaluation at $x_{3,5}$ becomes -1, which shows that we do not have an optimum solution any more. We can then make changes in the solution in proper patterns, as we have done earlier, and proceed to obtain an optimum solution with this new cost. Table 20 shows the results of the computations. It is important to note that there is an increase in cost of $240. From a naive point of view, we might have thought that, when the subsidy of $1 is changed to a cost of $3, there would be a net change of $4 per unit of goods, which would result in an increase in total cost of $320, as in the original solution 80 units were shipped from F_2 to W_5.

TABLE 20. Optimum Solution When Transportation Cost
from F_2 to W_5 Is Increased to $3 per Unit of Goods

(Minimum transportation cost is $520)

		Warehouses					Total
		W_1	W_2	W_3	W_4	W_5	
	F_1	40 ² *	40 ¹ *	20 ² *	0 ³ +2	0 ³ +1	100
Factories	F_2	0 ² 0	0 ² +1	60 ² *	40 ¹ *	0 ³ +1	100
	F_3	0 ³ +1	0 ³ +2	0 ² 0	40 ¹ *	80 ² *	120
Total		40	40	80	80	80	320

It is obvious that a further increase in the shipping cost from F_2 to
W_5 will make no change in the total transportation cost as this route
is not used in the optimum solution.

7. COMBINED TRANSPORTATION AND PRODUCTION ALLOCATION

We will consider now a new problem shown in Table 21: we have
4 factories and 4 warehouses, whose combined capacity is 980 units,
but the combined requirement is only 810 units. This means that

TABLE 21. Requirements, Capacities, Shipping Costs for Combined
Production and Transportation Problem, Involving Four Factories
and Four Warehouses

		Warehouses				Total
		W_1	W_2	W_3	W_4	
	F_1	28	40	36	38	140
	F_2	18	28	24	30	260
Factories	F_3	42	54	52	54	360
	F_4	36	48	40	46	220
Total		180	280	150	200	

some of the factories have excess capacities.   Furthermore, production
costs vary from factory to factory, the costs being for each unit of
goods:

Factory	Cost
F_1	$60
F_2	72
F_3	48
F_4	60

Our problem is to devise an allocation of shipping and production
facilities such that the total cost is minimized.   It is important to
realize that transportation and production costs are interrelated, and
that the problem cannot be solved by considering transportation and
production separately.

In order to solve this problem we prepare Table 22, where the combined   transportation   and   production   costs   are   tabulated.   For

**TABLE 22.   Requirements, Capacities, Combined Shipping,
and Production Costs**

(W_5 represents unused capacity)

		Warehouses					Total
		W_1	W_2	W_3	W_4	W_5	
Factories	F_1	88	100	96	98	0	140
	F_2	90	100	96	102	0	260
	F_3	90	102	100	102	0	360
	F_4	96	108	100	106	0	220
Total		180	280	150	200	170	980

instance, to produce and ship from F_2 to W_1 costs $90 per unit of goods,
where $18 is due to transportation and $72 to production.   The last
column under W_5 represents a hypothetical warehouse indicating the
unused capacity in each factory.   The bottom number in the column
shows that there will be a total of 170 units of unused capacity.
Production and transportation costs are zero for this hypothetical
warehouse, as, in fact, no goods are either manufactured or shipped.

We can now proceed to solve this problem as a conventional transportation problem according to the general method we have developed.

The optimum solution is shown in Table 23, and we find that all the square evaluations are positive. From this, and from the fact that this solution is basic (there are 12 zeros in the solution), it follows that the solution is optimal. (Incidentally, this is a unique optimum solution as all square evaluations are greater than zero.) Let us note that F_1, F_2, and F_3 are used with full capacity, but F_4 produces only 50 units and has an unused capacity of 170 units (listed under W_5).

TABLE 23. Lowest Cost Allocation of Production and Transportation Facilities

(Total cost, $78,880)

		Warehouses					Total
		W_1	W_2	W_3	W_4	W_5	
	F_1	0	0	0	140	0	140
Factories	F_2	0	160	100	0	0	260
	F_3	180	120	0	60	0	360
	F_4	0	0	50	0	170	220
Total		180	280	150	200	170	980

So far, we have not considered the possibility that some or all these factories can go on overtime. Suppose that the first factory has a capacity of 50 units on overtime, the second factory 80 units, the third factory 120 units, and the fourth factory 60 units. In order to bring this new situation into the framework of the transportation problem, we introduce four hypothetical factories, F_{10}, F_{20}, F_{30}, and F_{40}, and say that the capacities of these hypothetical factories are 50, 80, 120, and 60.

We recall that production costs are $60 in F_1; we say that production costs in the hypothetical factory F_{10} are $90 (there is a 50% overtime cost). We recall that transportation costs from F_1 to W_1 are $28. This led to the combined transportation and production cost of $88 from F_1 to W_1. Similarly, the combined transportation and production cost from F_{10} to W_1 is $118. This number is listed in Table 24 in the first row, first column. The other figures in Table 24 are developed in a similar fashion. For instance, combined production and transportation costs from F_{20} to W_3 are $132.

We can consider, then, our new problem as a problem in transportation allocation, with 4 real and 4 hypothetical factories and 5 warehouses. Using the method we have already developed, we can determine the cheapest allocation of production and transportation facilities. This appears, however, to be a problem without much interest, because we do not expect to use overtime when we have sufficient capacity to produce the required goods without overtime. However, let us inspect the optimum solution in Table 23. Note that F_4 is used way below capacity. This suggests that perhaps it would be wiser to shut down F_4 and go on overtime in F_1, F_2, or F_3.

TABLE 24. Overtime Capacities and Combined Production and Transportation Costs

(F_{10}, F_{20}, etc., represent hypothetical factories to take care of overtime production)

		Warehouses					Total
		W_1	W_2	W_3	W_4	W_5	
Factories	F_{10}	118	130	126	128	. . .	50
	F_{20}	126	136	132	138	. . .	80
	F_{30}	114	126	130	126	. . .	120
	F_{40}	126	138	130	136	. . .	60
Total		. . .	. . .	. . .	. . .	. . .	. . .

Now we have F_1, F_2, and F_3 on regular time, and we also have F_{10}, F_{20}, and F_{30} on overtime. We ask the question: what is the cheapest allocation of production and transportation facilities within these three factories?

It is important to realize that this problem cannot be solved purely from the production point of view by going to the plant with the lowest overtime production cost. This is a combined production and transportation allocation problem and must be solved as such. The solution obtained by the transportation method is shown in Table 25. This table reveals several things: (1) Overtime is used only in factory 3, and the 50 units produced on overtime are to be shipped to W_4. (2) F_1, F_2, and F_3 are all used to full capacity. This is to be expected as there would not be any point in going on overtime in factory 3 unless the three factories do not have sufficient regular time capacities. (3) Not all the overtime production capacity is used in F_3, as the last row of Table 25 (referring to overtime production) shows that there are 70 units to be shipped to the hypothetical W_5, representing excess overtime capacity.   (4) When the first three factories alone are used, the combined transportation and production cost is \$79,980.   When compared with the figures shown in Table 23, where we used F_4, we notice that there is an increase in cost of \$1,100.

We see, then, that shutting F_4 down and introducing overtime in F_3 leads to an increased cost of \$1,100.   This is, however, not enough

TABLE 25.   Lowest Cost Allocation of Production and Transportation
Facilities When F_4 Is Shut Down

(Overtime utilized in F_3 (F_{30}).   Total cost, \$79,980)

		Warehouses					Total
		W_1	W_2	W_3	W_4	W_5	
Factories	F_1	88 / +2	100 / +2	96 / +2	140 (98)	0 / +28	140
	F_2	90 / +2	110 (100)	150 (96)	102 / +2	0 / +26	260
	F_3	180 (90)	170 (102)	100 / +2	10 (102)	0 / +24	360
	F_{10}	118 / +4	130 / +4	126 / +4	128 / +2	50 (0)	50
	F_{20}	126 / +12	136 / +10	132 / +10	138 / +12	80 (0)	80
	F_{30}	114 / 0	126 / 0	130 / +8	50 (126)	70 (0)	120
Total		180	280	150	200	70	880

data to make a decision.   Cost estimates must be made to reveal how much is saved in fixed costs by shutting F_4 down.   If the saving is more than \$1,100, then there might be a reason to shut F_4 down.   Of course, there are many other cost considerations to be looked into which are beyond the scope of this discussion.

A few words about this increase of \$1,100.   Inspecting Table 23, we might reason the following way: if we shut down F_4 we will have a deficit of 50 units in W_3, and these 50 units must be produced somewhere else.   In which factory can these 50 units be produced at the cheapest combined cost?   By inspecting Table 24, we notice that the cheapest method of providing W_3 with these 50 units is to have them produced in F_1, that is in the hypothetical F_{10} at a unit cost of \$126. The total cost of producing and transporting these 50 units would be 50(126), that is, \$6,300.   Originally we produced these 50 units at F_4

at a cost of $100 each (Table 22), and, therefore, in our original solution the total cost of producing and transporting these 50 units was $5,000.   From this we might deduce that when shutting down F_4 we are to incur the cost of $1,300, which is the difference between the $6,300 and the $5,000.   This conclusion, however, is an error.   The solution we obtained by using the transportation method shows that the increase is only $1,100.   The fact of the matter is that the cheapest way to meet our needs (under the assumption that F_4 is to be shut down) is to go on overtime in F_3, and then to reallocate production and transportation.

We have a good illustration here of the concept of interdependence; when some of the factors of the problem are changed, the whole situation needs to be re-evaluated.

8. DEGENERACY

The transportation method described in this book fails in certain exceptional cases.   Let us consider a problem indicated by Table 26.

TABLE 26. Degeneracy

(The square for, say, $x_{2,3}$ cannot be evaluated)

		Warehouses					Total
		W_1	W_2	W_3	W_4	W_5	
Factories	F_1	140					140
	F_2	40	220				260
	F_3			150	200	10	360
	F_4					120	120
Total		180	220	150	200	130	880

The combined capacity of F_1 and F_2 (400 units) exactly satisfies the combined requirements at W_1 and W_2.   Let us look at the initial solution, as shown in Table 26, and attempt to evaluate the square for $x_{2,3}$.   It is obviously impossible to find a pattern such that none of the corners will have a zero.   This problem, then, is called "degenerate" and cannot be solved with our method.

Let us look at the solution in Table 26 from another point of view. We have $n = 4$ rows and $m = 5$ columns. According to the formula at the end of Section 5, a basic solution in this problem should have at least $5(4) - 5 - 4 + 1 = 12$ zeros. However, there are 13 zeros in Table 26. (This reminds us of the 2 by 2 problem where we observed we might have 2 zeros.) The fact that there are more zeros than the formula indicates causes the trouble called degeneracy.

Fortunately, there is a very simple way to remedy this situation. If we add a very small amount of requirement—say 0.1 unit—to each of the warehouses, and add this total of 0.5 unit to one of the factories

TABLE 27.   Changing a Degenerate Problem into a Nondegenerate One

(Every square can be evaluated)

		Warehouses					Total
		W_1	W_2	W_3	W_4	W_5	
Factories	F_1	140					140
	F_2	40.1	219.9				260
	F_3		0.2	150.1	200.1	9.6	360
	F_4					120.5	120.5
Total		180.1	220.1	150.1	200.1	130.1	880.5

—say to F_4—as a hypothetical capacity. This new problem shown in Table 27 is not degenerate any more and can be solved with our method. When the solution is obtained, all we have to do is to round off the numbers and thereby obtain a solution to the original problem.

9. MATHEMATICAL FORMULATION OF THE TRANSPORTATION PROBLEM

Let us first introduce a mathematical notation for the 2-factory, 2-warehouse problem—the one we discussed at the beginning of this chapter. Let x be the unknown quantity of units to be shipped from F_1 to W_1. Now we realize that F_1 produces 8 units of goods, and therefore F_1 will ship $(8 - x)$ units of goods to W_2. Furthermore, W_1 received x units from F_1, and, as the total requirement at W_1 is 7 units, W_1 must receive $(7 - x)$ units from F_2. Finally, it is easy to see that F_2 must ship $(x - 2)$ units to W_2. In tabular form this can be represented as:

	W_1	W_2	
F_1	x	$8 - x$	8
F_2	$7 - x$	$x - 2$	5
	7	6	

What about the cost associated with this transportation scheme? It costs \$2.00 to ship from F_1 to W_1, and as we ship x units we see that the cost here is $2(x)$ dollars. Similarly, the cost of shipping $(8 - x)$ units from F_1 to W_2 is $3(8 - x)$ dollars; the cost of shipping $(7 - x)$ units from F_2 to W_1 is $4(7 - x)$ dollars; the shipping of $(x - 2)$ units from F_2 to W_2 costs $7(x - 2)$ dollars. Adding all these costs, we get the total cost associated with this transportation allocation:

$$z = 2x + 3(8 - x) + 4(7 - x) + 7(x - 2) \tag{1}$$

If we carry out the arithmetic, we get

$$z = 2x + 38 \tag{2}$$

We recognize now that this is the equation of the straight line shown in Fig. 1. The problem is to make this transportation cost the smallest possible. However, we must recognize that the unknown x, that is, the shipment from F_1 to W_1, cannot be just any number, because we must insist that all the shipments from any other factory to any other warehouse be positive. Mathematically speaking, the fact that all the shipments must be either zeros or positive (that is, they cannot be negative numbers) can be written in the form of the following three inequalities:

$$8 - x \geq 0 \tag{3}$$

$$7 - x \geq 0 \tag{4}$$

$$x - 2 \geq 0 \tag{5}$$

(The sign $\geq$ in these equations is to be read "larger than or equal to," and it means that the quantity on the left-hand side is larger than or equal to the quantity on the right-hand side.) We see then that the problem is to determine the unknown x, subject to the restrictions as expressed by inequalities (3), (4), and (5), such that the cost function as given by equation (2) becomes a minimum.

Let us now proceed to introduce mathematical notations to the 2-factory, 3-warehouse problem.   Let us denote by x the quantity of goods shipped from F_1 to W_1, and by y the quantity to be shipped from F_1 to W_2.   This leads to a table of unknowns:

	W_1	W_2	W_3	
F_1	x	y	$10 - x - y$	10
F_2	$6 - x$	$7 - y$	$x + y - 5$	8
	6	7	5	

We can easily verify that this table is correct by adding each row and each column, and checking against the capacities and requirements. The cost associated with each route is given by

	W_1	W_2	W_3
F_1	$6x$	$4y$	$2(10 - x - y)$
F_2	$5(6 - x)$	$4(7 - y)$	$3(x + y - 5)$

From this table we can compute the total cost associated with this transportation allocation:

$$z = 6x + 4y + 2(10 - x - y) + 5(6 - x) + 4(7 - y)$$
$$+ 3(x + y - 5) \quad (6)$$

By carrying out the algebra, we get

$$z = 2x + y + 63 \quad (7)$$

Now we must put into mathematical form the fact that it is impossible to ship negative quantities.   This leads to the following six inequalities:

$$x \geq 0 \quad (8)$$

$$y \geq 0 \quad (9)$$

$$10 - x - y \geq 0 \quad (10)$$

$$6 - x \geq 0 \quad (11)$$

$$7 - y \geq 0 \quad (12)$$

$$x + y - 5 \geq 0 \quad (13)$$

The transportation problem discussed here, then, can be put into the following mathematical form: minimize the cost as expressed by equation (7) under the restrictions of the inequalities (8) through (13).

It is of some interest to show the relationship between these last inequalities and Fig. 2.

The first inequality simply says that x must be larger than or equal to zero. The vertical line on the left-hand side in Fig. 3 represents the

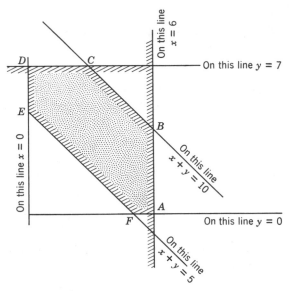

FIG. 3. Geometrical representation of inequalities (8)–(13). (Solution to the problem lies within the shaded area $ABCDEFA$.)

line on which x is zero. Therefore, we can say that inequality (8) states that the points we are interested in must lie on the right-hand side of the vertical axis shown. Similarly, inequality (9) tells us that the point we investigate must lie above the horizontal line shown. Inequality (10) can be written in the form

$$x + y \leq 10 \tag{14}$$

In Fig. 3 the line CB represents the line of those points for which the sum of x and y is exactly 10. Consequently, we can say that inequality (10) or (14) tells us that we should focus our attention to those points which lie below the line CB. Inequality (11) tells us that we are interested in the points that lie on the left-hand side of line AB, and inequality (12) tells us that we are interested in points that lie below the line DC. Finally, inequality (13) can be written in the form

$$x + y \geq 5 \tag{15}$$

and this inequality tells us that the point must lie above the line EF. If we put all these facts together we come to the conclusion that the points we are to investigate must lie inside the shaded area bordered by the polygon $ABCDEF$. This particular polygon has six sides corresponding to the six inequalities, and our problem is to select a point inside the polygon such that the cost associated with this point becomes a minimum. The fact of the matter is that *any* linear programming problem with two unknowns can be considered as a problem of searching the inside of a particular polygon. If we deal with linear programming with three unknowns, we are searching points inside of a three-dimensional polygon that is the inside of a polyhedron. Chapter 6, which describes the geometry of linear programming, will deal in more detail with this type of geometrical representation.

Let us finally proceed to the mathematical formulation of the problem of 3 factories and 5 warehouses. We could again call the unknowns x, y, z, etc., but as there are fifteen unknowns, this would be quite cumbersome. Another possibility would be to call the unknowns x_1, x_2, x_3, etc., on to x_{15}. This would be satisfactory, but it is more convenient to use the notation used in Table 3. We can put into mathematical form the fact that each row in Table 3 must add up to the particular capacity:

$$x_{1,1} + x_{1,2} + x_{1,3} + x_{1,4} + x_{1,5} = 100 \tag{16}$$

$$x_{2,1} + x_{2,2} + x_{2,3} + x_{2,4} + x_{2,5} = 100 \tag{17}$$

$$x_{3,1} + x_{3,2} + x_{3,3} + x_{3,4} + x_{3,5} = 120 \tag{18}$$

Similarly, each column must add up to the requirement in the particular warehouse:

$$x_{1,1} + x_{2,1} + x_{3,1} = 40 \tag{19}$$

$$x_{1,2} + x_{2,2} + x_{3,2} = 40 \tag{20}$$

$$x_{1,3} + x_{2,3} + x_{3,3} = 80 \tag{21}$$

$$x_{1,4} + x_{2,4} + x_{3,4} = 80 \tag{22}$$

$$x_{1,5} + x_{2,5} + x_{3,5} = 80 \tag{23}$$

The total transportation cost can be written as:

$$
\begin{aligned}
z = {} & 2x_{1,1} + {} & x_{1,2} + 2x_{1,3} + 3x_{1,4} + 3x_{1,5} \\
       & + 2x_{2,1} + 2x_{2,2} + 2x_{2,3} + {} & x_{2,4} - {} & x_{2,5} \\
       & + 3x_{3,1} + 3x_{3,2} + 2x_{3,3} + {} & x_{3,4} + 2x_{3,5}
\end{aligned} \tag{24}
$$

The problem in mathematical terminology is to minimize the cost function as it is given by equation (24) under the restrictions that the unknowns must satisfy the seven equations as given by equations (16) to (23).*

This completes the mathematical representation of the transportation problem when there are 3 factories and 5 warehouses. However, it is quite clear that it makes no difference how many warehouses and factories we have; we can always follow this scheme and represent the problem in a mathematical form.

At this point we might ask the question, "What is the use of putting the problem into mathematical form?" The answer is not much, because, in fact we have developed a method of solution without using the equations at all. However, later it will be recognized that the transportation problem is only a special type of linear programming problem, and that the more difficult problems in linear programming cannot be solved without setting up mathematical equations.

Let us add, furthermore, that the original development of the transportation method was based on a more formal argumentation than the one presented here. Only long after this mathematical argumentation was available was it possible to strip the method from its mathematical representation and develop the simplified presentation used in this book.

---

* There are eight equations, but one of them may be omitted. For, if seven of the equations are specified, it follows that the sum of the unknowns is 320. This makes the eighth equation superfluous.

CHAPTER 3

ILLUSTRATIONS

OF

MATHEMATICAL PROGRAMMING

1. ALLOCATION OF PRODUCTION FACILITIES WHEN ALTERNATE MACHINE ROUTING IS POSSIBLE

Let us imagine a hypothetical machine shop that is making plans for next week's production. This machine shop is producing only three products: cylinders, plates, and bushings. These various products are made on many machines, but only three groups of these machines form a bottleneck, and only these are to be considered for the production problem. These three groups are lathes, planers, and welders. The manager of the machine shop knows how much time is available on each of these machine groups. For instance, he has 236 hours available on lathes, 460 hours on planers, and 612 hours on welders, as shown in the right-hand column of Table 1. Each of the products can be manufactured through various routings; for instance, the cylinders can be routed through lathes, planers, or welders, as shown under column 1 of Table 1. It takes 0.4 hour for each of these cylinders on the lathes, on the planers, and on the welders. On the other hand, the same cylinder can be manufactured another way. The second column in Table 1 shows that it can be routed through lathes, taking 0.8 hour, and then directly through welding taking 0.6 hour. Table 1 shows that each of the products can be manufactured three different ways.

The selling price of these cylinders, plates, and bushings is different. It is $25 for each cylinder, $20 for each plate, and $30 for each bushing. It is assumed that there is an unlimited market for these products, and the problem that we are considering here is which of these products should be manufactured, on what routes, and in what quantities, in order to obtain a maximum revenue. We proceed now to set up the system of equations describing the problem, and to show that this is a problem in linear programming.

TABLE 1.   Allocation of Production Facilities When Alternate Machine Routing Is Possible[a]

	Products									Machine Hours Available
	Cylinders			Plates			Bushings			
	1	2	3	1	2	3	1	2	3	
	x_1	x_2	x_3	x_4	x_5	x_6	x_7	x_8	x_9	
Lathes 1	0.4	0.8	1.2	0.4	0.2		0.4	0.2		$h_1 = 236$
Planers 2	0.4		0.2	0.6	0.2	0.4	0.2	1.2	1.6	$h_2 = 460$
Welders 3	0.4	0.6	0.2	0.8	1.6	2.0	1.4	0.8	0.4	$h_3 = 612$
Minimum requirements	100			200			300			

[a] Shows hours required to manufacture each product, hours available on each machine group, and minimum quantity of each product required.

The first thing is to introduce names for the unknowns.   We denote by x_1 the number of cylinders manufactured according to first routing, by x_2 the number of cylinders manufactured through the second routing, and by x_3 the number of cylinders manufactured through the third routing.   Let us denote by x_4 the number of plates manufactured through the first routing, by x_5 the number of plates manufactured through the second routing, and by x_6 the number of plates manufactured through the third routing.   The unknowns, x_7, x_8, and x_9 have similar meaning for the bushings.   The first question we ask now is how much is the revenue associated with this production plan. This can be written in the following form:

$$z = 25(x_1 + x_2 + x_3) + 20(x_4 + x_5 + x_6) + 30(x_7 + x_8 + x_9) \quad (1)$$

The manager is then faced with the problem of making this revenue the largest possible. However, he cannot select the unknowns in an arbitrary fashion; he must consider the restrictions of the problem.

Let us compute first how many machine hours are required on the lathes. Let us call the number of hours required h_1; then

$$h_1 = 0.4x_1 + 0.8x_2 + 1.2x_3 + 0.4x_4 + 0.2x_5 + 0.4x_7 + 0.2x_8 \quad (2)$$

We know that we have only 236 hours available on lathes; therefore, h_1 must be less than 236.

$$0.4x_1 + 0.8x_2 + 1.2x_3 + 0.4x_4 + 0.2x_5 + 0.4x_7 + 0.2x_8 \leq 236 \quad (3)$$

We can similarly set up the restriction for the planers. This can be written as

$$0.4x_1 + 0.2x_3 + 0.6x_4 + 0.2x_5 + 0.4x_6 + 0.2x_7 + 1.2x_8 + 1.6x_9 \\ \leq 460 \quad (4)$$

The restriction for the welders is

$$0.4x_1 + 0.6x_2 + 0.2x_3 + 0.8x_4 + 1.6x_5 + 2.0x_6 + 1.4x_7 + 0.8x_8 \\ + 0.4x_9 \leq 612 \quad (5)$$

Our business problem can be described in mathematical language as follows: Determine the unknown x's, subject to the restrictions as given by equations (3), (4), and (5), that yield the maximum value of the revenue z as given in equation (1).

Let us make the problem somewhat more complicated. We will imagine that there is a fixed order (that must be satisfied) of 100 cylinders, 200 plates, and 300 bushings. (These numbers are shown in the bottom row of Table 1.) The customer pays $25, $20, and $30 for each cylinder, plate, and bushing in the fixed order. Furthermore, we will assume that the customer is willing to take any quantity of these products at a lower price. He is willing to pay $20 for each of the extra cylinders, $15 for each of the extra plates, and $20 for each of the extra bushings. The question is what should production allocation be, under these new conditions, in order to maximize revenue?

The first thing is to put these conditions into mathematical form. We must produce at least 100 of the cylinders. We are making cylinders in three different ways: Each of the three routings is allocated the quantity x_1, x_2, and x_3. Therefore, we make a total of $x_1 + x_2 + x_3$ number of cylinders. According to our requirement this must be equal to or more than 100:

$$x_1 + x_2 + x_3 \geq 100 \quad (6)$$

Similarly we can set up the condition for the plates:

$$x_4 + x_5 + x_6 \geq 200 \qquad (7)$$

and also for the bushings:

$$x_7 + x_8 + x_9 \geq 300 \qquad (8)$$

These are, then, the restrictions in the new problem. What about the revenue? This is a little more complicated, but it can be written as

$$\begin{aligned}
z = \ &25(100) + 20(x_1 + x_2 + x_3 - 100) + 20(200) \\
&+ 15(x_4 + x_5 + x_6 - 200) \\
&\qquad + 30(300) + 20(x_7 + x_8 + x_9 - 300) \quad (9)
\end{aligned}$$

The new problem in mathematical terms is how to maximize the revenue as given by equation (9) under the restrictions expressed by equations (3), (4), (5), (6), (7), and (8).

Let us suppose there is another complication in this problem. There is a market limitation on the number of cylinders that can be sold. Specifically, let us assume that not more than 200 of the cylinders can be sold. This market limitation results in

$$x_1 + x_2 + x_3 \leq 200 \qquad (10)$$

We see, then, that in order to handle this more complicated problem, all we have to do is to add the additional restriction given by (10).

Suppose now that there is the possibility of using overtime. How can we take this into account? Let x_{10} denote the number of cylinders made according to the first routing, not on regular time but on overtime. Let x_{11} denote the number of cylinders made on overtime according to the second routing. Similarly, we introduce the variable x_{12}. The overtime hours available on each group of machines are supposed to be known, and therefore three new inequalities can be obtained. We also have to replace our revenue function with a profit function, as overtime production is less profitable than regular production. However, in spite of the fact that there are more equations and more unknowns, and the fact that the payoff function is more complicated, we still have a problem in linear programming.

So far we have ignored the question of setup times: we have considered only the run time for each part. We did this because there is no general mathematical method of handling the problem of setup time. This does not mean that the problem cannot be handled at all; a systematic cut and try method can be used. For instance, we can make an estimate of what the setup time will be and reduce the available hours on the groups of machines by this estimated setup time.

Then we can proceed to obtain a solution based on linear programming. After this solution is obtained, we must verify whether the setup time estimate was correct. If it was, we are fortunate; however, if the estimate was off we must make a better estimate and carry through a new computation with the aid of linear programming.

Also we might discover that some of the runs are too short. The groups of machines with short runs should be excluded, and a new linear programming calculation should be carried through.

This is a systematic cut and try method and not as satisfactory as a straightforward linear programming solution. Notwithstanding, in some practical cases, it is possible to compute optimum solutions in a relatively short time. This is particularly true when there is a great deal of business experience or insight available.

Before we proceed to the next example, we will introduce a short-hand mathematical notation that is very useful in this type of problems. Table 1 has nine columns and three rows. This looks very similar to the tables used in connection with our transportation problem in Chapter 2. We propose to introduce symbols for each number in Table 1. As an example, take the number on the second row in the fifth column, 0.2. This is the number of hours it takes on the planers to make one of the plates according to the second routing scheme. We denote this number by $\tau_{2,5}$ where the first index refers to the second row and the second index refers to the fifth column. With this type of notation, equation (3) becomes

$$\tau_{1,1}x_1 + \tau_{1,2}x_2 + \tau_{1,3}x_3 + \tau_{1,4}x_4 + \tau_{1,5}x_5 + \tau_{1,6}x_6 + \tau_{1,7}x_7$$
$$+ \tau_{1,8}x_8 + \tau_{1,9}x_9 \leq h_1 \quad (11)$$

(We realize that both $\tau_{1,6}$ and $\tau_{1,9}$ have the value zero in this equation.) This does not look much like shorthand notation. However, this same equation can be written as

$$\sum_{j=1}^{9} \tau_{1,j}x_j \leq h_1 \quad (12)$$

where the Greek Σ denotes that the addition is to be carried through by substituting in the values of j as 1, 2, $\cdots$ 9. Using this notation, the restriction on planers, equation (4), can be written as

$$\sum_{j=1}^{9} \tau_{2,j}x_j \leq h_2 \quad (13)$$

or the restriction for welders as

$$\sum_{j=1}^{6} \tau_{3,j}x_j \leq h_3 \quad (14)$$

There is an even more abbreviated form of writing these three equations, namely:

$$\sum_{j=1}^{9} \tau_{i,j} x_j \leq h_i \qquad \text{for } i = 1, 2, 3 \tag{15}$$

This last equation says that i can be 1, 2, or 3. If we put any of these values of i into equation (15), we get back the old equations (12), (13), and (14). We can see, then, the equation (15) is a very compact way of writing all these equations. (It is recognized that it is rather difficult to get accustomed to this type of notation. Therefore, it is suggested that the reader take equation (15) and substitute the various values of i to get back equations (12), (13), and (14).)

The revenue or profit function in the problem can also be written in the abbreviated form:

$$z = \sum_{j=1}^{9} p_j x_j + C \tag{16}$$

For instance, if we want to get back equation (1) we have to make p_1, p_2, and p_3 all equal to 25, p_4, p_5, and p_6 all 15, and p_7, p_8, and p_9 all 20. In equation (1) the value of C is 0. On the other hand, if we want to get back equation (9) we have to assign to C the value of 4,500.

It is emphasized again that the shorthand notation does not tell us anything new, as we can always write out the equations in detail if necessary.

2. ALLOCATION OF LAND, CAPITAL, AND LABOR FOR A FARMING ENTERPRISE

A certain farm in North Carolina has a choice of growing potatoes, corn, soya beans, etc., as shown in Table 2.* Let us focus attention, say, on growing potatoes. According to the first column on Table 2, it can be seen that, for each acre of spring land, zero acres of fall land (i.e., no fall land) are required, and also a production capital of $99.4 is required. It is also shown that 2.4 hours of labor are required in January and February; in March and April only two hours of labor are required, etc. Table 2 also shows the requirements for growing corn or soya beans or for raising beef. Now, the farmer has only limited resources available; for instance, according to the last column

* F. W. Waugh and G. L. Burrows, "A Short Cut to Linear Programming," *Econometrica*, Vol. 23, 1955, p. 18.

TABLE 2. Allocation of Land, Capital, and Labor for a Farming Enterprise[a]

Resources		Potatoes x_1	Corn x_2	Soya Beans x_3	Beef x_4	Fall Cabbage x_5	Fall Lettuce x_6	Resources Available
Spring land	1	1.0	1.0	1.0	1.0	0	0	$a_1 = 60$
Fall land	2	0	1.0	1.0	1.0	1.0	1.0	$a_2 = 60$
Production capital	3	99.4	37.8	19.8	27.2	74.8	53.0	$a_3 = 2,000$
Jan.-Feb. labor	4	2.4	1.5	0	0	0	0	$a_4 = 351$
Mar.-April labor	5	2.0	2.0	0	0	0	0	$a_5 = 448$
May-June labor	6	1.8	3.3	5.3	0	0	0	$a_6 = 479$
July-Aug. labor	7	0	0	2.1	0	0	0	$a_7 = 388$
Sept.-Oct. labor	8	0	0	0.4	0	19.1	12.4	$a_8 = 424$
Nov.-Dec. labor	9	0	3.0	0.4	0	9.1	26.7	$a_9 = 359$
Net profit		83.4	72.4	27.3	36.0	20.7	45.5	

[a] Shows the quantity of resources required for each product, resources available, and the net profit on each product.

of Table 2 he has only 60 acres of land available either in the spring
or during the fall.   His production capital is $2,000.   His labor poten-
tial varies from month to month; during January and February it is
351 hours, in March and April it is 448 hours, etc.   Finally, the
bottom row on Table 2 shows his profit.   For instance, his net profit
is $83.4 on each acre of land producing potatoes.   On each acre of
corn cultivated, he can realize $72.4, etc.   The problem the farmer
is faced with is what is the best allocation of his resources (his land,
capital, and labor) to the various products he can grow.   This is a
linear programming problem, and we proceed now to set up a system
of equations describing the problem.

The first thing is again to introduce the unknowns.   Let x_1 denote
the acres of spring land allocated to growing potatoes, x_2 the land
allocated to corn, x_3 the land allocated to soya beans, x_4 to beef.
Finally, let x_5 and x_6 denote the acres of land allocated to fall production of cabbage and lettuce.   The restrictions on the available 60 acres
of spring land can be written as

$$x_1 + x_2 + x_3 + x_4 \leq 60 \tag{17}$$

and the restriction on fall acreage as

$$x_2 + x_3 + x_4 + x_5 + x_6 \leq 60 \tag{18}$$

According to Table 2, we can develop the restriction on capital as

$$99.4x_1 + 37.8x_2 + 19.8x_3 + 27.2x_4 + 74.8x_5 + 53.0x_6 \leq 2,000 \tag{19}$$

Similarly, we can proceed to set up each of the restrictions.   However, we propose to use a shorthand notation.   Let $r_{i,j}$ denote the
number in the ith row and the jth column in Table 2.   For instance,
$r_{7,3}$ is 2.1.   With this notation equation (19) becomes

$$r_{3,1}x_1 + r_{3,2}x_2 + r_{3,3}x_3 + r_{3,4}x_4 + r_{3,5}x_5 + r_{3,6}x_6 \leq 2,000 \tag{20}$$

or

$$\sum_{j=1}^{6} r_{3,j}x_j \leq a_3 \tag{21}$$

where a_3 is 2,000 as shown in the last column, third row, of Table 2.
We can write all the nine restrictions in the form

$$\sum_{j=1}^{6} r_{i,j}x_j \leq a_i \qquad i = 1, 2, \cdots, 9 \tag{22}$$

We can also compute the profit associated with this program.

$$z = 83.4x_1 + 72.4x_2 + \cdots + 45.5x_6 \tag{23}$$

or, in an abbreviated form:

$$z = \sum_{j=1}^{6} c_j x_j \qquad (24)$$

It is seen, then, that we have transformed this farming problem into a problem of linear programming; the problem is to maximize the profit as given by equation (24) subject to the restrictions expressed by (22).

As in the manufacturing problem discussed previously, the farmer might have some more complicated situations to deal with; he might have the problem of overtime, product discount, etc. These can be handled as described in Section 2 of this chapter.

3. ALLOCATION OF PRODUCTION FACILITIES WHEN PRODUCTS MAY BE MANUFACTURED ON ALTERNATE MACHINES

A machine shop manufactures five kinds of precision screws on three groups of automatic screw machines. Each product can be made on any of the machine groups, but the time required on each of the machine groups is different, as shown in the upper part of Table 3. As an example, it can be seen that each of the third type of precision screw, when manufactured on the second type of automatic machine, takes 0.4 hour. The machine shop is making plans for next week's production. There is an order for the different types of screws in quantities of 800, 1,800, 1,400, 1,800, and 800 as shown on the upper part of Table 3 in the last row. There is, of course, a limitation on available machine hours; this is 2,400 hours. The labor cost per hour for each machine is different. The labor cost for each product on each machine group is computed by multiplying labor costs by hours required. (See the lower part of Table 3.)

The labor market is assumed to be such that it is not necessary to work a 40-hour week. The shop can work 3, 4, or 5 days per week if it is necessary. This means then that production costs, and in particular labor costs, depend on the particular type of allocation of machine groups. The manager of the machine shop, then, is faced with the problem of allocating his machines to his product in such a way that the total cost will be at a minimum. This is a problem in linear programming, and we proceed now to set up the system of equations describing it.

TABLE 3. Allocation of Production Facilities When Products May Be Manufactured on Alternate Machines[a]

		Products					Machine Hours Available
		1	2	3	4	5	
Machine Groups	1	0.4	0.2	0.4	0.2	0.4	$h_1 = 2,400$
	2	0.8	0.6	0.4	0.6	0.6	$h_2 = 2,400$
	3	1.0	1.0	0.8	0.6	1.0	$h_3 = 2,400$
		$b_1 = 800$	$b_2 = 1,800$	$b_3 = 1,400$	$b_4 = 1,800$	$b_5 = 800$	

		Products				
		1	2	3	4	5
Machine Groups	1	0.4×12	0.2×12	0.4×12	0.2×12	0.4×12
	2	0.8×9	0.6×9	0.4×9	0.6×9	0.6×9
	3	1.0×9	1.0×9	0.8×9	0.6×9	1.0×9

[a]Table at top shows requirements for each product, hours available on each machine group, and standard times required. Table below shows labor costs.

The notation we are going to use is the following: let $x_{2,3}$ denote the number of products of type 3 that are made by machine type 2, etc. (This is very similar to the notation we used in the transportation problem in Chapter 2, as shown in Table 3.) The quantity of the first product to be made is 800, which can be expressed in equation form as

$$x_{1,1} + x_{2,1} + x_{3,1} = 800 \qquad (25)$$

Similarly, 1,800 of the second product must be made:

$$x_{1,2} + x_{2,2} + x_{3,2} = 1,800 \qquad (26)$$

Similar equations can be written to cover products 3, 4, and 5. Note that these equations look exactly like equation (19) in Chapter 2 on the transportation problem. We are, however, not through with the various restrictions of the problem. We must consider the machine hours available. This can be written for the first group of automatic screw machines as

$$0.4x_{1,1} + 0.2x_{1,2} + 0.4x_{1,3} + 0.2x_{1,4} + 0.4x_{1,5} \leq 2,400 \qquad (27)$$

The other two equations for machine groups 2 and 3 can be written in a similar form. We realize now that these equations are not entirely different from the ones we used in Chapter 2 in connection with the transportation problem. The difference is that in the transportation problem we added the unknowns in each row and the sum had to equal the total production in the particular plant. In the problem we are considering here, each of the unknowns must be multiplied by a factor before they are added together; this makes this problem somewhat more complicated.

The next thing is to compute the total cost associated with the manufacturing program. This can be written as

$$z = 4.8x_{1,1} + 2.4x_{1,2} + 1.8x_{1,3} \mid \cdots \mid 9x_{3,5} \qquad (28)$$

In order to make things simpler we will use an abbreviated notation.

The unknowns in each column must add up to the known requirements of each product:

$$\sum_{i=1}^{3} x_{i,j} = b_j \qquad \text{for } j = 1, 2, 3, 4, 5 \qquad (29)$$

On the right-hand side, the b represents the various requirements. (It must be remembered that equation (29) is the five different equations representing requirements for the five products. If the reader has difficulty following the notation in equation (29), it is suggested that he write these five equations out in detail.)

We proceed now to determine the machine hour restrictions. Let us use the notation that $\tau_{i,j}$ denotes the hours required for the jth product of the ith machine. For instance, $\tau_{2,3}$ equals the hours required for product 3 on machine 2, (0.4 hour, according to Table 3). We can write the machine hour restrictions as

$$\sum_{j=1}^{5} \tau_{i,j} x_{i,j} \leq h_i \qquad \text{for } i = 1, 2, 3 \tag{30}$$

where h_i denotes the hours available of each of the machine groups. (It so happens that h_1, h_2, and h_3 are each equal to 2,400 hours.) Finally, we write the cost in the form of

$$z = \sum_{j=1}^{5} \sum_{i=1}^{3} c_{i,j} x_{i,j} \tag{31}$$

Note that there are two Σ's in this equation. This expresses the fact that summation must be made both for rows and for columns. (Each element in each row must enter into the summation.) The little numbers show that i goes from 1 to 3. This means that the first, second, and third rows are to be added. The other numbers show that j goes from 1 to 5, indicating that summation must be made of the five different columns representing the five different products. The problem that the manager of this machine shop faces is to make the cost, represented by equation (31), the smallest possible, with the restrictions that both the quantities to be delivered, represented by equation (29), and the limitations on the machine hours, represented by equation (30), are satisfied. This is again a problem in linear programming, and the best possible allocation can be computed.

We have already indicated that this problem is somewhat similar to the transportation problem. Later we will see that problems of this type occur frequently and, therefore, that it will be convenient to call any of them the *generalized transportation problem*. It will be seen in Chapter 5 that there is a particular method of solution, tailored for this generalized transportation problem, which is somewhat more complicated than the solution to the original transportation problem but still much simpler than the method that must be used in solving linear programming problems in general. It will be noted that, if all the $\tau_{i,j}$'s are equal, we get back the old transportation problem in its original form.

The machine shop problem as presented here is, of course, highly idealized, but let us recognize that the problem can be solved under much more general conditions. For instance overtime can be introduced by assuming three hypothetical groups of overtime machines. This would make the upper part of Table 3 different, as there would be six instead of three rows. We would require twice as many unknowns, which would make the computations more time consuming. However, conceptually the problem is still the same.

Suppose now that the profit structure is not so simple. For instance, consider the possibility of discounts when selling in quantities. In Chapter 7, under the title "Convex Programming," we are going to develop a method of handling problems with this type of profit function.

We have again ignored here the problems associated with setup time. As mentioned before, there is no general mathematical method of handling this, and the only thing to do is to use a systematic cut and try method.

4. ALLOCATION OF RAW MATERIALS TO MATCH MARKET REQUIREMENTS

A manufacturer is engaged in producing four different products. Each of these products can be made of three different materials. The requirements for each product are shown on the upper part of Table 4. For instance, it can be seen that product 2 requires 3.0 units of material if it is made of material 1. On the other hand, if it is made of material 2, then it will require 4.5 units, etc. The manufacturer has only a limited amount of material available: 200 units of material 1, 300 units of material 2, and 500 units of material 3. The market for each product is limited: 200 units for product 1, 100 for product 2, 160 for product 3, and 50 for product 4. The price of each of the products is different and is independent of what material is used. Both material and production costs are different, and, therefore, the profit for each product depends on what material the particular product is made of. The lower part of Table 4 shows the profit for each product according to the material it is being made up of. What is the best allocation of materials to these products?

The first thing is to introduce the notation for the unknowns; let us use $x_{i,j}$ for the quantity of product j that is manufactured from material i. (This is the same type of notation we used before.) As there is a market limitation for each of the products, we can write the

TABLE 4. Allocation of Raw Materials to Match Market Requirements[a]

		Products				Materials Available
		1	2	3	4	
Materials	1	2.4	3.0	3.0	3.6	$a_1 = 200$
	2	3.6	4.5	4.5	5.4	$a_2 = 300$
	3	4.0	5.0	5.0	6.0	$a_3 = 500$
Potential market		$b_1 = 200$	$b_2 = 100$	$b_3 = 160$	$b_4 = 50$	

		Products			
		1	2	3	4
Materials	1	78	120	78	117
	2	66	90	72	90
	3	54	81	69	45

[a] Table at top shows the market potential for each product, quantity of raw materials available, and requirements for each product. Lower table shows profit for each product.

following four equations:

$$\sum_{i=1}^{3} x_{i,j} \leq b_j \qquad j = 1, 2, 3, 4 \tag{32}$$

where the b denotes the market limitation for each of the products. Next we have to introduce the limitation on the materials. We say that $r_{i,j}$ is the quantity of material i required for each product j; for instance, $r_{2,3}$ denotes the quantity of material 2 required for each unit of product 3, and this quantity is shown on the upper part of Table 4 as 4.5 units. With this notation, then we can write the material restrictions as follows:

$$\sum_{j=1}^{4} r_{i,j} x_{i,j} \leq a_i \qquad i = 1, 2, 3 \tag{33}$$

Finally, we can write the profit in the form of

$$z = \sum_{i=1}^{3} \sum_{j=1}^{4} p_{i,j} x_{i,j} \tag{34}$$

where the small p refers to the numbers shown on the lower part of Table 4.

This problem is a linear programming problem; we have to maximize the profit as shown by equation (34) under the restrictions of equations (32) and (33). Let us notice that these equations are the same as the ones in the problem we had in Section 3; we are dealing here with the generalized transportation problem. The only difference is that in this case we want to maximize our profit, whereas before we wanted to minimize the cost. Again, we notice that, if all the requirements, i.e., the $r_{i,j}$'s are equal, we get back the old transportation problem as developed in Chapter 2.

5. ALLOCATION OF TRANSPORTATION FACILITIES TO ALTERNATE ROUTING

A certain airline has four groups of airplanes; the first group consists of 10 four-engine postwar design airplanes, the second group consists of 19 two-engine postwar designs, the third of 25 two-engine prewar designs, and, finally, the fourth group consists of 15 four-engine prewar designs.* This particular airline flies from New York to Los Angeles with one stop or two stops. Furthermore, it flies from New York to Dallas without stops or with one stop, and finally from New York to Boston with no stops as shown in the upper part of Table 5. Revenues are $130 from New York to Los Angeles, $70 from New York to Dallas, and $10 from New York to Boston. The anticipated number of passengers per month is 25,000 from New York to Los Angeles, one stop; 12,000 on the same route with two stops; 18,000 from New York to Dallas, no stop; 9,000 from New York to Dallas, one stop; and 60,000 from New York to Boston. The lower part of Table 5 shows the variable operating costs for these different airplanes on the different routes. The problem the airline faces is how to allocate its airplane fleet to the various routes so that its profit will be maximum.

We will introduce the same type of notation we used before. Let $x_{i,j}$ denote the number of aircraft type i allocated to route j. (For instance, $x_{2,3}$ denotes the number of aircraft of type 2 allocated to the New York–Dallas no-stop flight.) Let b_1, b_2, etc., denote the anticipated passengers on each of the routes, and let $r_{i,j}$ denote the monthly passenger capacity of aircraft type i on route j. For instance, the upper part of Table 5 shows that the value of $r_{3,2}$ is 500. This means

* A. R. Ferguson and G. B. Dantzig, "The Problem of Routing Aircraft," *Aeronautical Engineering Review*, Vol. 14, No. 4, April, 1955, pp. 51–55.

TABLE 5. Allocation of Transportation Facilities to Alternate Routing[a]

		Routing					Number of Aircraft Available
		New York to Los Angeles, One Stop	New York to Los Angeles, Two Stops	New York to Dallas, No Stop	New York to Dallas, One Stop	New York to Boston	
		1	2	3	4	5	
Aircraft Type	1	1,600	1,500	2,800	2,300	8,100	$a_1 = 10$
	2	X	1,000	1,400	1,500	5,700	$a_2 = 19$
	3	X	500	X	700	2,900	$a_3 = 25$
	4	900	1,100	2,200	1,700	5,500	$a_4 = 15$
Passenger potential		$b_1 = 25,000$	$b_2 = 12,000$	$b_3 = 18,000$	$b_4 = 9,000$	$b_5 = 60,000$	

		Routing				
		1	2	3	4	5
Aircraft Type	1	18,000	21,000	18,000	16,000	10,000
	2	X	15,000	16,000	14,000	9,000
	3	X	10,000	X	9,000	6,000
	4	17,000	16,000	17,000	15,000	10,000

[a] Top table shows anticipated number of passengers per month at each route, number of aircraft available, capacity of each aircraft on each route per month. Lower table shows operating costs in dollars per month per airplane.

that aircraft type 3 can carry 500 passengers per month on the New York–Los Angeles two-stop trip. We can now put into mathematical form the fact that on each route the airline carries less than (or at most, equal to) the anticipated number of passengers:

$$\sum_{i=1}^{4} r_{i,j} x_{i,j} \leq b_j \qquad j = 1, 2, 3, 4, 5 \tag{35}$$

(Let us remember that we have in an abbreviated form five different inequalities.) Now we must put into mathematical form the fact that we have only a fixed number of airplanes available; let a_1 denote the number of aircraft type 1 available (i.e., 10); let a_2 denote the number of aircraft type 2 available, etc. Then:

$$\sum_{j=1}^{5} x_{i,j} = a_i \qquad i = 1, 2, 3, 4 \tag{36}$$

(Let us remember again that this last equation represents four different equations.) The profit can be written as the difference between revenues and costs:

$$z = \sum_{j=1}^{5} p_j \left(\sum_{i=1}^{4} r_{i,j} x_{i,j} \right) - \sum_{i=1}^{4} \sum_{j=1}^{5} c_{i,j} x_{i,j} \tag{37}$$

where p_1, p_2, etc., denote the revenue on each route per passenger, and $c_{i,j}$ denotes the cost for each aircraft on each route. (For instance, p_2 is $70, and $c_{3,4}$ is $9,000.) Our problem, in mathematical form, is to maximize the profit as represented by equation (37) under the restrictions of (35) and (36). We remember now that this is the type of problem we faced before. This is the generalized transportation problem. (If all the capacities $r_{i,j}$ were equal, we would get back our old transportation problem.)

It is interesting that there are quite a number of different business problems that lead to exactly the same mathematical problem, that is, the generalized transportation problem.

6. AN EXERCISE IN FUEL OIL BLENDING

A certain refinery produces on the average 1,000 gal./hr., of virgin pitch in its crude distillation operation.* Both the viscosity blending

* G. H. Symonds, *Linear Programming: The Solution of Refinery Problems*, Esso Standard Oil Company, New York, New York, 1955, p. 25.

number and the gravity blending number for the pitch are too low, and so it cannot be sold as commercial fuel oil. However, the pitch may be blended with flux stock or it may be sent in whole or in part to a visbreaker unit, and thereby the blending numbers can be improved. The problem here is what fraction of the 1,000 gal./hr. of pitch should be sent to the visbreaking unit, and how much flux stock should be purchased.

In order to put this problem into mathematical form, let us follow the notation introduced in Fig. 1. Let x denote the gallons per hour

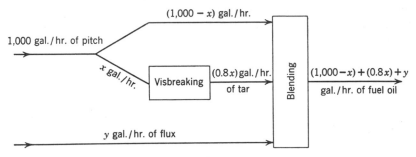

FIG. 1. An exercise in fuel oil blending.

of pitch going into visbreaking; then $(1,000 - x)$ gallons per hour of pitch go into blending. The visbreaking unit produces 80% of tar; i. e., there is $(0.8x)$ gallon per hour of tar produced by visbreaking. Suppose that the virgin pitch and the tar are blended with y gallons per hour of flux. We can see, then, that there are $(1,000 - x) + (0.8x) + y$ gallons per hour of fuel oil produced from blending.

Let us now look into the profit picture. There is a 5¢ per gallon profit for fuel oil, but there is an expense of 8¢ per gallon for the flux stock. The profit in this operation is given by

$$z = 5[(1,000 - x) + (0.8x) + y] - 8y \qquad (38)$$

Finally we need to consider the specifications for the fuel oil; the viscosity blending number must be equal to or more than 21, and the gravity blending number must be equal to or more than 12.

In order to be able to evaluate these performance numbers, we must take into account the specifications for pitch, tar, and flux. The

	Viscosity Blending Number	Gravity Blending Number
Pitch	5	8
Tar	11	7
Flux	37	24

viscosity blending number of the product can be computed from the formula:

Viscosity blending number of fuel oil

$$= \frac{5(\text{quantities of pitch}) + 11(\text{quantities of tar}) + 37(\text{quantities of flux})}{\text{quantities of fuel oil}}$$

According to the specification on the fuel oil, the viscosity blending number must be equal to or more than 21, that is, we must have

$$\frac{5(1{,}000 - x) + 11(0.8x) + 37y}{(1{,}000 - x) + (0.8x) + y} \geq 21 \qquad (39)$$

We multiply both sides of equation (39) by the denominator and get

$$5{,}000 + 3.8x + 37y \geq 21(1{,}000 - 0.2x + y) \qquad (40)$$

We can use the same type of formula for the gravity blending number, and get the inequality

$$\frac{8(1{,}000 - x) + 7(0.8x) + 24y}{(1{,}000 - x) + (0.8x) + y} \geq 12 \qquad (41)$$

or

$$8{,}000 - 2.4x + 24y \geq 12(1{,}000 - 0.2x + y) \qquad (42)$$

The problem is, then, to maximize the profit as given by equation (38), under the restrictions of inequalities (39) and (41). Furthermore, both x and y must be positive and x must be less than 1,000, or:

$$0 \leq x \leq 1{,}000 \qquad (43)$$

Equation (40) can be simplified after a little arithmetic to

$$x + 2y \geq 2{,}000 \qquad (44)$$

and equation (42) can be simplified to

$$y \geq 333 \qquad (45)$$

Finally, the profit equation, (38), can be simplified to the following:

$$z = 5{,}000 - x - 3y \qquad (46)$$

It can be seen, then, that in the final mathematical form the problem is to maximize the profit as given by equation (46), under the restrictions of (43), (44), and (45). This is a problem in linear programming and can be solved as such.

Let us remind ourselves, however, that this is only an exercise, and that such a simple problem can be solved without linear programming.

It is obvious that visbreaking is either a profitable or an unprofitable operation. From this, it follows that either we do not send any of the 1000 gal./hr. pitch to vixbreaking or we send all of it to visbreaking. If we do not use visbreaking, we have $x = 0$. The least amount of flux that must be used is $y = 1,000$, as both equations (44) and (45) must be satisfied. The profit can be computed from equation (46), and we get \$20. On the other hand, if we send the 1,000 gal./hr., to visbreaking, we get $x = 1,000$ and $y = 500$, which leads to the profit of \$25. It is seen, then, that each gallon of pitch, when sent through visbreaking, increases the profit by half a cent, and, therefore, that we should send all the pitch to visbreaking. (If the capacity of vis-breaking is only, say, 800 gal./hr., then the best thing is to send this quantity to visbreaking.)

7. BLENDING OF CONSTITUENTS: WHAT AND HOW TO PRODUCE

After working through the previous exercise, we are in a position to consider a more realistic situation. Let us consider a refinery that has a daily supply of 3,800 bbl./day of alkylate, 2,652 bbl./day of catalytic cracked gasoline, 4,081 bbl./day of straight-run gasoline, and 1,300 bbl./day of isopentane.* These four constituents are blended into three grades of aviation gasoline, A, B, and C, the rest of the constituents are sold as gasoline for automobiles. The blending process is shown graphically in Fig. 2. The selling price of aviation gasoline A is \$5.00/bbl.; of aviation gasoline B, \$5.80/bbl.; of aviation gasoline C, \$6,40/bbl.; and the automobile gasoline sells for \$4.80/bbl. The problem is to determine the mix of the four constituents that will result in maximum profit.

We introduce a notation shown in Fig. 2 and Table 6. For instance, $x_{2,3}$ denotes the barrels of straight-run gasoline that is blended into aviation gasoline B. Furthermore, y_2 denotes the barrels of aviation gasoline to be produced per day. As the daily supply of alkylate is 3,800 bbl., we can write

$$x_{1,1} + x_{2,1} + x_{3,1} + x_{4,1} = 3,800 \qquad (47)$$

Or we can write for each of the constituents

$$x_{1,j} + x_{2,j} + x_{3,j} + x_{4,j} = b_j \qquad j = 1, 2, 3, 4 \qquad (48)$$

* A. Charnes, W. W. Cooper, and B. Mellon, "Blending Aviation Gasolines, A Study in Program-ming Interdependent Activities in an Integrated Oil Company," *Econometrica*, Vol. 20, No. 2, April, 1952.

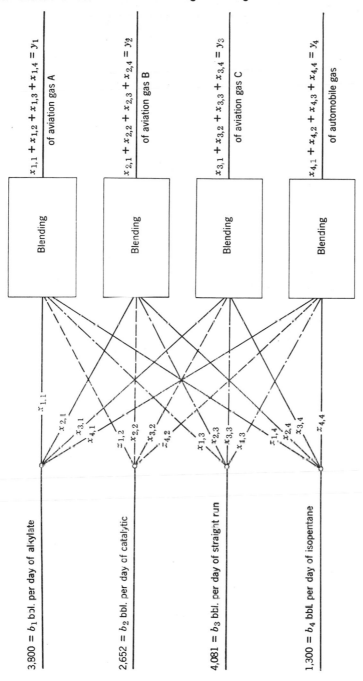

FIG. 2. Gasoline blending.

TABLE 6. Blending of Constituents[a]

		Constituents				Quantity Produced
		Alkylate	Catalytic	Straight Run	Isopentane	
		1	2	3	4	
Aviation gas A	1	$x_{1,1}$	$x_{1,2}$	$x_{1,3}$	$x_{1,4}$	y_1
Aviation gas B	2	$x_{2,1}$	$x_{2,2}$	$x_{2,3}$	$x_{2,4}$	y_2
Aviation gas C	3	$x_{3,1}$	$x_{3,2}$	$x_{3,3}$	$x_{3,4}$	y_3
Auto gas	4	$x_{4,1}$	$x_{4,2}$	$x_{4,3}$	$x_{4,4}$	y_4
Constituents available		$b_1 = 3,800$	$b_2 = 2,652$	$b_3 = 4,081$	$b_4 = 1,300$	

[a] Shows designation of unknown quantity of each constituent allocated to each product, designation of total quantities produced, and quantities of constituents available.

where b_1, b_2, b_3, and b_4 denote the barrels of alkylate, catalytic cracked gasoline, straight-run gasoline, and isopentane available per day. The barrels of aviation gasoline C produced per day is given by

$$x_{3,1} + x_{3,2} + x_{3,3} + x_{3,4} = y_3 \qquad (49)$$

In general we can write

$$x_{i,1} + x_{i,2} + x_{i,3} + x_{i,4} = y_i \qquad i = 1, 2, 3, 4 \qquad (50)$$

The revenue gained from selling these gasolines is given by

$$z = 5y_1 + 5.8y_2 + 6.4y_3 + 4.8y_4 \qquad (51)$$

which can be written in the form

$$z = 5(x_{1,1} + x_{1,2} + \cdots) + 5.8(x_{2,1} + x_{2,2} + \cdots) + \cdots$$
$$+ 4.8(x_{4,1} + x_{4,2} + \cdots) \qquad (52)$$

or

$$z = \sum_{i=1}^{4} \sum_{j=1}^{4} p_{i,j} x_{i,j} \qquad (53)$$

So far we have ignored the performance characteristics imposed on the aviation gasolines. One of these characteristics is the Reid vapor pressure, which is abbreviated RVP. The RVP for aviation gasoline must be less than 7.0. For each of the constituents the RVP is 5.0, 8.0, 4.0, and 20.5. How do we put this performance characteristic restriction into a mathematical form? The formula is very similar to the one we used for the viscosity blending number of fuel oil in the last section, equation (39). The RVP for aviation gasoline A is given by

$$\text{RVP of aviation gasoline A} = \frac{5x_{1,1} + 8x_{1,2} + 4x_{1,3} + 20.5x_{1,4}}{y_1} \qquad (54)$$

This must be less than (or equal to) 7.0:

$$\frac{5x_{1,1} + 8x_{1,2} + 4x_{1,3} + 20.5x_{1,4}}{x_{1,1} + x_{1,2} + x_{1,3} + x_{1,4}} \leq 7.0 \qquad (55)$$

This can be written in the form

$$5x_{1,1} + 8x_{1,2} + 4x_{1,3} + 20.5x_{1,4} \leq 7x_{1,1} + 7x_{1,2} + 7x_{1,3} + 7x_{1,4} \qquad (56)$$

which can be written as

$$-2x_{1,1} + x_{1,2} - 3x_{1,3} + 13.5x_{1,4} \leq 0 \qquad (57)$$

Similar equations hold for aviation gasoline B and aviation gasoline C. Therefore, we can write

$$-2x_{i,1} + x_{i,2} - 3x_{i,3} + 13.5x_{i,4} \leq 0 \qquad i = 1, 2, 3 \qquad (58)$$

(This represents three different inequalities for $i = 1, 2, 3$. However, (58) does *not* hold for $i = 4$, that is, for automobile gasoline, as there is no restriction there on the RVP.)

If the only restriction on the aviation gasolines is the RVP, then the problem is to maximize the profit as given by equation (53) under the three restrictions given by equations (48) and (58). However, usually there are some other performance numbers that must be restricted. For instance, the octane number must be above a certain limit, both for lean and for rich mixtures. Each of these new restrictions leads to three inequalities similar to the ones given by equation (58). Instead of going into the details of deriving these inequalities here, we write them in a general form:

$$\sum_{j=1}^{4} q_j{}^k x_{i,j} \geq 0 \qquad i = 1, 2, 3; k = 1, 2, 3 \qquad (59)$$

This last inequality is an abbreviated expression of the fact that there are three inequalities for each value of k, that is, for $k = 1, 2, 3$. The first of these three (i.e., $k = 1$) refers to the RVP, the second, $k = 2$, to the lean mixture octane number, and the third, $k = 3$, to the rich mixture octane number.

We see, then, that this problem in gasoline blending can be expressed in mathematical form, maximizing the profit as given by equation (53) under the restrictions given by equations (48) and (59). In the problem described here, there would be thirteen of these restrictions. This is a problem in linear programming.

8. A STUDY OF AN OIL CORPORATION

An oil corporation is committed to buy a certain minimum of each of six different crudes every day.* Market conditions are such that the corporation can obtain more than this minimum amount of each crude if necessary. The crudes received are put through the primary stage of a refining process as shown in Fig. 3. However, capacity at this primary stage is limited and, therefore, it can happen that there

---

* A. Charnes, W. W. Cooper, and B. Mellon; "A Model for Programming and Sensitivity Analysis in an Integrated Oil Company," *Econometrica*, Vol. 22, 1954, p. 193.

is a surplus crude which must be sold on the market.   The primary
stage of the refinery process results in two intermediate products.
Each of these products can be sold directly on the market or can be
refined further through a secondary stage of refining as shown in Fig. 3.
The capacities in the secondary stages of each intermediate product
are also limited.   The problem is to determine how much of each

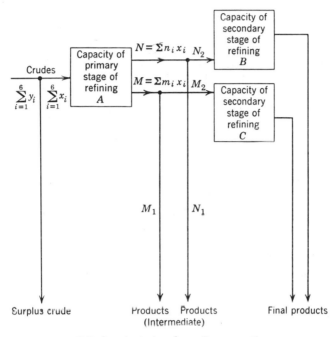

FIG. 3.   A study of an oil corporation.

crude should be purchased and what is the best allocation of the refinery
capacities to the various products.

Let $y_1, y_2 \cdots y_6$ denote the quantity of each crude to be purchased
every day; let $a_1, a_2 \cdots a_6$ denote the minimum quantities of these
crudes that must be purchased.   The fact that a certain amount of
each crude must be purchased can be put into the following mathematical form:

$$y_i \geq a_i \qquad i = 1, 2, \cdots, 6 \qquad (60)$$

(Let us remember that equation (60) represents six different inequalities.)   Let $x_1, x_2 \cdots x_6$ denote the quantity of crude actually refined
each day.   We cannot refine more than purchase, and so

$$x_i \leq y_i \qquad i = 1, 2, \cdots, 6 \qquad (61)$$

(Again, let us remember that equation (61) contains six different inequalities.) We proceed now to express the fact that the primary stage of the refinery process has a limited capacity. Let us denote this limited capacity by A; then

$$x_1 + x_2 + x_3 + x_4 + x_5 + x_6 \leq A \tag{62}$$

The next thing is to determine the yield of the two different intermediate products from the primary stage of the refinery. Let us assume that out of the x_1 of crude 1 refined, n_1 fraction goes into the first intermediate product, where n_1 is a fixed factor known from refinery technology. This means that $n_1 x_1$ is the quantity of first intermediate product produced from the first crude. Similarly, the quantity produced from the second crude is $n_2 x_2$, etc. This, then, leads to

$$n_1 x_1 + n_2 x_2 + n_3 x_3 + n_4 x_4 + n_5 x_5 + n_6 x_6 = N \tag{63}$$

where N denotes the total quantity of the first intermediate product. Let us denote by M the total quantity of the second intermediate product produced from the primary stage of the refinery. Using a similar notation to the one above, we get

$$m_1 x_1 + m_2 x_2 + m_3 x_3 + m_4 x_4 + m_5 x_5 + m_6 x_6 = M \tag{64}$$

Now we assume that the quantity N of the first intermediate product is split two ways: N_1 is sold, whereas N_2 is further refined in a secondary stage; then

$$N_1 + N_2 = N \tag{65}$$

However, there is a limit of the quantity of each product that can be refined in the secondary stage. This leads to the inequality

$$N_2 \leq B \tag{66}$$

where B is the capacity of the secondary stage for the first intermediate product. Similarly, we split the second intermediate product, which results in the relation

$$M_1 + M_2 = M \tag{67}$$

with the restriction

$$M_2 \leq C \tag{68}$$

where C is capacity limitation of the other secondary stage of the refinery process. The problem in mathematical form is to determine the x's, y's, N_1, N_2, M_1, M_2 so that the profit becomes a maximum.

We assume that the profit can be written as

$$z = \nu_1 N_1 + \mu_1 M_1 + \nu_2 N_2 + \mu_2 M_2 - \sum_{i=1}^{6} c_i y_i \qquad (69)$$

but we will omit here a derivation of this formula. (Those interested in the derivation are referred to the paper cited in the footnote on p. 76.) It is easy to recognize that the formula is a plausible one. The first two terms on the right-hand side represent the profit for each crude that is refined only through the primary stage. The next two terms represent additional profit from the secondary stages of refinery. The last term is associated with the cost of the purchase and transportation of the crudes.

It can be seen that this problem of the oil refinery is a problem in linear programming. The unknowns are the x's, y's, N's, and M's; the restrictions are given in equations (60) through (68); and the profit function is given by equation (69).

The reader might wonder at this point how practical it is to solve a problem involving such a large number of equations. It will be a surprise, perhaps, that such a problem can be solved relatively easily. We will discuss the solution in Chapter 7, where this problem will be considered as a problem in convex programming.

9. A PROBLEM IN PRODUCTION AND INVENTORY CONTROL

The production department of a certain corporation is making plans for the next calendar year. It is customary for the production department to plan in production periods consisting, say, of two months and, therefore, next year's production is to be divided up into six production periods. The corporation manufactures goods only when there are firm orders for these goods. The number of units required in each of these production periods is

Periods	1	2	3	4	5	6
Requirements	5	5	10	30	50	8

As it is more convenient to work with cumulative requirements, the above table is changed into the following:

Period	1	2	3	4	5	6
Cumulative requirements	5	10	20	50	100	108

A graphical representation of these requirements is given in Fig. 4. The problem with which the production department is confronted is to determine how many of these units should be produced in each production period. Any production plan that meets requirements can be represented in Fig. 4 by a broken line, lying *above* the requirement line.

In this plant it is possible to operate a day or a night shift. Capacity is 15 units for each two-month period on daytime production, and

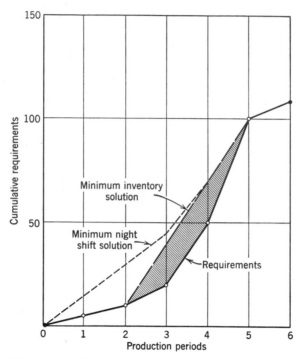

FIG. 4. A problem in production and inventory control.

15 units during night shift production. Labor costs are $100 for each unit if the unit is produced during the day shift. If the unit is produced on the night shift, the labor cost is somewhat higher, namely, $120. A graphical representation of the labor cost is shown on the left-hand side of Fig. 5 where labor cost, as a function of the number of units produced, is shown. Let us assume that at the beginning of the year there is no inventory of these units, and that at the end of the year there will be no inventory either. This means that in Fig. 4 a proper production plan is represented by a broken line lying

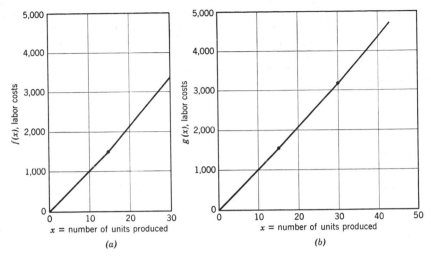

FIG. 5.   Labor costs as function of number of units produced.   (a) Two-shift operation.   (b) Three-shift operation.

above the requirement line, but that both ends of the production line are anchored at the level of the requirements (0 and 108 units).

A possible production plan is shown in Table 7.   The first column shows the requirements r_i, and the second column shows the cumulative requirements R_i.   The third column, x_i, shows the production plan, and X_i shows the cumulative production plan.   It can be seen that during the first three periods 15 units are produced, utilizing

TABLE 7.   A Problem in Production and Inventory Control [a]

	r_i	R_i	x_i	X_i	u_i
1	5	5	15	15	10
2	5	10	15	30	20
3	10	20	15	45	25
4	30	50	25	70	20
5	50	100	30	100	0
6	8	108	8	108	0

[a] Respective columns show production periods, requirements, cumulative requirements, units produced, cumulative units produced, and inventory at hand.   This production plan represents a minimum night shift plan.

all of the day shift capacities. During the fourth and fifth periods, additional night shift is utilized, 10 units being produced during the night shift in the fourth period and 15 units in the fifth period. Finally, in the sixth production period, production is reduced to 8 units, all day shift. In Table 7 in the last column under u_i, the inventory at the end of each period is shown. For instance, at the end of the first period there will be 10 units in inventory as 15 will be produced and only 5 units are required.

The rationale behind this production schedule is obvious. The manager of the production department is minimizing the night shift production. Consequently, during the first three periods he produces at capacity during the day shift. In the fourth period he has to go on overtime because otherwise he is not going to be able to meet the requirements. He must produce at least an additional 10 units, and this brings up production in the fourth period to 25. In the fifth production period, it is necessary to go on full-time night shift operation to meet requirements. Finally, in the sixth period, only a partial day shift operation is utilized.

The combined production costs can be easily computed as

$$83(100) + 25(120) = \$11,300$$

This production plan is good from the point of view of minimizing night shift operation. However, there is another consideration to be taken into account. This is the problem of the inventory levels associated with this production plan. Let us assume that inventory costs (including all the various expenses), amount to 24% per year. Assuming that the total cost of each unit is $400, this results in 4% carrying cost per production period, or $16 for each unit per production period. By inspecting the last column, the inventory column, in Table 7, we can make the following observation: at the beginning of the first period there is no inventory, and at the end of the first period there is an inventory of 10 units. Therefore, the average inventory in the first production period is 5 units. Similarly, in the second period the inventory varies between 10 and 20 units. Therefore, the average inventory is 15 units. The average inventory in the third period is 22.5 units, during the fifth period it is 10 units, and, finally, in the sixth period there is no inventory at all. Consequently, the total inventory cost can be computed as

$$16(5 + 15 + 22.5 + 22.5 + 10 + 0) = 16(75) = \$1,200$$

We can see, then, that the combined production and inventory cost associated with this plan is $12,500.

In Table 8, an alternate production plan is listed. The rationale behind this plan is to minimize inventory costs. It can be seen that during the first and second periods only 5 units are produced to meet requirements. During the third period 30 units are produced, 15 on day shift and 15 on night shift, resulting in an inventory of 20 units. This has to be done because otherwise future requirements cannot be

TABLE 8. A Problem in Production and Inventory Control [a]

	r_i	R_i	x_i	X_i	u_i
1	5	5	5	5	0
2	5	10	5	10	0
3	10	20	30	40	20
4	30	50	30	70	20
5	50	100	30	100	0
6	8	108	8	108	0

[a] This production plan represents a minimum inventory plan.

met. In production periods 4 and 5, again 30 and 30 units are produced, so that by the end of the fifth period a total of 100 units is produced to meet the requirements. Finally, in the sixth production period, 8 units are produced. The combined production cost can be computed for this plan as

$$63(100) + 45(120) = \$11,700$$

Furthermore, inventory costs can be computed as

$$16(0 + 0 + 10 + 20 + 10 + 0) = 16(40) = \$640$$

It can be seen that the combined production and inventory costs in this second plan amount to $12,340, which is $160 less than the first plan we considered.

The problem we propose to solve now is the development of the *best* production plan, that is, the production plan which results in a minimum combined production and inventory cost.

Let x_1 denote production in the first period, x_2 in the second period, $\cdots$, x_6 in the sixth period. The first thing is to put into a mathematical form the fact that there is a capacity limitation. This can be expressed by the inequality,

$$x_i \leq \alpha \qquad i = 1, 2, \cdots, 6 \tag{70}$$

Here, α denotes the total capacity of production (which includes day or night shift). In the particular problem we are discussing here, α is 30 units. We will now introduce a notation for the cumulative production in each period. Let X_1 denote the cumulative production in the first production period, X_2 in the second period, etc. We can then write the following equations:

$$X_1 = x_1$$
$$X_2 = x_1 + x_2 \tag{71}$$
$$\cdots \cdots \cdots \cdots \cdots$$
$$X_6 = x_1 + x_2 + \cdots + x_6$$

We will denote by R_1, R_2 the cumulative requirements for each production period. So far, we have assumed that there is no inventory at the beginning of the first period. In order to make the mathematics somewhat more general, we assume now that there is an inventory of u_0 at the beginning of the first period. The fact that at the end of each production period the requirements must be met can be expressed by the following set of inequalities

$$u_0 + X_i \geq R_i \tag{72}$$

The inventory levels at the end of each period are related to the cumulative production schedule and to the cumulative requirements by the following set of equations

$$u_i = u_0 + X_i - R_i \qquad i = 1, 2, \cdots, N \tag{73}$$

Here, u_1 denotes inventory at the end of the first period, u_2 at the end of the second period, etc. In our particular example, we assume that both the initial and final inventories are zero. These can be expressed then by the equations

$$u_0 = 0 \tag{74}$$

$$u_6 = 0 \tag{75}$$

The next problem is to put into a mathematical form the production cost. How can this be done?

The left-hand side of Fig. 5 shows a graphical representation of labor costs as functions of number of units produced. In mathematical language we say that

$$\text{Labor cost} = f(x) \tag{76}$$

where the sign $f(x)$ is to be read "ef of ex." This is the way a mathematician refers in a symbolic form to a given graph or table of numbers. The important thing to remember is that the notation does not refer to a particular shape of curve like the one on the left-hand side of Fig. 5, but that it includes all possible types of curves that one might encounter. For instance, we could write

$$g(x) = 2x^2 + 5 \qquad (77)$$

where an explicit rule for the function dependence is given. An illustrative function from trigonometry would be the following:

$$h(x) = \sin x \qquad (78)$$

Another type of function could be the following:

$$y(x) = \text{The largest integer smaller than } x \qquad (79)$$

Another possible function is

$$\left. \begin{array}{l} F(x) = 0 \text{ when } x \text{ is negative or zero} \\ F(x) = 1 \text{ when } x \text{ is positive} \end{array} \right\} \qquad (80)$$

Again, another type of function is the following:

$$\left. \begin{array}{l} R(x) = 0 \text{ when } x \text{ is an integer} \\ R(x) = 1 \text{ when } x \text{ is not an integer} \end{array} \right\} \qquad (81)$$

Now that we understand the concept of a *function*, let us return to our problem and continue with the mathematical formulation.

The total labor cost for the six periods is given by

$$z_p = f(x_1) + f(x_2) + \cdots + f(x_6) \qquad (82)$$

In order to compute the inventory carrying cost, let us first compute the average inventory level. The average inventory over the first period is given by

$$\frac{u_0 + u_1}{2}$$

Similarly, the average inventory over the second period is given by

$$\frac{u_1 + u_2}{2}$$

The average inventory over all the n periods is given by

$$\frac{u_0 + u_1}{2} + \frac{u_1 + u_2}{2} + \cdots + \frac{u_{n-1} + u_n}{2}$$

which simplifies to

$$\frac{u_0}{2} + u_1 + u_2 + \cdots + u_{n-1} + \frac{u_n}{2}$$

Let us denote by q the inventory carrying cost for each unit, for each period. Then the inventory carrying cost is given by

$$z_I = \tfrac{1}{2}q(u_0 + u_1) + \tfrac{1}{2}q(u_1 + u_2) + \cdots + \tfrac{1}{2}q(u_{n-1} + u_n) \quad (83)$$

An interesting geometrical interpretation of the inventory cost can be given by recognizing that, if we omit q in the above formula, we

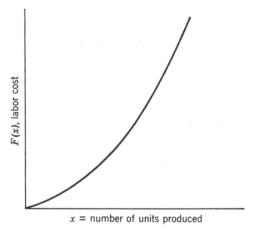

x = number of units produced

FIG. 6.   Convex labor cost function.

get the area between the actual cumulative production curve and the requirements curve, as illustrated by the shaded area in Fig. 4. Minimizing inventory costs can be interpreted as minimizing the area between the production and requirements curve. For instance, it can be directly seen in Fig. 4 that the minimum night shift plan involves a higher inventory cost than the minimum inventory solution. We can say now that the combined production and inventory costs are given by

$$z = z_p + z_I = \sum_{i=1}^{6} f(x_i) + \tfrac{1}{2}q \sum_{i=1}^{6} (u_i + u_{i-1}) \quad (84)$$

Mathematically speaking, then, the problem is to minimize the expression as given by equation (84) under the constraints of equations (70) to (75). This is not a problem in linear programming, as the cost function is not linear, that is, the cost function cannot be represented by a straight line. In Chapter 7, under the title "Convex Programming," it will be shown that a problem of this type can be reduced to a linear programming problem, and the method of solution will be worked out.

Suppose now that we are dealing with a somewhat more complicated situation. Say that there are three possible shifts involved. The right-hand side in Fig. 5 shows a labor cost function when there are three shifts. The mathematics we have developed applies to this case too, as all we have to do is to interpret our cost function as given by this new curve.

Another type of cost function is shown in Fig. 6, where we really deal with a curve and not with a function that is composed of straight-line segments. In Chapter 8, under the title "Dynamic Programming," we will develop a general method which permits the solution of problems of this type.*

10. A PROBLEM RELATED TO THE ATTRITION OF PRODUCTION FACILITIES

The production department of a certain corporation is making a four-year plan for the assignment of production facilities. Suppose that the corporation has 1,000 of certain automatic machines which can produce only two different products. If x number of these machines are allocated to produce the first product, the yearly profit will be represented by the upper $f(x)$ curve shown in Fig. 7. On the other hand, if y number of machines are assigned to the second product, the yearly profits are shown by the lower curve $g(y)$ in Fig 7. How many machines should be allocated to the first and second product each year? Observing that profits on the first product are higher than on the second product, one would think at first that all production should be allocated to the first product.

There is, however, another factor that must be considered: the attrition rates of the machines are different. Thus, if 100 machines are assigned to the first product, then after the first year there will be only 60 machines in working condition. On the other hand, if 100 machines are assigned to the second product, then there will still be 80 machines in working condition at the end of the first year. At the end of the first year, that is, at the beginning of the second year, there will still be a certain number of machines available, depending

---

* For more details on this problem, read F. Modigliani and F. E. Hohn, "Production Planning over Time and the Nature of the Expectation and Planning Horizons," *Econometrica*, Vol. 23, No. 1, January, 1955.

on how the machines were allocated during the first year. (We will assume that the machines that stay in working condition remain as good as new.) Now a new decision has to be made on how to allocate the machines in the second year of production. At the end of the

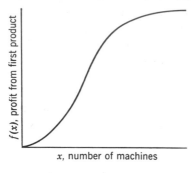

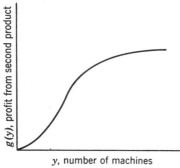

y, number of machines

FIG. 7. A problem related to the attrition of production facilities.

second year of production a decision must be made again, and finally at the end of the third year a final decision must be made as far as the allocation of machines for the fourth year is concerned. It can be seen that this factor of attrition makes the problem more complicated, and we propose now to set up the mathematical equation for the solution of this problem.

Let us assume that we allocate x_1, x_2, x_3, and x_4 number of machines to the first product during each of the four years, and that we allocate y_1, y_2, y_3, and y_4 number of machines to the second product. We assume that we start with A_1 number of machines, and so we have

$$x_1 + y_1 = A_1 \qquad (85)$$

(In our particular case, the value of A_1 is 1,000). Let us denote by A_2 the number of machines in working condition at the beginning of the second period. Then we have

$$A_2 = 0.6x_1 + 0.8y_1 \qquad (86)$$

Consequently, we must have

$$x_2 + y_2 = A_2 \qquad (87)$$

Similarly, we get for the third and fourth years, the following equations

$$A_3 = 0.6x_2 + 0.8y_2 \qquad (88)$$

$$x_3 + y_3 = A_3 \qquad (89)$$

and

$$A_4 = 0.6x_3 + 0.8y_3 \qquad (90)$$

$$x_4 + y_4 = A_4 \qquad (91)$$

In order to make the problem more manageable, we will assume that at the end of the fourth year the machines all become obsolete and that they have no value. Then the total profit for the four years can be expressed by

$$Z = f(x_1) + f(x_2) + f(x_3) + f(x_4) + g(y_1) + g(y_2)$$
$$+ g(y_3) + g(y_4) \quad (92)$$

It can be seen that, mathematically speaking, the problem is to maximize the profit as given by equation (92) under the restrictions of the equations (85) to (91). This problem is not a problem in linear programming, as the profit is not a straight-line function. In Chapter 8, under "Dynamic Programming," a method will be developed which allows the solution of problems of this type.

11. WHAT TO PRODUCE IN FACE OF COMPETITION: AN APPLICATION OF THE THEORY OF GAMES

Suppose that I am the manager of a refinery and am producing insufficient quantities of gasoline and Diesel oil, but am producing a surplus of bunker fuel oil. As a result it is necessary for me to export the surplus of bunker fuel, and to import gasoline and Diesel oil to meet market requirements. This leads to excessive transportation costs and lower profits. In order to improve my profit picture, I get four different proposals from my staff. The proposals are that some of the production facilities be modernized, and that some new promotional means be introduced. Each of these proposals leads to a different increase in profit. Current profits are 30 cents per barrel. The first proposal would make profits go up to 35 cents, the second to 39 cents, the third to 42 cents, and the fourth to 44 cents per barrel. (These figures include depreciation costs associated with the capital expense required to modernize the refinery.) Which of these proposals should I accept? At first glance it would appear that I should take the fourth proposal which leads to a profit of 44 cents per barrel.

A more complete examination of the facts, however, uncovers some additional important information.* The total market in this market-ing area is essentially fixed and split between my refinery and my principal competitor's; there is no way to change the total market requirement. Furthermore, the competitor is also considering chang-ing his refinery equipment and considering new promotional methods

* See G. H. Symonds, *Linear Programming: The Solution of Refinery Problems,* Esso Standard Oil Company, New York, New York, 1955, p. 25.

of improving his profit.   As I know a great deal about my competitor's operation, and about the market, I can figure out the possible improvements he is considering.   Evaluation of his possible actions leads to a table of potential profits per barrel of product, as shown in Table 9.

The first column shows that, if he stands still, my first policy (that is, standing still) gives me 30 cents profit per barrel.   If he stands still (his policy [1]), and I accept the first recommendation (that is, my policy (2)) I get 35 cents per barrel; if I accept the second (my

TABLE 9.   What to Produce in the Face of Competition; an Application of the Theory of Games"

		1/3 ↓				2/3 ↓
		[1]	[2]	His Policy [3]	[4]	[5]
	(1)	30	34	37	39	40
1/3 ⟶	(2)	35	38	40	41	39
2/3 ⟶ My Policy	(3)	39	41	42	40	37
	(4)	42	43	41	38	34
	(5)	44	42	39	35	30

" Shows my profits for each barrel of oil.   If I choose policy (2) and my competitor policy [4], my profit is $0.41 per barrel.

policy (3)) I get 39 cents; if I accept the third (my policy (4)) I get 42 cents; if I accept the fourth (my policy (5)) I get 44 cents.   However, if he proceeds with his policy [2] as his method of improving his business, my profit will change.   If I stand still I get 34 cents a barrel; if I introduce my policy (2) I get 38 cents; my policy (3) leads to 41 cents, etc.   Thus Table 9 shows my profit, whatever policy is accepted by my competitor, and whatever policy is accepted by my own refinery.

What should my action be in this case?   If I accept my policy (5), what would happen?   If he makes no improvements, that is, if he accepts his policy [1], I get 44 cents per barrel.   On the other hand, if he "plays," say, his policy [5], I only get 30 cents per barrel.   Perhaps I should accept my policy (3)?   Then I would be certain to get at least 37 cents profit on each barrel.   Moreover, if he does not select his policy [5], I might even get more than 37 cents per barrel.   However, the question is this, is the acceptance of policy (3) the best possible choice on my part? Is it possible to assure a profit of more than 37 cents per barrel?

It is clear from Table 9 that there is no fixed policy that can assure a profit of more than 37 cents per barrel. However, I might decide to change my policy from month to month, and, in this way, perhaps I can improve my profit to a higher figure than 37 cents per barrel. In fact, perhaps I could prepare a plan specifying in what months I am going to "play" my various policies. This is not practical though, as it is likely that my competitor would find out about my plan, and then he could counteract it by selecting an appropriate sequence of policies.

At this point, let us consider the following plan: At the beginning of each month, I take a coin and throw it; when I get heads, I "play" my policy (2), and when I get tails I "play" my policy (5). In this way, I can be sure that my competitor will not know what policy I am going to "play." This "game" is somewhat restricted because I can select from only two different policies. Suppose I take dice and select my policy according to the numbers thrown, or I take an urn and fill it up with tokens, with the numbers 1, 2, 3, 4, 5. I pull one of these tokens each month, and the number shown is the policy to be played that particular month. The question I have now is the following: How many tokens should have the number 1? How many the number 2, etc.? Is it possible by playing this "game" to get more (in the long run) than 37 cents of profit per barrel? If the answer is yes, I would like to know which marking of tokens yields the highest possible profit, and what is this highest profit.

The problem we have formulated here is a problem in the branch of mathematics called *theory of games*. This mathematical theory yields the answer to the problem posed: let us place a single token in the urn with the number 2 written on it, and place two tokens with the number 3 written on them. Let us pull one of the three tokens from the urn and play the particular policy that is written on the token. We will replace the token and pull one again next month, etc. It can be shown on the basis of the theory of games that this is the *best* possible "strategy," and that this strategy leads to the highest profit, $37\frac{2}{3}$ cents per barrel. Using this "strategy" improves the profit from the previous figure by $\frac{2}{3}$ of a cent per barrel.

To be more specific, accepting this strategy insures getting (in the long run) $37\frac{2}{3}$ cents per barrel of profit. On the basis of the theory of games we can also conclude that if my competitor "plays" the same sort of a "game," that is, if he places in his urn one token with his policy [1] and two tokens with his policy [5], then he will restrict me to the (long run) profit of $37\frac{2}{3}$ cents per barrel. On the other hand, if he "plays" any other "strategy," my profit will be higher than $37\frac{2}{3}$ cents.

This is a problem, then, in the theory of games; and in Chapter 9 it will be shown that problems of this type can be solved with the aid of linear programming.

12. THE GENERAL MATHEMATICAL FORMULATION OF THE PROBLEM OF LINEAR PROGRAMMING

We are in a position now to proceed to a general definition of linear programming. Let us denote the unknowns of the business problem by x_1, x_2, etc. We claim that any of the restrictions we have used so far in this book can be written in the form:

$$A_1x_1 + A_2x_2 + A_3x_3 + \cdots + A_nx_n = B \qquad (93)$$

Let us see whether this statement is true. As an example, take equation (6). Can this be brought to the form of equation (93)? Let us introduce a new "nonnegative"* variable x_{10}, which denotes the quantity produced in excess of 200. With this notation, we can write equation (6) in the following form:

$$x_1 + x_2 + x_3 - x_{10} = 100 \qquad (94)$$

Is this an equation of the type of (93)? Let us rewrite equation (94) as

$$x_1 + x_2 + x_3 + 0x_4 + 0x_5 + 0x_6 \\ + 0x_7 + 0x_8 + 0x_9 - x_{10} = 100 \quad (95)$$

This indeed shows that the equation (94) can be written in the desired form by putting A_1, A_2, A_3 equal to 1, A_4, A_5, A_6, A_7, A_8, A_9 equal to zero, A_{10} equal to -1, and B equal to 100. A variable like x_{10} is called a slack variable in the theory of linear programming.

Suppose we want to put equation (7) into this form; we need to introduce a new slack variable x_{11}. Similarly, to put equation (8) into this form requires a slack variable x_{12}. Moreover, any other restrictions that we have used in this book can be written in the form of (93), and the reader is advised to work through some of the equations to verify this statement.

Mathematicians call such restrictions *linear*. Not every restriction

---

* Nonnegative means positive or zero.

is linear.   For instance, the equation

$$x_1{}^3 + x_3 = 5 \tag{96}$$

is nonlinear because the variable x_1 appears to the third power.   In the theory of linear programming no such restrictions are permitted.

Now suppose we take our first illustration from this chapter and write equations (3) to (8), all of them in the form of equation (93). There would be 6 slack variables in the problem because each of the inequalities requires a slack variable, and we would need a total of 15 unknowns.   The reader is advised to work through these equations. For convenience, we have put the coefficients of all the equations into tabular form in Table 10.   In the literature on linear programming it is usual to write the restrictions in tabular form as shown in the table.   When the coefficient of an x is zero, there should be a zero in the table.   However, often the zeros are omitted.

We will now write the equations for these restrictions in a more general fashion.   Let $a_{i,j}$ denote the coefficient in the ith equation, which refers to the jth unknown.   For instance, in Table 10, $a_{5,4}$ is 0.6.   Let us denote by A_1, A_2, etc., the right-hand term in each of these equations.   For instance, in Table 10, A_3 is 300.   With this notation the restrictions can be written in the following form:

$$
\begin{aligned}
a_{1,1}x_1 + a_{1,2}x_2 + \cdots + a_{1n}x_n &= A_1 \\
a_{2,1}x_1 + a_{2,2}x_2 + \cdots + a_{2n}x_n &= A_2 \\
&\ \ \vdots \\
a_{m,1}x_1 + a_{m,2}x_2 + \cdots + a_{mn}x_n &= A_m
\end{aligned}
\tag{97}
$$

or, in an abbreviated form, as

$$\sum_{j=1}^{n} a_{i,j}x_j = A_i \qquad i = 1, 2, \cdots, m \tag{98}$$

Let us finally write the *payoff function* as

$$z = c_1x_1 + c_2x_2 + \cdots + c_nx_n \tag{99}$$

or, in an abbreviated form, as

$$z = \sum_{i=1}^{n} c_i x_i \tag{100}$$

(It is to be noted that the c's referring to the slack variables should be zero.)   We use the term payoff here, as is customary in the theory of

TABLE 10. Coefficients for the Allocation of Production Facilities When Alternate Routing Is Possible

Equations	Unknowns									Slack Variables						a
	x_1	x_2	x_3	x_4	x_5	x_6	x_7	x_8	x_9	x_{10}	x_{11}	x_{12}	x_{13}	x_{14}	x_{15}	
1	1.0	1.0	1.0							−1.0						100
2				1.0	1.0	1.0					−1.0					200
3							1.0	1.0	1.0			−1.0				300
4	0.4	0.8	1.2	0.4	0.2		0.4	0.2					+1.0			236
5	0.4		0.2	0.6	0.2	0.4	0.2	1.2	1.6					+1.0		460
6	0.4	0.6	0.2	0.8	1.6	2.0	1.4	0.8	0.4						+1.0	
Payoff	25	25	25	20	20	20	30	30	30							

linear programming, to denote either the profit or the cost. In Table 10 these payoff coefficients are shown in the last row. A payoff function of the type of equation (99) is called linear. All the costs and profits that we have studied in this book (except the ones given by equations (84) and (92)) are of the form of equation (100) and are, therefore, linear.

We are in a position now to give a definition of linear programming: Let us consider n nonnegative unknowns $x_1, x_2, \cdots, x_n$, subject to m linear restrictions as given by equation (98). Linear programming is a computational method of determining the values of these unknowns such that the payoff function as given by equation (100) becomes a maximum (or minimum).

This is, then, the definition of linear programmming. The concept of scientific programming is broader and it is more vague. Generally speaking, we mean by scientific programming that the restriction of dealing with linear equations is removed. However, the theory of scientific programming has not progressed yet to a point where a complete definition can be given.

PART II

MATHEMATICAL
PROGRAMMING

CHAPTER 4

THE SIMPLEX METHOD
OF
LINEAR PROGRAMMING

1. STATEMENT OF THE PROBLEM: HOW NOT TO SOLVE IT

Instead of following George Dantzig's original exposition* of the simplex method, we will develop the method through an illustrative example. We propose to consider a special case of the so-called nutrition problem. Let us assume that we can purchase seven types of vitamin pills, and that each of these pills contains a certain proportion of vitamins of three different types. Table 1 shows that pill 1, i.e., P_1, contains 5 units of vitamin 1, 3 units of vitamin 2, and 1 unit of vitamin 3. The table also shows that pill 3, i.e., P_3, contains 2 units of vitamin 1, 5 units of vitamin 2, and 3 units of vitamin 3. The bottom row in Table 1 shows that pills of the first type sell for $0.40, pills of the second type for $0.10, etc.

Suppose that we desire to purchase a combination of vitamin pills to meet a daily requirement of exactly 100 units of vitamin 1, 80 units of vitamin 2, and 120 units of vitamin 3. (Vitamin requirements are shown in the last column of Table 1.) The question is what combination of pills should be purchased to meet this requirement in the cheapest way?

We notice that a pill of type 2, or P_2, contains exactly 1 unit of vitamin 2, or V_2, and that each P_2 sells for $0.10. Clearly then, 80 of P_2 will meet the requirement of vitamin V_2 and these 80 P_2's

* G. B. Dantzig, in *Activity Analysis of Production and Allocation, Cowles Commission Monograph 13,* edited by T. C. Koopmans, John Wiley & Sons, New York, 1951.

will cost \$8.   Furthermore, P_4 contains nothing but V_3 so 120 of P_4 will fulfill the requirement of vitamin V_3, and these 120 of P_4 will cost \$7.20.   Finally, pill P_6 contains nothing but vitamin V_1 and so 100 of these at a price of \$7 will meet the requirements.   In summary then, 80 of P_2, 120 of P_4, and 100 of P_6 at a total cost of \$22.20 meet the required quota of vitamins.   Is this the cheapest combination of pills?

TABLE 1.   Vitamin Pills, Requirements, and Costs

	P_1	P_2	P_3	P_4	P_5	P_6	P_7	
V_1	5	0	2	0	3	1	2	100
V_2	3	1	5	0	2	0	1	80
V_3	1	0	3	1	2	0	6	120
Costs	40	10	50	6	35	7	40	

Suppose we meet our requirements by buying P_1, P_3, and P_5. How many of each of these pills do we need?   Let us call by x_1 the number of P_1's to be purchased, by x_3 the number of P_3's to be purchased, and by x_5 the number of P_5's to be purchased.   The unknowns x_1, x_3, and x_5 must satisfy the following equations:

$$5x_1 + 2x_3 + 3x_5 = 100 \tag{1}$$

$$3x_1 + 5x_3 + 2x_5 = \ \ 80 \tag{2}$$

$$1x_1 + 3x_3 + 2x_5 = 120 \tag{3}$$

In order to solve these equations for the unknowns, multiply equation (3) by 5 and subtract it from equation (1).   Then we get:

$$-13x_3 - 7x_5 = -500 \tag{4}$$

Now we multiply equation (3) by 3, subtract it from equation (2), and get:

$$-4x_3 - 4x_5 = -280 \tag{5}$$

Finally, we multiply equation (5) by 13/4 subtract it from equation (4), and get:

$$6x_5 = 410$$

or

$$x_5 = 205/3 \sim 68$$

Substituting this value of x_5 into equation (5), we get the value of:

$$x_3 = 5/3 \sim 1.6$$

Finally, from equation (1) we compute the value of x_1 as:

$$x_1 = -65/3 \sim -21$$

We have succeeded, then, in solving equations (1), (2), and (3), and it is easy to verify by substitution that these values really satisfy the equations. To put it in words, we see that we can meet our quota of vitamins by purchasing $-65/3$ number of P_1, $5/3$ number of P_3, and $205/3$ number of P_5. This is, of course, nonsense, as there is no way to buy a negative number of pills P_1. In other words, it is impossible to meet the vitamin requirements by purchasing a combination of the pills P_1, P_3, and P_5.*

Remembering that we are trying to get the cheapest combination, we could select some three other types of pills and try that combination. There is a total of 35 different combinations of three types of pills; we could solve the three equations with three unknowns for each of these 35 combinations and select the combination which is the least expensive. This would be quite a lot of work, but even if we did it we might still wonder whether we have the cheapest combination of pills. Why not use, say, a combination of four pills or five, instead of three?

Perhaps the most important single result of the theory of linear programming is the *fundamental theorem* that states that this is not necessary. *The cheapest combination of pills cannot require four, five, six, or seven kinds of pills.* It follows from the fundamental theorem of linear programming that the cheapest combination may require a single type of pill, or two types of pills, or three types, but certainly not more than *three* types. (This is due to the fact that there are *three* equations.)

To repeat, then: if all combinations of three types of pills are surveyed and the one with the minimum cost is selected, then this combination represents the cheapest of all possible combinations of pills that meet requirements.

We proceed now to state the fundamental theorem of linear programming in a more precise form.

2. THE FUNDAMENTAL THEOREM OF LINEAR PROGRAMMING

Let x_1 denote the number of pills P_1 to be purchased, x_2 the number of P_2's, and so on. In order to meet the requirements, the following

---

* If we were permitted to have an excess of vitamins, then it would be possible to meet the requirements by purchasing pills P_1, P_3, and P_5.

equations must hold:

$$5x_1 + 0x_2 + 2x_3 + 0x_4 + 3x_5 + x_6 + 2x_7 = 100 \qquad (6)$$

$$3x_1 + x_2 + 5x_3 + 0x_4 + 2x_5 + 0x_6 + x_7 = 80 \qquad (7)$$

$$x_1 + 0x_2 + 3x_3 + x_4 + 2x_5 + 0x_6 + 6x_7 = 120 \qquad (8)$$

The cost (in cents) of this combination of pills will be:

$$z = 40x_1 + 10x_2 + 50x_3 + 6x_4 + 35x_5 + 7x_6 + 40x_7 \qquad (9)$$

The problem is, then, how to select the x's satisfying equations (6), (7), and (8) such that the cost expressed by equation (9) becomes a minimum.

The fundamental theorem of linear programming states that there is a solution to this problem such that at least four of the x's are zero. (Not more than three of the x's are nonzero.)

In a more general case we would have m equations and n unknowns, where we assume that there are more unknowns than equations. Then the fundamental theorem states that there is a solution such that $n - m$ of the unknowns are zero. The rest of the unknowns may or may not be zero.

We will now introduce the concept of the *basic solution*. Any solutions of equations (6), (7), and (8) which have the property that not more than three of the x's are nonzero is called a *basic solution*. In general, when there are m equations and n unknowns, $(n \geq m)$ a basic solution is one in which at least $n - m$ of the unknowns are zero. We see, then, that the fundamental theorem can be stated in the following way: *there is a solution to the minimization (or maximization) problem which is a basic solution.* This theorem, although very useful, is not obvious at all. However, we will not include the proof to the theorem in this book.

The problem of linear programming is, then, to search the basic solutions in order to find the optimum solution. In our particular nutrition problem we need to select the combination of three pills which have the cheapest cost and satisfy our vitamin requirements.

As we mentioned before, in our problem we could get an answer by solving, 35 times, three equations with three unknowns. But suppose we had a problem where there were ten equations and thirty unknowns. In this case, we would have to solve approximately 30 million times ten equations with ten unknowns. It is well known that to solve ten equations with ten unknowns takes a lot of work. To do this 30 million times would be utterly impractical, even if we used the largest electronic computing machine.

The simplex method of linear programming can be looked upon as a strategy to search the basic solutions in an efficient way and to find the optimum. The central idea of the method is to modify a basic solution step by step in such a way that after a reasonable number of steps the optimum solution is obtained.

3. TECHNIQUE OF MODIFYING A SOLUTION

Suppose that we have a set of x's that satisfies equations (6), (7), and (8). To abbreviate our presentation, we denote this by:

$$[x_1, x_2, x_3, x_4, x_5, x_6, x_7] \tag{10}$$

As an example, we know that 80 of P_2, 120 of P_4, and 100 of P_6 form a solution and so we can say:

$$[0, 80, 0, 120, 0, 100, 0] \tag{11}$$

as these seven numbers do satisfy the equations. (In fact, we know that this is a basic solution as four of the unknowns are zero.) We also know that, for instance, the equations are satisfied by:

$$\left[\frac{-65}{3}, 0, \frac{5}{3}, 0, \frac{205}{3}, 0, 0\right] \tag{12}$$

Now we pose the question of how to change the x's in equation (10) in order to get another solution to the equations. Suppose we change x_1 by y_1. We get the numbers $x_1 + y_1$, x_2, x_3, and so on. However, this is not a solution to the equations. Because of interdependence of the variables, we cannot change just one of the variables, we must change a few of them in order to get another solution. Suppose, then, that we change x_1 by y_1, x_2 by y_2, and so on. In order that these numbers form a solution, we must have:

$$5(x_1 + y_1) + 0(x_2 + y_2) + 2(x_3 + y_3) + 0(x_4 + y_4) + 3(x_5 + y_5)$$
$$+ (x_6 + y_6) + 2(x_7 + y_7) = 100 \tag{13}$$

$$3(x_1 + y_1) + (x_2 + y_2) + 5(x_3 + y_3) + 0(x_4 + y_4) + 2(x_5 + y_5)$$
$$+ 0(x_6 + y_6) + (x_7 + y_7) = 80 \tag{14}$$

$$1(x_1 + y_1) + 0(x_2 + y_2) + 3(x_3 + y_3) + (x_4 + y_4) + 2(x_5 + y_5)$$
$$+ 0(x_6 + y_6) + 6(x_7 + y_7) = 120 \tag{15}$$

We now subtract equation (6) from equation (13), equation (7) from equation (14), and equation (8) from equation (15). Then we get:

$$5y_1 + 0y_2 + 2y_3 + 0y_4 + 3y_5 + y_6 + 2y_7 = 0 \qquad (16)$$

$$3y_1 + y_2 + 5y_3 + 0y_4 + 2y_5 + 0y_6 + y_7 = 0 \qquad (17)$$

$$1y_1 + 0y_2 + 3y_3 + y_4 + 2y_5 + 0y_6 + 6y_7 = 0 \qquad (18)$$

This system of equations is very similar to our equations (6), (7), and (8) except there are zeros on the right-hand side. We call this system of equations the homogeneous equations. If we had a set of y's satisfying the homogeneous equations, then we could modify our original solution and get a new solution to our equations. Such a set of y's we denote by:

$$\{y_1, y_2, y_3, y_4, y_5, y_6, y_7\}$$

The problem of how to modify a solution is equivalent to the problem of how to find a solution to the homogeneous equations. Suppose we want to modify the following solution:

$$[0, 80, 0, 120, 0, 100, 0] \qquad (19)$$

Say we modify x_1 by y_1. As originally x_1 was zero, this y_1 denotes the number of P_1's to be purchased. We now modify x_2 by y_2, which means that we buy $80 + y_2$ of P_2. Similarly, we buy $120 + y_4$ of P_4 and $100 + y_6$ of P_6, but do not buy any P_3 and P_5. As we buy more and more of P_1 we buy less and less of P_2, P_4, and P_6, and, in fact, when the quantity of P_1 bought reaches a certain maximum, one of the pills P_2 or P_4 or P_6 becomes unnecessary. At this point, we satisfy requirements with exactly three types of pills and, consequently, have a basic solution to our problem. Now we know from the fundamental theorem that the optimum solution is a basic solution and is composed only of three types of pills. Consequently, if we find a method of shifting from a combination of three pills to another combination of three pills, we will have a method of shifting from one basic solution to another and so we will be on our way to finding the optimum (basic) solution.

In order to determine these modifications to our solutions we need to set up a system of equations for the unknowns y_1, y_2, y_4, and y_6.

These can be obtained from equations (16), (17), and (18) by substituting $y_3 = y_5 = y_7 = 0$. We get

$$5y_1 + 0y_2 + 0y_4 + y_6 = 0 \qquad (20)$$

$$3y_1 + y_2 + 0y_4 + 0y_6 = 0 \qquad (21)$$

$$1y_1 + 0y_2 + y_4 + 0y_6 = 0 \qquad (22)$$

These can be written as:

$$y_6 = -5y_1$$

$$y_2 = -3y_1$$

$$y_4 = - y_1$$

This shows that we can assign any value to y_1 and then y_2, y_4, and y_6 can be computed. This is to be expected, as when we introduce any amount of P_1 we should be able to compute how many of P_2, P_4, and P_6 are to be purchased. We will say that we introduce pill P_1 with the aid of the factor $F = y_1$, that is, for any value of F,

$$\{F, -3F, 0, -F, 0, -5F, 0\} \tag{23}$$

is a solution of the homogeneous equation. For instance, if $F = -1$, then:

$$\{-1, +3, 0, +1, 0, +5, 0\} \tag{24}$$

is a solution to the homogeneous equation. In other words, equation (23) expresses a possible modification to our original solution of the problem. Or, again that:

$$[F, 80 - 3F, 0, 120 - F, 0, 100 - 5F, 0] \tag{25}$$

is a solution to our problem for any value of the factor F. This expression, then, shows in general what combination of pills P_1, P_2, P_4, and P_6 should be purchased in order to get exactly the right amount of vitamins. We can also interpret equation (25) as showing that pill P_1 is equivalent (as far as vitamins are concerned) to three of P_2, one of P_4, and five of P_6. (Note that we have not said whether this exchange is advantageous or disadvantageous from the point of view of cost.)

We have succeeded, then, in determining how to modify the amount of P_2, P_4, and P_6 to be purchased when P_1 is brought into the combination. Suppose we want to answer the same question when P_3 is brought in. Repeating the procedure we have followed previously, we find that for $F = -1$

$$\{0, 5, -1, 3, 0, 2, 0\} \tag{26}$$

is the solution to the homogeneous equation which introduces P_3. Consequently

$$[0, 80 - 5F, F, 120 - 3F, 0, 100 - 2F, 0] \tag{27}$$

represents a possible combination of pills P_2, P_3, P_4, and P_6 for any value of the factor F. Similarly, we can compute that P_5 can be brought in with the aid of the solutions:

$$\{0,\ 2,\ 0,\ 2,\ -1,\ 3,\ 0\} \qquad (F = -1) \tag{28}$$

and

$$[0,\ 80 - 2F,\ 0,\ 120 - 2F,\ F,\ 100 - 3F,\ 0] \tag{29}$$

Finally, pill P_7 can be brought in with the aid of the solutions:

$$\{0,\ 1,\ 0,\ 6,\ 0,\ 2,\ -1\} \qquad (F = -1) \tag{30}$$

and

$$[0,\ 80 - F,\ 0,\ 120 - 6F,\ 0,\ 100 - 2F,\ F] \tag{31}$$

We see, then, that equation (19) is a solution to the equations, whereas equations (24), (26), (28), and (30) are solutions to the homogeneous equations associated with the original equation. As a sum-

TABLE 2.   The First Family of Solutions[a]

		P_1	P_2	P_3	P_4	P_5	P_6	P_7
Row 0		0	80	0	120	0	100	0
Row 1	P_1	−1	3	0	1	0	5	0
Row 2	P_3	0	5	−1	3	0	2	0
Row 3	P_5	0	2	0	2	−1	3	0
Row 4	P_7	0	1	0	6	0	2	−1

[a] The top row (row 0) is a solution to equations (6), (7), (8). The other rows are solutions to the homogeneous equations (16), (17), (18). Total cost of pills is $22.20.

mary, we present these numbers in a tabular form in Table 2.   The top row or row 0 is a solution to the equation.   The rest of the rows are solutions to the homogeneous equations.   (The reader is urged to verify by substitution that these numbers really satisfy the equations.) In the left-hand column we show that row 1 is capable of modifying the solution in such a way that pill P_1 is brought in.   Row 2 brings in P_3; row 3 brings in P_5; and row 4 brings in P_7.   We call such a set of solutions a *family of solutions* and to make it clear what we mean, we show the pattern of such a family:

		P_1	P_2	P_3	P_4	P_5	P_6	P_7
Row 0		0	*	0	*	0	*	0
Row 1	P_1	-1	*	0	*	0	*	0
Row 2	P_3	0	*	-1	*	0	*	0
Row 3	P_5	0	*	0	*	-1	*	0
Row 4	P_7	0	*	0	*	0	*	-1

On the very top of the table the various pills are listed. Below that we have a basic solution; this means that four of the numbers (at least) must be zero. The remaining three numbers are represented by an asterisk (*). (In the present case P_2, P_4, and P_6 enter into the solution, and so there are asterisks under P_2, P_4, and P_6.) The first column on the left-hand side is a list of pills that are not required for the particular combination. These are indicated by the zeros in the top row. (In the present case, P_1, P_3, P_5, and P_7 are not in the solution.) The pattern is such that there are asterisks in the second, fourth, and sixth column corresponding to pills P_2, P_4, and P_6. Then the row referring to P_1 can bring in pill P_1, and we have -1 in row 1 under P_1. We have -1 in row 2 under P_3, as this row can bring in P_3. Row 3 brings in P_5, so we have -1 under P_5. Finally, row 4 brings in P_7, and so we have -1 under P_7. The rest of the numbers in the table are zero.

This is, then, the pattern of what we call a family of solutions. We proceed now to show how one modifies a family of solutions in order to get another family of solutions.

4. TECHNIQUE OF MODIFYING A FAMILY OF SOLUTIONS

We recall that we are looking for a method to search the basic solutions and to select the best one. We plan to do this search with the aid of developing, step by step, new families of solutions. We proceed now to show how to get a new family of solutions from the one we obtained in the previous section.

The solution we had (Table 2) combines pills P_2, P_4, and P_6. (These were the pills containing single vitamins.) Suppose we want a solution that introduces pill P_5 and removes pill P_4. In other words, we try to meet the vitamin requirements with pills P_2, P_5, and P_6. We observe equation (29) and note that the factor F brings in P_5.

The question is "What value should we assign to this factor F?" In order to eliminate pill P_4, we must have

$$120 - 2F = 0 \tag{32}$$

which gives

$$F = 60$$

We now have the solution:

$$(0, -40, 0, 0, 60, -80, 0)$$

which is indeed a solution that introduces P_5 and removes P_4.

We note that this is not a useful solution, as not all quantities are positive. If we bring in P_5 and insist on having positive numbers, we must have

$$80 - 2F \geq 0$$

$$120 - 2F \geq 0 \tag{33}$$

$$100 - 3F \geq 0$$

or

$$F \leq 40$$

$$F \leq 60 \tag{34}$$

$$F \leq \tfrac{100}{3} = 33.3$$

This means, then, that the factor F must be less than, or equal to, $100/3$ and as we wish to have one of the pills disappear, we must make $F = 100/3$. *When P_5 is introduced, P_6 must be removed.* So we have now the desired combination:

$$(0, \tfrac{40}{3}, 0, \tfrac{160}{3}, \tfrac{100}{3}, 0, 0) \tag{35}$$

We started out by trying to get a combination of pills P_2, P_5, and P_6, and ended up with a combination P_2, P_4, and P_5.

Suppose we want a solution combining P_3, P_4, and P_5. We can obtain such a solution by modifying the solution given by equation (35). We need to remove P_2 and introduce P_3. In order to do this, we need the entire family of solutions associated with equation (35). We could get such a family by solving the associated homogeneous equations. This would be a lot of work, but fortunately there is a short cut.

The family of solutions we need has the pattern:

$$[\quad 0, \tfrac{40}{3}, \quad 0, \tfrac{160}{3}, \tfrac{100}{3}, \quad 0, \quad 0] \tag{36a}$$

$$\{ -1, \quad *, \quad 0, \quad *, \quad *, \quad 0, \quad 0\} \tag{36b}$$

$$\{ \quad 0, \quad *, \quad -1, \quad *, \quad *, \quad 0, \quad 0\} \tag{36c}$$

$$\{ \quad 0, \quad *, \quad 0, \quad *, \quad *, \quad -1, \quad 0\} \tag{36d}$$

$$\{ \quad 0, \quad *, \quad 0, \quad *, \quad *, \quad 0, \quad -1\} \tag{36e}$$

If we had this pattern, we could remove P_2 and introduce P_1, P_3, P_6, or P_7.

We recall now that the top row in this pattern was obtained with the aid of equation (29). But this equation was obtained with the aid of Table 2 by subtracting the proper multiples of row 3 from row 0. Let us now subtract from row 1, row 2, and row 4 various multiples of row 3. This leads to the following family of solutions:

$$[\quad 0, 80 - 2F_0, \quad 0, 120 - 2F_0, F_0, 100 - 3F_0, \quad 0] \tag{37a}$$

$$\{ -1, 3 - 2F_1, \quad 0, \quad 1 - 2F_1, F_1, \quad 5 - 3F_1, \quad 0\} \tag{37b}$$

$$\{ \quad 0, 5 - 2F_2, -1, \quad 3 - 2F_2, F_2, \quad 2 - 3F_2, \quad 0\} \tag{37c}$$

$$\{ \quad 0, \quad - 2F_3, \quad 0, \quad - 2F_3, F_3, \quad - 3F_3, \quad 0\} \tag{37d}$$

$$\{ \quad 0, 1 - 2F_4, \quad 0, \quad 6 - 2F_4, F_4, \quad 2 \cdot 3F_4, \quad 1\} \tag{37e}$$

(Note that equation (37d) was obtained by taking row 3 on Table 2 and multiplying it by $-F_3$.)

We have implicitly assumed that solutions to the homogeneous equations can be combined into new solutions. This is, in fact, the case, and the proof, being very simple, is left to the reader.

The question now is what values to assign to the various F's. We already know that $F_0 = 100/3$, as $100 - 3F_0$ must be 0. According to our pattern the sixth number in equation (37b) must be 0, which leads to $F_1 = 5/3$. Similarly, the sixth number in equation (37c) must be 0, which gives $F_2 = 2/3$. Furthermore, the sixth number in equation 37d must be -1; this gives $F_3 = 1/3$. Finally the sixth number in equation (37e) must be 0, which gives $F_4 = 2/3$.

Substituting these values of the factors, we get Table 3a or, after carrying out the computations, Table 3b.

We see, then, that in Table 3b, we do have the desired family of solutions. Row 0 is the solution combining P_2, P_4, and P_5. The other rows are the associated solutions to the homogeneous equations.

TABLE 3a. Modification of the First Family of Solutions[a]

| | | | | | ↓In | ↓Out | |
	P_1	P_2	P_3	P_4	P_5	P_6	P_7
Row 0	$0-0$	$80-2\times\frac{100}{3}$	$0-0$	$120-2\times\frac{100}{3}$	$0+\frac{100}{3}$	$100-3\times\frac{100}{3}$	$0-0$
Row 1 P_1	$-1-0$	$3-2\times\frac{5}{3}$	$0-0$	$1-2\times\frac{5}{3}$	$0+\frac{5}{3}$	$5-3\times\frac{5}{3}$	$0-0$
Row 2 P_3	$0-0$	$5-2\times\frac{2}{3}$	$-1-0$	$3-2\times\frac{2}{3}$	$0+\frac{2}{3}$	$2-3\times\frac{2}{3}$	$0-0$
Row 3 P_6	$-0\times\frac{1}{3}$	$-2\times\frac{1}{3}$	$-0\times\frac{1}{3}$	$-2\times\frac{1}{3}$	$\frac{1}{3}$	$-3\times\frac{1}{3}$	$-0\times\frac{1}{3}$
Row 4 P_7	$0-0$	$1-2\times\frac{2}{3}$	$0-0$	$6-2\times\frac{2}{3}$	$0+\frac{2}{3}$	$2-3\times\frac{2}{3}$	$-1-0$

[a] Multiples of row 3, Table 2, are subtracted from each row in Table 2, resulting in row 0, row 1, row 2, and row 4 of this table. This introduces pill P_5. The proper factors for each row are determined by the fact that pill P_6 is to be removed.

As an exercise, the reader is urged to verify the fact that the numbers on Table 3 form a family of solutions.

To summarize, we have described a technique that allows us to go from one family of solutions to a second one, to a third one, etc. We do have a method now to survey all the basic solutions to our original

TABLE 3b. The New Family of Solutions Obtained from Table 3a[a]

		P_1	P_2	P_3	P_4	P_5	P_6	P_7
Row 0		0	40/3	0	160/3	100/3	0	0
Row 1	P_1	−1	−1/3	0	−7/3	5/3	0	0
Row 2	P_3	0	11/3	−1	5/3	2/3	0	0
Row 3	P_5	0	−2/3	0	−2/3	1/3	−1	0
Row 4	P_7	0	−1/3	0	14/3	2/3	0	−1
Cost row		40	10	50	6	35	7	40

[a] The top row is a solution to equations (6), (7), (8). The other rows are solutions to the homogeneous equations (16), (17), and (18).

equations, with the aid of developing, one after the other, the proper families of solutions.

5. SYMBOLIC FORMULATION OF MODIFICATION PRINCIPLE

In order to be sure that we have a clear understanding of the method of going from one family of solutions to another, we formulate the technique in a symbolic fashion. This will be somewhat cumbersome, but necessary for reasons of clarity and completeness. Assume then that the first family is given by:

$$[x_1, \quad x_2, \quad x_3, \quad x_4, \quad x_5, \quad x_6, \quad x_7 \,] \tag{38a}$$

$$\{y_{1,1}, \ y_{1,2}, \ y_{1,3}, \ y_{1,4}, \ y_{1,5}, \ y_{1,6}, \ y_{1,7}\} \tag{38b}$$

$$\{y_{2,1}, \ y_{2,2}, \ y_{2,3}, \ y_{2,4}, \ y_{2,5}, \ y_{2,6}, \ y_{2,7}\} \tag{38c}$$

$$\{y_{3,1}, \ y_{3,2}, \ y_{3,3}, \ y_{3,4}, \ y_{3,5}, \ y_{3,6}, \ y_{3,7}\} \tag{38d}$$

$$\{y_{4,1}, \ y_{4,2}, \ y_{4,3}, \ y_{4,4}, \ y_{4,5}, \ y_{4,6}, \ y_{4,7}\} \tag{38e}$$

Then the second family is given by:

$$[x_1 \quad - y_{3,1}F_0, \; x_2 \quad - y_{3,2}F_0, \; x_3 \quad - y_{3,3}F_0, \; x_4 \quad - y_{3,4}F_0, \; x_5 \quad - y_{3,5}F_0, \; x_6 \quad - y_{3,6}F_0, \; x_7 \quad - y_{3,7}F_0]$$
$$(39a)$$

$$\{y_{1,1} - y_{3,1}F_1, \; y_{1,2} - y_{3,2}F_1, \; y_{1,3} - y_{3,3}F_1, \; y_{1,4} - y_{3,4}F_1, \; y_{1,5} - y_{3,5}F_1, \; y_{1,6} - y_{3,6}F_1, \; y_{1,7} - y_{3,7}F_1\}$$
$$(39b)$$

$$\{y_{2,1} - y_{3,1}F_2, \; y_{2,2} - y_{3,2}F_2, \; y_{2,3} - y_{3,3}F_2, \; y_{2,4} - y_{3,4}F_2, \; y_{2,5} - y_{3,5}F_2, \; y_{2,6} - y_{3,6}F_2, \; y_{2,7} - y_{3,7}F_2\}$$
$$(39c)$$

$$\{ \quad - y_{3,1}F_3, \quad\quad - y_{3,2}F_3, \quad\quad - y_{3,3}F_3, \quad\quad - y_{3,4}F_3, \quad\quad - y_{3,5}F_3, \quad\quad - y_{3,6}F_3, \quad\quad - y_{3,7}F_3\}$$
$$(39d)$$

$$\{y_{4,1} - y_{3,1}F_4, \; y_{4,2} - y_{3,2}F_4, \; y_{4,3} - y_{3,3}F_4, \; y_{4,4} - y_{3,4}F_4, \; y_{4,5} - y_{3,5}F_4, \; y_{4,6} - y_{3,6}F_4, \; y_{4,7} - y_{3,7}F_4\}$$
$$(39e)$$

where equation (39a) is obtained by multiplying equation (38d) by F_0 and subtracting it from equation (38a). Equations (39b), (39c), and (39e) are obtained from equations (38b), (38c), and (38e) in a similar manner. However, equation (39d) is obtained by multiplying equation (38d) by $-F_3$. Let us call the second family the following:

$$[X_1, \quad X_2, \quad X_3, \quad X_4, \quad X_5, \quad X_6, \quad X_7 \;] \tag{40a}$$

$$\{Y_{1,1}, \; Y_{1,2}, \; Y_{1,3}, \; Y_{1,4}, \; Y_{1,5}, \; Y_{1,6}, \; Y_{1,7}\} \tag{40b}$$

$$\{Y_{2,1}, \; Y_{2,2}, \; Y_{2,3}, \; Y_{2,4}, \; Y_{2,5}, \; Y_{2,6}, \; Y_{2,7}\} \tag{40c}$$

$$\{Y_{3,1}, \; Y_{3,2}, \; Y_{3,3}, \; Y_{3,4}, \; Y_{3,5}, \; Y_{3,6}, \; Y_{3,7}\} \tag{40d}$$

$$\{Y_{4,1}, \; Y_{4,2}, \; Y_{4,3}, \; Y_{4,4}, \; Y_{4,5}, \; Y_{4,6}, \; Y_{4,7}\} \tag{40e}$$

The relationship between the new and old families is given by:

$$\boxed{X_j = x_j - y_{3,j}F_0} \qquad j = 1, 2, 3, \cdots, 7 \tag{41}$$

$$Y_{1,j} = y_{1,j} - y_{3,j}F_1 \tag{42}$$

$$Y_{2,j} = y_{2,j} - y_{3,j}F_2 \tag{43}$$

$$\boxed{Y_{3,j} = \qquad - y_{3,j}F_3} \tag{44}$$

$$Y_{4,j} = y_{4,j} - y_{3,j}F_4 \tag{45}$$

or

$$\boxed{Y_{i,j} = y_{i,j} - y_{3,j}F_i} \qquad i = 1, 2, 4 \tag{46}$$

(This last equation does not apply to $Y_{3,j}$.)   The value of F_0 is given by the smallest positive value of

$$\frac{x_1}{y_{3,1}}, \frac{x_2}{y_{3,2}}, \frac{x_3}{y_{3,3}}, \ldots, \frac{x_7}{y_{3,7}}$$

In the illustrative example we are using in this chapter, we get

$$F_0 = \frac{x_6}{y_{3,6}} = \frac{100}{3}$$

It follows from this that we must have:

$$Y_{1,6} = Y_{2,6} = Y_{4,6} = 0 \quad \text{and} \quad Y_{3,6} = -1$$

These give then the factors for equations (42), (43), (44), and (45), as

$$F_1 = \tfrac{5}{3}, F_2 = \tfrac{2}{3}, F_3 = \tfrac{1}{3}, F_4 = \tfrac{2}{3}$$

Let us finally point out that there is a somewhat simpler symbolic representation of the relationship between the old and new family of solutions.   This can be written as:

$$(\text{New row } 0) = (\text{Old row } 0) - F_0 \,(\text{Old row } 3)$$

$$(\text{New row } 1) = (\text{Old row } 1) - F_1 \,(\text{Old row } 3)$$

$$(\text{New row } 2) = (\text{Old row } 2) - F_2 \,(\text{Old row } 3) \qquad (47)$$

$$(\text{New row } 3) = \qquad\qquad - F_3 \,(\text{Old row } 3)$$

$$(\text{New row } 4) = (\text{Old row } 4) - F_4 \,(\text{Old row } 4)$$

6. THE SIMPLEX TRANSFORMATION

Let us summarize the state of affairs.   We started with a family of solutions which was obtained by solving a system of equations.   Then we developed a technique to survey other families of solutions, this without solving any more equations.   In order to select the cheapest solution, we would have to compute the cost for each of these solutions.   If we had ten equations and thirty unknowns, we would have to survey approximately 30,000,000 solutions, though we would not have to solve ten equations with thirty unknowns 30,000,000 times. This survey represents an impractical amount of work.   Is there any way we could reduce the search from the 30,000,000 to a reasonable number?   Let us remember that we must look for the cheapest solution, and so far we have not capitalized on this fact at all.   We

proceed now to show that the costs associated with each family of
solutions can guide us to the next family of solutions to be surveyed.

First of all, let us determine the *change* in costs when we move from a
solution:

$$[x_1, \ x_2, \ x_3, \ x_4, \ x_5, \ x_6, \ x_7]$$

to the next solution

$$[Fy_1, \ Fy_2, \ Fy_3, \ Fy_4, \ Fy_5, \ Fy_6, \ Fy_7]$$

The change in cost is given by:

$$40(x_1 - Fy_1) + 10(x_2 - Fy_2) + 50(x_3 - Fy_3) + 6(x_4 - Fy_4)$$
$$+ \ 35(x_5 - Fy_5) + 7(x_6 - Fy_6) + 40(x_7 - Fy_7) \quad (48)$$

or by

$$(40x_1 + 10x_2 + 50x_3 + 6x_4 + 35x_5 + 7x_6 + 40x_7)$$
$$- \ F(40y_1 + 10y_2 + 50y_3 + 6y_4 + 35y_5 + 7y_6 + 40y_7) \quad (49)$$

In equation (49) the first term is the original cost. The second is the
differential cost due to the modification. This second term, of course,

TABLE 4. First Family of Solutions[a]

		P_1	P_2	P_3	P_4	P_5	P_6	P_7	D	
Row 0		0	80	0	120	0	100	0		
Row 1	P_1	-1	3	0	1	0	5	0	$+31$	
Row 2	P_3	0	5	-1	3	0	2	0	$+32$	←
Row 3	P_5	0	2	0	2	-1	3	0	$+18$	
Row 4	P_7	0	1	0	6	0	2	-1	$+20$	
Cost row		40	10	50	6	35	7	40		

[a] The last column shows the differential costs. The row with the largest differential cost, row
2, is to be introduced next.

is proportional to F, and the proportionality factor in the bracket
we will denote by D.

We now inspect Table 4, which is the same as Table 2 except that in
the bottom the cost of each pill is listed, and in the right-hand side
a new column listing the differential costs is given. We consider
row 1, which introduces pill P_1. Clearly, for each P_1 introduced

there is a saving (in cents) of

$$40(-1) + 10(3) + 50(0) + 6(1) + 35(0) + 7(5) + 40(0) = +31$$

Let us put it this way: As far as vitamin contents are concerned, each P_1 is equivalent to 3 of P_2, 1 of P_4, and 5 of P_6. The cost of these is $3(10) + 1(6) + 5(7) = \$0.71$. On the other hand a single P_1 costs $\$0.40$. Therefore, by introducing a single P_1, we can save $\$0.31$. This rule of computation can be expressed symbolically by stating that the row of costs is to be combined with one of the rows or

$$(\text{Row of costs}) \times (\text{Row 1}) = 31$$

The number 31, then, is listed in the column under D in row 1.

We can proceed similarly to row 2, which introduces P_3. We get for the differential cost

$$(\text{Row of costs}) \times (\text{Row 2})$$
$$= 40(0) + 10(5) + 50(-1) + 6(3) + 35(0) + 7(2) + 40(0) = 32$$

The differential cost for row 3, which introduces P_5, is

$$40(0) + 10(2) + 50(2) + 6(2) + 35(-1) + 7(3) + 40(0) = 18$$

Finally, the cost of row 4, introducing P_7, is:

$$40(0) + 10(1) + 50(0) + 6(6) + 35(0) + 7(2) + 40(-1) = 20$$

It can be seen that, whatever pill is introduced, there is a saving. However, it is reasonable to introduce the pill which offers the greatest saving. This can be expressed as the following rule: *Introduce the pill which offers the largest differential saving.*

If we had followed this rule, we would not have gone from Table 2 to Table 3, as we would have introduced P_3 and not P_5. We should have subtracted the proper multiples of row 2, which leads, then, to the following pattern:

$$[\quad 0, \; 80 - 5F_0, \; F_0, \; 120 - 3F_0, \quad 0, \; 100 - 2F_0, \quad 0] \quad (50a)$$

$$\{-1, \quad 3 - 5F_1, \; F_1, \quad 1 - 3F_1, \quad 0, \quad 5 - 2F_1, \quad 0\} \quad (50b)$$

$$\{ \quad 0, \qquad -5F_2, \; F_2, \qquad -3F_2, \quad 0, \qquad -2F_2, \quad 0\} \quad (50c)$$

$$\{ \quad 0, \; 2 - 5F_3, \; F_3, \quad 2 - 3F_3, \; -1, \quad 3 - 2F_3, \quad 0\} \quad (50d)$$

$$\{ \quad 0, \; 1 - 5F_4, \; F_4, \quad 6 - 3F_4, \quad 0, \quad 2 - 2F_4, \; -1\} \quad (50e)$$

How many pills P_3 should we introduce? What is the largest permissible value of F_0? We remove P_2 if

$$80 - 5F_0 = 0$$

or when $F_0 = 16$. On the other hand, we can remove P_4 by putting

$$120 - 3F_0 = 0$$

or putting $F_0 = 40$. This value of F_0 is, however, not permissible as it leads to -120 number of pills P_2, which makes no sense. Or, finally. we can remove pill P_6 by putting

$$100 - 2F_0 = 0$$

which leads to $F_0 = 50$. This is again a forbidden value, as it leads to a negative quantity of P_2. In summary, we see that the possibilities

TABLE 5a. Modifications of First Family of Solutions Leading to the Second Family of Solutions[a]

| | Out | | | In | | | |
| | ↓ | | | ↓ | | | |

	P_1	P_2	P_3	P_4	P_5	P_6	P_7
	$0-0$	$80-5\times16$	$0+16$	$120-3\times16$	0	$100-2\times16$	0
P_1	$-1-0$	$3-5\times0.6$	$0+0.6$	$1-3\times0.6$	$0-0$	$5-2\times0.6$	$0-0$
P_2	-0	-5×0.2	0.2	-3×0.2	-0	-2×0.2	-0
P_5	$0-0$	$2-5\times0.4$	$0+0.4$	$2-3\times0.4$	$-1-0$	$3-2\times0.4$	$0-0$
P_7	$0-0$	$1-5\times0.2$	$0+0.2$	$6-3\times0 2$	$0-0$	$2-2\times0.2$	$-1-0$

[a] With the aid of row 2, Table 4, P_3 is introduced and P_2 is removed.

TABLE 5b. Second Family of Solutions[a]

(Total cost, $17.08)

		P_1	P_2	P_3	P_4	P_5	P_6	P_7	
Row 0		0	0	16	72	0	68	0	
Row 1	P_1	-1	0	0.6	-0.8	0	3.8	0	$+11.8$
Row 2	P_2	0	-1	0.2	-0.6	0	-0.4	0	-6.4
Row 3	P_5	0	0	0.4	0.8	-1	2.2	0	$+5.2$
Row 4	P_7	0	0	0.2	5.4	0	1.6	-1	$+13.6$ ←
Cost row		40	10	50	6	35	7	40	

[a] The row with the largest differential cost (row 4) is to be introduced next.

TABLE 6a. Modifications of Second Family of Solutions Leading to the Third Family of Solutions[a]

	P_1	P_2	P_3	P_4 (Out ↓)	P_5	P_6	P_7 (In →)
P_1	$0 - 0$	$0 - 0$	16 $-(0.2 \times 13.3)$	72 $-(5.4 \times 13.3)$	$0 - 0$	68 $-(1.6 \times 13.3)$	$0 + 13.3$
P_2	$-1 - 0$	$0 - 0$	0.6 $-(0.2 \times -0.143)$	-0.8 $-(5.4 \times -0.148)$	$0 - 0$	3.8 $-(1.6 \times -0.148)$	$0 + 0.148$
P_5	$0 - 0$	$-1 - 0$	0.2 $-(0.2 \times -0.111)$	-0.6 $-(5.4 \times -0.111)$	$0 - 0$	-0.4 $-(1.6 \times -0.111)$	$0 + 0.111$
P_4	$0 - 0$	$0 - 0$	0.4 $-(0.2 \times 0.148)$	0.8 $-(5.4 \times 0.148)$	$-1 - 0$	2.2 $-(1.6 \times 0.148)$	$0 - 0.148$
	0	0	-0.2×0.185	-5.4×0.185	0	-1.6×0.185	$0 + 0.185$

[a] With the aid of row 4, Table 5b, P_7 is introduced and P_6 is removed.

TABLE 6b.   Third Family of Solutions[a]
(Total cost, $15.26)

		P_1	P_2	P_3	P_4	P_5	P_6	P_7	
Row 0		0	0	13.33	0	0	46.66	13.33	
Row 1	P_2	0	−1	0.222	0	0	−0.222	−0.111	−4.89
Row 2	P_4	0	0	−0.037	−1	0	−0.296	0.185	−2.52
Row 3	P_5	0	0	0.370	0	−1	1.96	0.148	+3.14
Row 4	P_1	−1	0	0.630	0	0	4.04	−0.148	+13.86 ←
Cost row		40	10	50	6	35	7	40	

[a] The row with the largest differential cost (row 4) is to be introduced next.

for F_0 are 16, 40, and 50, and we must select the smallest of these numbers, namely, 16. This means then, that the new family of solutions will not contain P_2. We are led to the equations:

$$3 - 5F_1 = 0$$
$$-5F_2 = -1$$
$$2 - 5F_3 = 0$$
$$1 - 5F_4 = 0$$

which give:

$$F_1 = \tfrac{3}{5}, F_2 = \tfrac{1}{5}, F_3 = \tfrac{2}{5}, F_4 = \tfrac{1}{5}$$

Table 5a represents this family of solutions, and Table 5b shows results of the computations. These tables replace, then, Tables 3a and 3b.

We continue now to process by computing the differential costs. We get the numbers:

$$40(-1) + 10(\ 0) + 50(\tfrac{3}{5}) + 6(-\tfrac{4}{5}) + 35(\ 0) + 7(\tfrac{19}{5})$$
$$+ 40(\ 0) = +11.8$$

$$40(\ 0) + 10(-1) + 50(\tfrac{1}{5}) + 6(-\tfrac{3}{5}) + 35(\ 0) + 7(\ \tfrac{2}{5})$$
$$+ 40(\ 0) = -6.4$$

$$40(\ 0) + 10(\ 0) + 50(\tfrac{2}{5}) + 6(\ \tfrac{4}{5}) + 35(-1) + 7(\tfrac{11}{5})$$
$$+ 40(\ 0) = +5.2$$

$$40(\ 0) + 10(\ 0) + 50(\tfrac{1}{5}) + 6(\ \tfrac{27}{5}) + 35(\ 0) + 7(\ \tfrac{8}{5})$$
$$+ 40(-1) = +13.6$$

which are listed on the last column in Table 5b.

TABLE 7a. Modification of the Third Family of Solutions Leading to the Fourth Family of Solutions[a]

In →   Out →

	P_1	P_2	P_3	P_4	P_5	P_6	P_7
	0 + 11.55	0	13.33 -(0.630 × 11.55)	0	0	46.66 -(4.04 × 11.55)	13.33 -(-0.148 × 11.55)
P_2	0 - 0.055	-1	0.222 -(0.630 × -0.055)	0	0	-0.222 -(4.04 × -0.055)	-0.111 -(-0.148 × -0.055)
P_4	0 - 0.073	0	-0.037 -(0.630 × -0.037)	-1	0	-0.296 -(4.04 × -0.073)	0.185 -(-0.148 × -0.073)
P_5	0 + 0.485	0	0.370 -(0.630 × 0.485)	0	-1	1.96 -(4.04 × 0.485)	0.148 -(-0.148 × 0.485)
P_6	+0.247	0	-0.630 × 0.247	0	0	-4.04 × 0.247	0.148 × 0.247

[a] With the aid of row 4, Table 6b, P_1 is introduced and P_4 is removed.

It can be seen, then, that we now have a guide that specifies at each step which new family of solutions to choose. Table 6a shows modifications of the second family of solutions leading to the third family of solutions. Table 6b shows the third family of solutions. In our illustrative example, after four steps we reach the final solution, shown in Tables 7a and 7b. We suspect that this is the cheapest solution, for, as the last column indicates, the introduction of any pill results

TABLE 7b. Fourth and Optimal Family of Solutions[a]

(Total cost, $13.66)

	P_1	P_2	P_3	P_4	P_5	P_6	P_7	
	11.55	0	6.05	0	0	0	15.05	
P_2	−0.055	−1	+0.257	0	0	0	−0.119	−4.11
P_4	−0.073	0	0.009	−1	0	0	0.174	−1.51
P_5	0.485	0	0.065	0	−1	0	0.220	−3.55
P_6	0.248	0	−0.156	0	0	−1	0.037	−3.40
Cost row	40	10	50	6	35	7	40	

[a] All differential costs are negative. No further cost saving is possible.

in a negative saving or increase in cost. (Rigorous proof that this method does lead to the optimum solution is omitted here.)

The economy of work that results from following these rules is spectacular. For our hypothetical example of ten equations and thirty unknowns, the number of solutions to be surveyed would be cut from 30,000,000 to perhaps 50. Without the simplex method, linear programming could not have become an important tool of the business world.

7. TECHNIQUE OF COMPUTING THE FIRST FAMILY OF SOLUTIONS

Let us recall the way we computed the first family of solutions. Pills P_2, P_4, and P_6 happen to be pure vitamins, and therefore we could immediately write down a first solution to the equations by simply combining these pure vitamin pills. The associated solutions to the homogeneous equations were determined by solving the homogeneous equations.

This method of obtaining the first family of solutions is too restrictive and cumbersome. What should we do if we do not happen to have pure vitamin pills, if, moreover, we have a large number of unknowns? The difficulty of not having pure vitamin pills can be overcome by using an ingenious artifice to modify the problem. We will simply add some hypothetical vitamin pills and assume that these hypothetical pills are extremely expensive. Referring to our particular example, we could introduce the hypothetical pills P_8, P_9, P_{10} (even i. P_2, P_4, and P_6 were not pure pills) and replace Table 1 by Table 8f

TABLE 8. Vitamin Pills, Requirements, and Costs for Modified Problem

	P_1	P_2	P_3	P_4	P_5	P_6	P_7	P_8	P_9	P_{10}	
V_1	5	0	2	0	3	1	2	1	0	0	100
V_2	3	1	5	0	2	0	1	0	1	0	80
V_3	1	0	3	1	2	0	6	0	0	1	120
Costs	40	10	50	6	35	7	40	1,000	1,000	1,000	

(The cost of the hypothetical pills is assumed to be $10 or 1,000 cents.) We can start now solving this modified problem by meeting the vitamin requirements with these pure hypothetical pills. Then, as the solution proceeds from one family of solutions to the next, the expensive hypothetical pills will automatically disappear, and we will obtain a solution to our original problem.

We still do not know, though, how to obtain the first set of solutions to the homogeneous equations without going to the trouble of *solving* these equations. We will proceed to show that for the modified problem these solutions can be written down directly without any computations.

In order to show this, we formulate the linear programming problem in a more general fashion. We assume that the system of equations to be solved is the following:

$$a_{1,1}x_1 + a_{1,2}x_2 + a_{1,3}x_3 + a_{1,4}x_4 + \cdots + a_{1,n}x_n = b_1$$
$$a_{2,1}x_1 + a_{2,2}x_2 + a_{2,3}x_3 + a_{2,4}x_4 + \cdots + a_{2,n}x_n = b_2$$
$$a_{3,1}x_1 + a_{3,2}x_2 + a_{3,3}x_3 + a_{3,4}x_4 + \cdots + a_{3,n}x_n = b_3 \quad (51)$$
$$\vdots$$
$$a_{m,1}x_1 + a_{m,2}x_2 + a_{m,3}x_3 + a_{m,4}x_4 + \cdots + a_{m,n}x_n = b_m$$

where there are n unknowns and m equations. The cost function is

$$z = c_1x_1 + c_2x_2 + c_3x_3 + c_4x_4 + \cdots + c_nx_n \qquad (52)$$

where the c's are the costs associated with the various unknowns. These last two equations replace equations (6)–(9), which we had for our illustrative example of the nutrition problem.

We introduce now m number of hypothetical pills in quantities $x_{n+1}, x_{n+2}, \cdots, x_{n+m}$. Mathematically speaking, this means that equations (51) are replaced by the following equations:

$$a_{1,1}x_1 + a_{1,2}x_2 + \cdots + a_{1,n}x_n + x_{n+1} = b_1$$

$$a_{2,1}x_1 + a_{2,2}x_2 + \cdots + a_{2,n}x_n + x_{n+2} = b_2$$

$$a_{3,1}x_1 + a_{3,2}x_2 + \cdots + a_{3,n}x_n + x_{n+3} = b_3 \qquad (53)$$

$$\vdots$$

$$a_{m,1}x_1 + a_{m,2}x_2 + \cdots + a_{m,n}x_n + x_{n+m} = b_m$$

In the theory of linear programming, the quantities of these hypothetical pills are referred to as the *slack variables*.

The cost function given by equation (52) is to be replaced by:

$$z = c_1x_1 + c_2x_2 + \cdots + c_nx_n + Mx_{n+1} + Mx_{n+2} + \cdots \\ + Mx_{n+m} \quad (54)$$

where the letter M denotes a very large price associated with the hypothetical pills.

Referring again to our particular example, equation (53) takes the form:

$$5x_1 \qquad + 2x_3 \qquad + 3x_5 + x_6 + 2x_7 + x_8 \qquad\qquad = 100$$

$$3x_1 + x_2 + 5x_3 \qquad + 2x_5 \qquad + x_7 \qquad + x_9 \qquad = 80 \quad (55)$$

$$x_1 \qquad + 3x_3 + x_4 + 2x_5 \qquad + 6x_7 \qquad\qquad + x_{10} = 120$$

and equation (54) takes the form:

$$z = 40x_1 + 10x_2 + 50x_3 + 6x_4 + 35x_5 + 7x_6 + 40x_7 + 1000x_8 \\ + 1000x_9 + 1000x_{10} \quad (56)$$

We claim now that the first family of solutions associated with equation (53) or (55) can be directly written down as shown in Table 9. Consider the top row or row 0 in Table 9. This row is claimed to be a solution to equation (53).   The first n numbers are all 0.   This means that:

$$x_1 = x_2 = \cdots = x_n = 0 \qquad (57)$$

and so, by inspecting equation (53), we conclude that we must have

$$x_{n+1} = b_1,\ x_{n+2} = b_2,\ x_{n+3} = b_3,\ \cdots,\ x_{n+m} = b_m \qquad (58)$$

This is, however, exactly what is listed on the right-hand side of Table 9 in row 0.   So we see that row 0 is indeed a solution to equation (53).

TABLE 9.   First Family of Solutions to Modified Problem

	P_1	P_2	P_3	P_4				P_n	P_{n+1}	P_{n+2}			P_{n+m}
Row 0	0	0	0	0				0	b_1	b_2	b_3		b_m
Row 1	−1	0	0	0				0	$a_{1,1}$	$a_{2,1}$	$a_{3,1}$		$a_{m,1}$
Row 2	0	−1	0	0				0	$a_{1,2}$	$a_{2,2}$	$a_{3,2}$		$a_{m,2}$
Row 3	0	0	−1	0				0	$a_{1,3}$	$a_{2,3}$	$a_{3,3}$		$a_{m,3}$
	0	0	0	−1				0	$a_{1,4}$	$a_{2,4}$	$a_{3,4}$		$a_{m,4}$
							−1	0					
Row n							0	−1	$a_{1,n}$	$a_{2,n}$	$a_{3,n}$		$a_{m,n}$

Does row 1 in Table 9 represent a solution to the homogeneous equations?   The first n numbers in row 1 are

$$x_1 = -1,\ x_2 = x_3 = \cdots,\ x_n = 0 \qquad (59)$$

Inspecting equations 53, we see that we must have

$$a_{1,1} - x_{n+1} = 0,\ a_{2,1} - x_{n+2} = 0,\ a_{3,1} - x_{n+3} = 0,$$
$$\cdots\ a_{m,1} - x_{n+m} = 0 \qquad (60)$$

These last equations precisely assign the values to the unknowns listed in the right-hand side of row 1 in Table 6.

Similarly, it can be seen that the other rows represent the other solutions to the homogeneous equations.

We can apply this method to our particular example.   Table 10 shows the first family of solutions to the modified problem.

In summary then, we can see that we indeed have a method to get the first family of solutions to our modified problem, and we can do this

TABLE 10. First Family of Solutions to Modified Problem[a]

		P_1	P_2	P_3	P_4	P_5	P_6	P_7	P_8	P_9	P_{10}	
Row 0		0	0	0	0	0	0	0	100	80	120	
Row 1	P_1	−1	0	0	0	0	0	0	5	3	1	9,000 − 40
Row 2	P_2	0	−1	0	0	0	0	0	0	1	0	1,000 − 10
Row 3	P_3	0	0	−1	0	0	0	0	2	5	3	10,000 − 50
Row 4	P_4	0	0	0	−1	0	0	0	0	0	1	1,000 − 6
Row 5	P_5	0	0	0	0	−1	0	0	3	2	2	7,000 − 35
Row 6	P_6	0	0	0	0	0	−1	0	1	0	0	1,000 − 7
Row 7	P_7	0	0	0	0	0	0	−1	2	1	6	9,000 − 40
Cost row		40	10	50	6	35	7	40	1,000	1,000	1,000	

[a] Row with largest differential cost row 3, is to be removed.

without solving the system of equations even a single time. When combining this with the method of moving from one family of solutions to the next one, we recognize the full economy of the simplex method for solving linear programming problems.

8. RECAPITULATION OF THE SIMPLEX METHOD

Suppose that we have a first family of solutions:

$$
\begin{matrix}
x_1, & x_2, & x_3, & \cdots, & x_n \\
y_{1,1}, & y_{1,2}, & y_{1,3}, & \cdots, & y_{1,n} \\
y_{2,1}, & y_{2,2}, & y_{2,3}, & \cdots, & y_{2,n} \\
\cdot & \cdot & \cdot & & \cdot \\
\cdot & \cdot & \cdot & & \cdot \\
\cdot & \cdot & \cdot & & \cdot \\
y_{m,1}, & y_{m,2}, & y_{m,3}, & \cdots, & y_{m,n}
\end{matrix}
\tag{61}
$$

Let us denote the next family of solutions by

$$
\begin{matrix}
X_1, & X_2, & X_3, & \cdots, & X_n \\
Y_{1,1}, & Y_{1,2}, & Y_{1,3}, & \cdots, & Y_{1,n} \\
Y_{2,1}, & Y_{2,2}, & Y_{2,3}, & \cdots, & Y_{2,n} \\
\cdot & \cdot & \cdot & & \cdot \\
\cdot & \cdot & \cdot & & \cdot \\
\cdot & \cdot & \cdot & & \cdot \\
Y_{m,1}, & Y_{m,2}, & Y_{m,3}, & \cdots, & Y_{m,n}
\end{matrix}
\tag{62}
$$

What are the rules for getting these solutions?

Step 1

We compute the differential costs:

$$
\begin{aligned}
D_1 &= c_1 y_{1,1} + c_2 y_{1,2} + c_3 y_{1,3} + \cdots + c_n y_{1,n} \\
D_2 &= c_1 y_{2,1} + c_2 y_{2,2} + c_3 y_{2,3} + \cdots + c_n y_{2,n} \\
& \quad \cdot \qquad \cdot \qquad \cdot \qquad\qquad \cdot \\
& \quad \cdot \qquad \cdot \qquad \cdot \qquad\qquad \cdot \\
& \quad \cdot \qquad \cdot \qquad \cdot \qquad\qquad \cdot \\
D_m &= c_1 y_{m,1} + c_2 y_{m,2} + c_3 y_{m,3} + \cdots + c_n y_{m,n}
\end{aligned}
\tag{63}
$$

We then select the largest of these numbers and denote the corresponding row number by s. This is the row whose multiple has to be subtracted when going to the next family of solutions. As an example, we apply this to Table 10. We get:

$$D_1 = (-1)40 + (5 \times 1{,}000) + (3 \times 1{,}000) + (1 \times 1{,}000)$$
$$= 9{,}000 - 40 \sim 9{,}000$$

$$D_2 = (-1)10 + (0 \times 1{,}000) + (1 \times 1{,}000) + (0 \times 1{,}000)$$
$$= 1{,}000 - 10 \sim 1{,}000$$

$$D_3 = (-1)50 + (2 \times 1{,}000) + (5 \times 1{,}000) + (3 \times 1{,}000)$$
$$= 10{,}000 - 50 \sim 10{,}000$$

$$D_4 = (-1)\ 6 + (0 \times 1{,}000) + (0 \times 1{,}000) + (1 \times 1{,}000)$$
$$= 1{,}000 - \ 6 \sim 1{,}000$$

$$D_5 = (-1)35 + (3 \times 1{,}000) + (2 \times 1{,}000) + (2 \times 1{,}000)$$
$$= 7{,}000 - 35 \sim 7{,}000$$

$$D_6 = (-1)\ 7 + (1 \times 1{,}000) + (0 \times 1{,}000) + (0 \times 1{,}000)$$
$$= 1{,}000 - \ 7 \sim 1{,}000$$

$$D_7 = (-1)40 + (2 \times 1{,}000) + (1 \times 1{,}000) + (6 \times 1{,}000)$$
$$= 9{,}000 - 40 \sim 9{,}000$$

This shows that the third row is the one to be subtracted, or

$$s = 3$$

Step 2

We select the smallest positive number from the group:

$$\frac{x_1}{y_{s,1}}, \frac{x_2}{y_{s,2}}, \ \cdot \ \cdot \ \cdot \ , \frac{x_n}{y_{s,n}} \tag{64}$$

Let this smallest number be

$$\frac{x_r}{y_{s,r}}$$

where r is the column number of the unknown to be removed. We now compute

$$F_0 = \frac{x_r}{y_{s,r}}$$

In our illustrative example, we choose from the numbers:

$$\tfrac{100}{2} = 50 \qquad \tfrac{80}{5} = 16 \qquad \tfrac{120}{3} = 40$$

The smallest of these is 16. This refers to the column under P_9, and so P_9 is to be removed, or

$$r = 9$$

(We also know that $F_0 = 16$.)

Step 3

We compute the numbers:

$$F_1 = \frac{y_{1,r}}{y_{s,r}}, \; F_2 = \frac{y_{2,r}}{y_{s,r}}, \; \cdots, \; F_n = \frac{y_{n,r}}{y_{s,r}}$$

but omit from the above F_s, as this is given by:

$$F_s = \frac{1}{y_{s,r}}$$

Referring to our illustrative example, we have:

$$y_{s,r} = y_{3,9} = 5$$

So we have $F_3 = \frac{1}{5}$. The rest of the factors are obtained by taking the ninth column and dividing each of the numbers by 5. This gives:

$$F_1 = \tfrac{3}{5}, F_2 = \tfrac{1}{5}, F_4 = 0, F_5 = \tfrac{2}{5}, F_6 = 0, F_7 = \tfrac{1}{5}$$

Step 4

The top row of the new family of solutions is given by:

$$X_1 = x_1 - y_{s,1}F_0$$

$$= x_2 - y_{s,2}F_0$$

$$\vdots \qquad \vdots \qquad \vdots \qquad (65)$$

$$X_n = x_n - y_{s,n}F_0$$

Equations (65) follow the rule given at the end of Section 5:

New row 0 = Old row 0 − F_0 (old row 5)

The ith row (provided that i does not equal s is given by:

$$Y_{i,1} = y_{i,1} - y_{s,1}F_i$$
$$Y_{i,2} = y_{i,2} - y_{s,2}F_i$$

$$\begin{matrix} \cdot & \cdot & \cdot \\ \cdot & \cdot & \cdot \\ \cdot & \cdot & \cdot \end{matrix} \qquad (66)$$

$$Y_{i,n} = y_{i,n} - y_{s,n}F_i$$

Equations (66) follow the previously given rule:

New row i = Old row $i - F_i$ (old row 5)

Finally the sth row is given by

$$Y_{s,1} = -y_{s,1}F_s$$
$$Y_{s,2} = -y_{s,2}F_s$$

$$\begin{matrix} \cdot & \cdot \\ \cdot & \cdot \\ \cdot & \cdot \end{matrix} \qquad (67)$$

$$Y_{s,n} = -y_{s,n}F_s$$

Equations (67) follow the rule:

New row $s = -F_s$ (old row s)

For our illustrative example, Table 11a shows the application of these equations. In Table 11b, the computations are carried through.

Step 5

We repeat the whole process.

In our illustrative example, the largest differential cost is in row 7, so P_7 is to be removed. The reader is urged to carry the computation through, as it is very difficult to understand all the details without actually carrying through the computations. Tables 11a and 11b show the second family of solutions. Finally, row 0 in Table 12 shows

TABLE 11a Modifications of the First Family of Solutions to Modified Problem[a]

In → P_3 Out → P_9

	P_1	P_2	P_3	P_4	P_5	P_6	P_7	P_8	P_9	P_{10}
	0	0	16	0	0	0	0	$100 - 2 \times 16$	$80 - 5 \times 16$	$120 - 3 \times 16$
P_1	-1	0	$\frac{3}{5}$	0	0	0	0	$5 - 2 \times \frac{3}{5}$	$3 - 5 \times \frac{3}{5}$	$1 - 3 \times \frac{3}{5}$
P_2	0	-1	$\frac{1}{5}$	0	0	0	0	$0 - 2 \times \frac{1}{5}$	$1 - 5 \times \frac{1}{5}$	$0 - 3 \times \frac{1}{5}$
P_3	0	0	$\frac{1}{5}$	0	0	0	0	$-2 \times \frac{1}{5}$	$-5 \times \frac{1}{5}$	$-3 \times \frac{1}{5}$
P_4	0	0	0	-1	0	0	0	$0 - 2 \times 0$	$0 - 5 \times 0$	$1 - 3 \times 0$
P_5	0	0	$\frac{2}{5}$	0	-1	0	0	$3 - 2 \times \frac{2}{5}$	$2 - 5 \times \frac{2}{5}$	$2 - 3 \times \frac{2}{5}$
P_6	0	0	0	0	0	-1	0	$1 - 2 \times 0$	$0 - 5 \times 0$	$0 - 3 \times 0$
P_7	0	0	$-\frac{1}{5}$	0	0	0	-1	$2 - 2 \times \frac{1}{5}$	$1 - 5 \times \frac{1}{5}$	$6 - 3 \times \frac{1}{5}$

[a] With the aid of row 3, Table 10, P_3 is introduced and P_9 is removed.

TABLE 11b. Second Family of Solutions to Modified Problem[a]

		P_1	P_2	P_3	P_4	P_5	P_6	P_7	P_8	P_9	P_{10}	
Row 0		0	0	16	0	0	0	0	68	0	72	
Row 1	P_1	−1	0	3/5	0	0	0	0	19/5	0	−4/5	2,990
Row 2	P_2	0	−1	1/5	0	0	0	0	−2/5	0	−3/5	−1,000
Row 3	P_3	0	0	1/5	0	0	0	0	−2/5	−1	−3/5	−1,990
Row 4	P_4	0	0	0	−1	0	0	0	0	0	1	− 994
Row 5	P_5	0	0	2/5	0	−1	0	0	11/5	0	4/5	2,985
Row 6	P_6	0	0	0	0	0	−1	0	1	0	0	993
Row 7	P_7	0	0	1/5	0	0	0	−1	8/5	0	27/5	6,970
Cost row		40	10	50	6	35	7	40	1,000	1,000	1,000	

[a] The row with the largest differential saving, row 7, is to be introduced next.

TABLE 12. Final Family of Solutions to Modified Problem

		P_1	P_2	P_3	P_4	P_5	P_6	P_7	P_8	P_9	P_{10}	
Row 0		11.56	0	6.06	0	0	0	15.05	0	0	0	
Row 1	P_8	0.248	0	−0.156	0	0	0	0.037	−1	0	0	3.60 − 1,000
Row 2	P_2	−0.055	−1	+0.257	0	0	0	−0.119	0	0	0	−4.11
Row 3	P_9	−0.055	0	+0.257	0	0	0	−0.119	0	−1	0	5.89 − 1,000
Row 4	P_4	−0.073	0	0.009	−1	0	0	0.174	0	0	0	−1.51
Row 5	P_5	0.485	0	0.065	0	−1	0	0.220	0	0	0	−3.55
Row 6	P_6	0.248	0	−0.156	0	0	−1	0.037	0	0	0	−3.40
Row 7	P_{10}	−0.073	0	0.009	0	0	0	0.174	0	0	−1	4.49 − 1,000
Cost row		40	8	50	6	35	7	40	1,000	1,000	1,000	

the optimum solution, and it can be seen that this solution is identical with the one shown in Table 7b.   We also note that row 1 and row 6, row 2 and row 3, and row 4 and 7 are identical.   The reason is that P_6, P_2, and P_4 are all pure pills, and so are not different from the hypothetical pills P_8, P_9, P_{10}.   In the general case, none of the pills would be pure, and therefore we would be compelled to introduce P_8, P_9, and P_{10}.

9.   DEGENERACY

In Section 8 of Chapter 2, in connection with the transportation problem we discussed the case of degeneracy.   We have seen that, under certain conditions, our method of solving the transportation problem may not work, and modifications in the approach need to be introduced.   We want to discuss here a similar difficulty that may arise in connection with the simplex method.

We present the modified simplex method (to be applied in the case of degeneracy), with the aid of an illustrative example of the nut-mix problem borrowed from Charnes, Cooper, and Henderson,* a problem similar to the one in Chapter 3, Section 4 (p. 65), which concerns the allocation of products.

A business enterprise mixes cashews, hazelnuts, and peanuts into three different products.   This hypothetical business enterprise purchases cashews at a price of $0.65 a pound, hazelnuts at $0.35 a pound, and peanuts at $0.25 a pound.   These various nuts are mixed in three different products, and the specifications for the products are as follows: Product 1 must have at least 50% cashews and at most 25% peanuts.   Product 2 must have at least 25% cashews and at most 50% peanuts.   Finally, product 3 can be any mixture of these various nuts. The sale price of the first product is $0.50 a pound, of the second is $0.35 a pound, and of the third is $0.25 a pound.   A further restriction is that there is only a limited supply of these nuts available, namely, there are only 100 pounds of cashews, 100 pounds of peanuts, and 60 pounds of hazelnuts available.   The question is, then, in what proportion should these nuts be mixed in order to maximize profit?

Let us denote by x_1 the quantity of cashews that go into product 1, by x_2 the quantity of peanuts that go into product 1, and so on, as shown by the table:

* A. Charnes, W. W. Cooper, A. Henderson, *An Introduction to Linear Programming*, John Wiley & Sons, New York, 1953.

	Products			
	1	2	3	
Cashews 1	x_1	x_4	x_7	100
Peanuts 2	x_2	x_5	x_8	100
Hazelnuts 3	x_3	x_6	x_9	60

We have a limited supply of each of these nuts, and, therefore, we have

$$x_1 + x_4 + x_7 \leq 100 \tag{68}$$

$$x_2 + x_5 + x_8 \leq 100 \tag{69}$$

$$x_3 + x_6 + x_9 \leq 60 \tag{70}$$

We must have at least 50% cashews in the first product, and so we must have

$$\frac{x_1}{x_1 + x_2 + x_3} \geq 0.5 \tag{71}$$

We cannot allow more than 25% peanuts in the same product, and therefore we must have

$$\frac{x_2}{x_1 + x_2 + x_3} \leq 0.25 \tag{72}$$

We must have at least 25% cashews in product 2 and, therefore, we must have

$$\frac{x_4}{x_4 + x_5 + x_6} \geq 0.25 \tag{73}$$

Finally, we cannot allow more than 50% peanuts in product 2 and, therefore, we must have

$$\frac{x_5}{x_4 + x_5 + x_6} \leq 0.50 \tag{74}$$

Let us multiply both sides of equations (71) and (72) by $(x_1 + x_2 + x_3)$ and collect all terms on the left-hand side. We get

$$-\tfrac{1}{2}x_1 + \tfrac{1}{2}x_2 + \tfrac{1}{2}x_3 \leq 0 \tag{75}$$

and

$$-\tfrac{1}{4}x_1 + \tfrac{3}{4}x_2 - \tfrac{1}{4}x_3 \leq 0 \tag{76}$$

Let us multiply both sides of equations (73) and (74) by $(x_4 + x_5 + x_6)$ and collect all terms on the left-hand side. We get

$$-\tfrac{3}{4}x_4 + \tfrac{1}{4}x_5 + \tfrac{1}{4}x_6 \leq 0 \tag{77}$$

$$-\tfrac{1}{2}x_4 + \tfrac{1}{2}x_5 - \tfrac{1}{2}x_6 \leq 0 \tag{78}$$

There are no restrictions in product 3 as these can contain any mixture of nuts.

The first product sells for $0.50 a pound, the second one at $0.35 a pound, and the third one at $0.25 a pound. Cashews cost $0.65 a pound, hazelnuts $0.35 a pound, and peanuts $0.25 a pound, and consequently the total profit can be written as

$$z = 50(x_1 + x_2 + x_3) + 35(x_4 + x_5 + x_6) + 25(x_7 + x_8 + x_9) \\ - 65(x_1 + x_4 + x_7) - 25(x_2 + x_5 + x_8) - 35(x_3 + x_6 + x_9) \tag{79}$$

This can be written as

$$z = -15x_1 + 25x_2 + 15x_3 - 30x_4 + 10x_5 - 40x_7 - 10x_9 \tag{80}$$

We can see, then, that we have here a linear programming problem; we are to maximize the payoff function as expressed by equation (80) under the restrictions of equations (68), (69), (70), (75), (76), (77), and (78).

In order to solve this problem with the simplex method, we introduce slack variables and get the following system of equations

$$-\tfrac{1}{2}x_1 + \tfrac{1}{2}x_2 + \tfrac{1}{2}x_3 + x_{10} = 0 \tag{81}$$

$$-\tfrac{1}{4}x_1 + \tfrac{3}{4}x_2 - \tfrac{1}{4}x_3 + x_{11} = 0 \tag{82}$$

$$-\tfrac{3}{4}x_4 + \tfrac{1}{4}x_5 + \tfrac{1}{4}x_6 + x_{12} = 0 \tag{83}$$

$$-\tfrac{1}{2}x_4 + \tfrac{1}{2}x_5 - \tfrac{1}{2}x_6 + x_{13} = 0 \tag{84}$$

$$x_1 + x_4 + x_7 + x_{14} = 100 \tag{85}$$

$$x_2 + x_5 + x_8 + x_{15} = 100 \tag{86}$$

$$x_3 + x_6 + x_9 + x_{16} = 60 \tag{87}$$

In Table 13 we summarize matters by showing the table of coefficients for this nut-mix problem.

TABLE 13. Table of Coefficients for the Nut-Mix Problem[a]

Equations	Unknowns									Slack Variables							
	x_1	x_2	x_3	x_4	x_5	x_6	x_7	x_8	x_9	x_{10}	x_{11}	x_{12}	x_{13}	x_{14}	x_{15}	x_{16}	
1	$-1/2$	$+1/2$	$+1/2$							$+1$							$= 0$
2	$-1/4$	$+3/4$	$-1/4$								$+1$						$= 0$
3				$-3/4$	$+1/4$	$-1/4$						$+1$					$= 0$
4				$-1/2$	$+1/2$	$-1/2$							$+1$				$= 0$
5	$+1$			$+1$			$+1$							$+1$			$= 100$
6		$+1$			$+1$			$+1$							$+1$		$= 100$
7			$+1$			$+1$			$+1$							$+1$	$= 60$
	-15	$+25$	$+15$	-30	$+10$		-40		-10								

[a] This is a degenerate problem.

TABLE 14.　First Family of Solutions for Nut-Mix Problem

		P_1	P_2	P_3	P_4	P_5	P_6	P_7	P_8	P_9	P_{10}	P_{11}	P_{12}	P_{13}	P_{14}	P_{15}	P_{16}	
Row 0															100	100	60	
Row 1	P_1	-1									$-1/2$	$-1/4$			$+1$			$+15$
2	P_2		-1								$+1/2$	$\boxed{+3/4}$				$+1$		-25 ←
3	P_3			-1							$+1/2$	$-1/4$					$+1$	-15
4	P_4				-1								$-3/4$	$-1/2$	$+1$			$+30$
5	P_5					-1							$+1/4$	$+1/2$		$+1$		-10
6	P_6						-1						$+1/4$	$-1/2$				0
7	P_7							-1								$+1$		$+40$
8	P_8								-1									
9	P_9									-1							$+1$	$+10$
		-15	$+25$	$+15$	-30	$+10$	0	-40	0	-10								

Let us try to apply the simplex method to this problem. We can immediately write down the first family of solutions as shown in Table 14, and we can compute the differential savings as shown in the last column. We recognize that the largest saving is in row 2, and consequently we should introduce this row into the solution. However, we find that there is no way to introduce this row, for if we subtract this row from the top row we get negative numbers in the tenth and eleventh column. But this is not permissible as the solution to the equation must be positive. How can we get around this difficulty?

What we need is solutions to the homogeneous equation such that in the tenth, eleventh, twelfth, and thirteenth column only negative numbers appear. Then, when we subtract this row from the top row, we do get positive numbers in the top row. Now we proceed to show how we can combine the solutions to the homogeneous equations, so that in each of these columns we get a single -1. (The rest of the numbers will be 0 in each column.)

We begin by introducing row 2 in our solution and multiplying every number in it by $-\frac{4}{3}$. This gives a solution to the homogeneous equations as listed in row 2 in Table 15 (second family of solutions.) Now we proceed to multiply our old row 2 by a proper factor and subtract it from old row 1, old row 3, old row 4, old row 5, old row 6, old row 7, old row 8, and old row 9. Now we get everywhere a zero in the eleventh column. For instance, we multiply our old row 2 by the factor of $-\frac{1}{3}$, and then subtract it from the old row 1. We get the new row 1 in Table 15, and, indeed, the number in the eleventh column is 0. We see, then, that the second family of solutions has only a single -1 in the eleventh column and that all the other numbers in the eleventh column are zero. We are one step closer to our purpose of having only negative numbers in the tenth, eleventh, twelfth, and thirteenth columns.

Incidentally, we could have achieved the same result by taking the old row 2 and multiplying it by -2. Then we would have a -1 in the tenth column, and could have changed into zero the numbers in the tenth column. (Instead of turning the $\frac{3}{4}$ into -1, we could have turned the $+\frac{1}{2}$ into -1.) Let us agree to the convention that we take the largest positive number in the row that is being introduced and turn that number into -1. (This is the convention we have used when we selected $\frac{3}{4}$ instead of $\frac{1}{2}$.)

Now we compute the differential savings as shown in the last column of Table 15; we recognize that row 3 offers the greatest saving and, therefore, this is the row that we are to introduce into the solution. In this row the number in the tenth column, the $\frac{2}{3}$, is the largest posi-

TABLE 15. Second Family of Solutions for Nut-Mix Problem

	P_1	P_2	P_3	P_4	P_5	P_6	P_7	P_8	P_9	P_{10}	P_{11}	P_{12}	P_{13}	P_{14}	P_{15}	P_{16}	
Row 0	-15	$+25$	$+15$	-30	$+10$	0	-40	0	-10					100	100	60	
1 P_1	-1	$-1/3$								$-1/3$				1	$1/3$	$1/3$	$+20/3$
2 P_2		$4/3$								$-2/3$	-1				$-4/3$		$+100/3$
3 P_3		$-1/3$	-1							$\boxed{2/3}$					$1/3$	$1/3$	$-70/3 \leftarrow$
4 P_4				-1								$-3/4$	$-1/2$	$+1$			$+90/3$
5 P_5					-1							$+1/4$	$+1/2$		$+1$		$-30/3$
6 P_6						-1						$+1/4$	$-1/2$			$+1$	0
7 P_7							-1							$+1$			$+120/3$
8 P_8								-1							$+1$		0
9 P_9									-1							$+1$	$+30/3$

tive number, and this is the one to be changed into -1. We multiply this row by $-\frac{3}{2}$ and thereby obtain the new row 3 in the third family of solutions (Table 16). The new rows in the third family of solutions are obtained by taking the old row 3 and subtracting its proper multiple from the old rows 1, 2, 4, 5, 6, 7, 8, and 9. (We must use the proper factors when subtracting so that the numbers will disappear in the tenth column.)

Next we compute the differential savings in the third family (Table 16) and note that the fifth row is the one that must be introduced into the solution. The $\frac{1}{2}$ in the thirteenth column must be made into -1, and, consequently, we multiply row 5 by -2 and get the new row 5 in the fourth family of solutions (Table 17). The rest of the rows in the fourth family of solutions are obtained by combining the old rows of the third family of solutions. We realize now that, in the fourth family of solutions, we have positive numbers only in the twelfth column. With the procedure outlined previously, we can get rid of these numbers and get the fifth family of solutions (Table 18) which, indeed, has the property that there are only negative numbers in the tenth, eleventh, twelfth, and thirteenth columns. Now we can proceed with the conventional simplex method and introduce the first row into the solution, as this offers the largest potential saving. It so happens that the next (or sixth) family of solutions (Table 19) is already the final solution to the problem since, for this family, all the differential savings are positive and therefore no further improvement can be made.

We see, then, that the solution to our nut-mix problem is to make only product 1 and to use 100 pounds of cashews, 50 pounds of peanuts, and 50 pounds of hazelnuts. The other products are not profitable to make. (This result could be obtained by a simple analysis; our emphasis is not on the problem but on the method of solution.)

This method of getting around the difficulty of degeneracy works also in any other linear programming problem. There is one further point, though. We selected the proper row to come into the solution by taking the largest differential cost, as is always the case in the simplex method. We chose the number to be made into -1 by selecting the largest positive number in the row. Under certain peculiar conditions, it might be necessary to have a different way to select the number that is to be turned into -1. The reader who has interest in this particular subject is referred to the original work of Charnes, Cooper, and Henderson.*

* A. Charnes, W. W. Cooper, A. Henderson, *An Introduction to Linear Programming*, John Wiley & Sons, New York, 1953.

TABLE 16. Third Family of Solutions for Nut-Mix Problem

	P₁	P₂	P₃	P₄	P₅	P₆	P₇	P₈	P₉	P₁₀	P₁₁	P₁₂	P₁₃	P₁₄	P₁₅	P₁₆	
Row 0	-15	+25	+15	-30	+10	0	-40	0	-10					100	100	60	
1 P₁	-1	-1/2	-1/2								-1			+1	+1/2	+1/2	-10/2
2 P₂	+1	-1													-1	+1	+20/2
3 P₃	+1/2	+1/2								-1					-1/2	-3/2	+45/2
4 P₄				-1								-3/4	-1/2	+1			+60/2
5 P₅					-1							+1/4	[+1/2]		+1		-20/2 ↓
6 P₆						-1						+1/4	-1/2				0
7 P₇							-1							+1	+1		+80/2
8 P₈								-1								+1	0
9 P₉									-1							+1	+20/2

TABLE 17. Fourth Family of Solutions for Nut-Mix Problem

Row	P_1	P_2	P_3	P_4	P_5	P_6	P_7	P_8	P_9	P_{10}	P_{11}	P_{12}	P_{13}	P_{14}	P_{15}	P_{16}	
0														100	100	60	↓
1 P_1	−1	−1/2	−1/2											+1	+1/2	+1/2	−10/2
2 P_2		+1	−1								−1				−1	+1	+20/2
3 P_3	+1/2		+3/2	−1											−1/2	−3/2	+70/2
4 P_4				−1	−1					−1		−1/2		+1	+1		+40/2
5 P_5					+2							−1/2			−2		+40/2
6 P_6					−1	−1						[+1/2]	−1		+1	+1	−20/2
7 P_7							−1										+80/2
8 P_8								−1							+1		0
9 P_9									−1							+1	+29/2
	−15	+25	+15	−30	+10	0	−40	0	−10								

142 Mathematical Programming

TABLE 18. Fifth Family of Solutions for Nut-Mix Problem

	P_1	P_2	P_3	P_4	P_5	P_6	P_7	P_8	P_9	P_{10}	P_{11}	P_{12}	P_{13}	P_{14}	P_{15}	P_{16}	
Row 0	-15	$+25$	$+15$	-30	$+10$	0	-40	0	-10					100	100	60	$\leftarrow$
1 P_1	-1	$-1/2$	$-1/2$											$+1$	$+1/2$	$+1/2$	$-10/2$
2 P_2		$+1$	-1								-1				-1	$+1$	$+20/2$
3 P_3		$+1/2$	$+3/2$							-1					$-1/2$	$-3/2$	$+70/2$
4 P_4				-1	-2	-1								$+1$	$+2$	$+1$	$+20/2$
5 P_5					$+1$	-1							-1		-1	$+1$	$+20/2$
6 P_6					$+2$	$+2$						-1			-2	-2	$+40/2$
7 P_7							-1										$+80/2$
8 P_8								-1							$+1$		0
9 P_9									-1							$+1$	$+20/2$

TABLE 19. Sixth and Final Family of Solutions for Nut-Mix Problem

	P_1	P_2	P_3	P_4	P_5	P_6	P_7	P_8	P_9	P_{10}	P_{11}	P_{12}	P_{13}	P_{14}	P_{15}	P_{16}	
Row 0	100	50	50												50	10	
1 P_1	+1	+1/2	+1/2											−1	−1/2	−1/2	+10/2
2 P_2		+1	−1								−1				−1	+1	+20/2
3 P_3		+1/2	+1/2							−1					−1/2	−3/2	+70/2
4 P_4		+1/2	+1/2	−1	−2	−1									+3/2	+1/2	+60/2
5 P_5					+1	−1							−1		−1	+1	+20/2
6 P_6					+2	+2						−1			−2	−2	+40/2
7 P_7		+1/2	+1/2				−1								−1/2	−1/2	+120/2
8 P_8								−1									0
9 P_9									−1						+1	+1	20/2
	−15	+25	+15	−30	+10	0	−40	0	−10								

10.   CONCLUDING REMARKS

We now know how to carry through computations to solve a linear programming problem.   The various steps required in the computations can be worked out into a routine that can be programmed on an electronic computer.   However, it is beyond the purpose of this book to present a "recipe" for computations, as we are concentrating on providing the reader with an insight and understanding of the subject.

One of the great difficulties in understanding a complicated mathematical argument lies in the fact that it is not sufficient to understand each of the steps but rather that it is necessary to have a grasp of the whole at once.   If we insisted on remembering every step in detail when contemplating the whole, we would face an impossible task of remembering.   Therefore, it is necessary to try to grasp the sequence of arguments in their totality in a fashion which does not burden the memory with all the details involved.   To put it another way, the problem should be broken down into a few large concepts whose interrelationship is recognized.

In order to understand the simplex method, we must first understand that the problem is to find a solution to a system of linear equations which minimizes the cost function.   However, we recognize that we do not need to search all possible solutions but only basic solutions, since, according to the fundamental theorem of linear programming, the solution to the problem will be a basic solution.   (Our book is incomplete in the sense that we have not given a proof of the fundamental theorem.)

After understanding the fundamental theorem, we come to the central feature of the method.   This is embodied in the concept of the family of solutions.   We must understand what we mean by a family of solutions, what is the homogeneous system of equations, and what is the particular pattern that the family of solutions forms.

We can imagine every family of solutions represented by an object or by a point in space.   There would be very many of these points. There is a cost associated with each of the points, and we can imagine that the higher the cost the higher the point is in space.   The problem is to survey the points and find the lowest one.

We have developed a technique for moving from one family of solutions to another.   We can imagine in our geometrical representation that, if we can go from one point to another, then there is a route connecting these points.   Now we have the image of a complicated network in space (as only some of the points are connected with each other). The problem is to reach the point on the bottom by moving along these connecting routes.

We have a device to help us find a first point in this space. We know how to move along these routes from one point to another. We have a guide that tells us in which direction to move.

Finally, we have a way to know when we are on the bottom, though we have not included in our book a proof that the method guarantees that we reach the bottom.

This general description of the simplex method allows comprehension of the whole method at once. To understand each of the steps completely requires the step by step understanding we have demonstrated. The geometrical representation of the simplex method can be made more exact, and in Chapter 6 we will develop in detail this geometrical representation of linear programming.

We have presented in this chapter the simplex method through an illustrative example and have tacitly assumed that the method is valid for any linear programming problem. The discerning reader may ask whether this is true. The fact of the matter is that the method as presented here does not always work, but it does work in most practical problems and also it can be slightly modified to include any linear programming problem. We have omitted in this book the precise distinction between when the method works and when it does not work, as we did not want to go into the detailed discussion of the problem of degeneracy. The reader who is particularly interested in this subject is referred to the literature on linear programming* to explore this matter further.

* A. Charnes, W. W. Cooper, and A. Henderson, *An Introduction to Linear Programming*, John Wiley & Sons, New York, 1953.

CHAPTER 5

THE DUAL THEOREM
OF
LINEAR PROGRAMMING

1. PRICE IMPUTATIONS: A NEW WAY OF LOOKING AT THE PROBLEM

Let us return to our nutrition problem considered in Chapter 4. How much do we pay for the various units of vitamins we purchase to meet the daily requirements?

The first solution to the problem consists of a combination of the pure pills P_2, P_4, and P_6. As pill P_6 costs 7 cents and contains 1 unit of vitamin 1, we can say that each unit of vitamin 1 costs 7 cents. Similarly, from the cost of P_2 and P_4, we deduce that each unit of V_2 costs 10 cents and each unit of V_3 costs 6 cents. These costs lead to the total cost of

$$(100 \times 7) + (80 \times 10) + (120 \times 6) = 2220 \quad \text{or} \quad \$22.20$$

In the optimum solution, the total cost was reduced to \$13.66. What is the cost of each vitamin when we are using this combination? Let us introduce the following notation: each unit of V_1 costs $\bar{w}_1$, each unit of V_2 costs $\bar{w}_2$, and each unit of V_3 costs $\bar{w}_3$. How can we determine these costs?

P_1 contains 5 units of V_1, 3 of V_2, and 1 of V_3. The costs of the various units of vitamins will be proper if by adding the costs of the vitamin contents of P_1 we get back the cost of P_1, which is 40 cents. In equation form, this means that we must have

$$5\bar{w}_1 + 3\bar{w}_2 + \bar{w}_3 = 40 \tag{1a}$$

Similarly, the cost of P_3 implies that we must have

$$2\bar{w}_1 + 5\bar{w}_2 + 3\bar{w}_3 = 50 \qquad (1b)$$

Finally, the cost of P_7 implies that

$$2\bar{w}_1 + \bar{w}_2 + 6\bar{w}_3 = 40 \qquad (1c)$$

We can now solve this system of equations and get for the vitamin costs the figures:

$$\bar{w}_1 = 3.578 \text{ cents}, \quad \bar{w}_2 = 5.872 \text{ cents}, \quad \bar{w}_3 = 4.495 \text{ cents}$$

As a check for these figures, let us compute the total costs of buying the required 100 units of V_1, 80 units of V_2 and 120 units of V_3. We get

$$100\bar{w}_1 + 80\bar{w}_2 + 120\bar{w}_3 = 13.67$$

which is in agreement with the result that the minimum cost is \$13.66.

We can look at the same problem of determining the vitamin costs from a different point of view. Suppose our daily requirements are reduced to 99 units of V_1, 80 units of V_2, and 120 units of V_3. How can be compute the cost of meeting these reduced requirements? We have just discovered that each unit of V_1 costs 3.578 cents. Therefore, the cost of the reduced vitamin requirements should turn out to be less than the original cost of \$13.66 by this amount.

Let us denote by x'_1 the number of pills P_1 needed to meet the reduced vitamin requirements, by x'_3 the number of P_3's required to meet the reduced requirements, and by x'_7 the number of P_7's required. These three unknowns must satisfy the equations

$$5x'_1 + 2x'_3 + 2x'_7 = \quad 99 \qquad (2a)$$

$$3x'_1 + 5x'_3 + \quad x'_7 = \quad 80 \qquad (2b)$$

$$x'_1 + 3x'_3 + 6x'_7 = 120 \qquad (2c)$$

The cost associated with reduced requirements is given by

$$z_1 = 40x'_1 + 50x'_2 + 40x'_7 \qquad (3)$$

as each P_1, P_2, or P_7 costs \$0.40, \$0.50, or \$0.40. Furthermore, as we said before, we must have

$$z_{\min} - z_1 - \bar{w}_1 \qquad (4)$$

where $z_{\min}$ is the minimum cost when 100 units of V_1 are required, z_1 is the minimum cost when 99 units of V_1 are required, and $\bar{w}_1$ is the price of each unit of vitamin V_1.

Suppose we want to verify equation (4). We could do this by solving equation (2) and then computing z from equation (3) and, finally, $\bar{w}_1$ from equation (4). We should find agreement with our original evaluation of the cost of V_1. However, it will be more convenient to do this checking in another fashion. Let x_1 denote the number of pills P_1 needed to meet the original vitamin requirements. Similarly, let x_3 and x_7 denote the number of pills P_3 and P_7 required to meet the original vitamin requirements. Then

$$5x_1 + 2x_3 + 2x_7 = 100 \tag{5a}$$

$$3x_1 + 5x_3 + x_7 = 80 \tag{5b}$$

$$x_1 + 3x_3 + 6x_7 = 120 \tag{5c}$$

The minimum cost associated with this combination of pills is given by:

$$z_{\min} = 40x_1 + 50x_3 + 40x_7 \tag{6}$$

Let us now subtract equation (2a) from equation (5a), equation (2b) from equation (5b), and equation (2c) from equation (5c); we get

$$5(x_1 - x'_1) + 2(x_3 - x'_3) + 2(x_1 - x'_7) = 1$$

$$3(x_1 - x'_1) + 5(x_3 - x'_3) + (x_1 - x'_7) = 0 \tag{7}$$

$$(x_1 - x'_1) + 3(x_3 - x'_3) + 6(x_1 - x'_7) = 0$$

Let us also subtract equation (3) from equation (6); we get for the cost of V_1:

$$\bar{w}_1 = z_{\min} - z_1 = 40(x_1 - x'_1) + 50(x_3 - x'_3) + 40(x_7 - x'_7) \tag{8}$$

Let us now introduce the new variables:

$$u_1 = x_1 - x'_1$$

$$u_3 = x_3 - x'_3 \tag{9}$$

$$u_7 = x_7 - x'_7$$

We get the system of equations:

$$5u_1 + 2u_3 + 2u_7 = 1$$

$$3u_1 + 5u_3 + u = 0 \tag{10}$$

$$u_1 + 3u_3 + 6u_7 = 0$$

and

$$\bar{w}_1 = 40u_1 + 50u_3 + 40u_7 \tag{11}$$

So far we have not accomplished much as it does not seem to be any easier to solve equations (10) than to solve equations (2). But here comes the surprise: Let us consider Table 12, Chapter 4 and in particular row 1. Here we have a solution to the homogeneous equations,

$$\{0.248,\ 0,\ -0.156,\ 0,\ 0,\ 0,\ 0.037,\ -1,\ 0,\ 0\}$$

or, replacing the numbers with y's,

$$\{y_1,\ 0,\ y_3,\ 0,\ 0,\ 0,\ y_7,\ -1,\ 0,\ 0\}$$

These numbers are a solution to the homogeneous equations, which means that

$$5y_1 + 2y_3 + 2y_7 - 1 = 0$$

$$3y_1 + 5y_3 +\ \ y_7\ \ \ \ \ = 0 \tag{12}$$

$$y_1 + 3y_3 + 6y_7\ \ \ \ \ = 0$$

These equations are precisely the same as equations (10), which means that the y's are identical with the u's. Therefore row 1 represents the solution to our problem of determining the combination of pills that meets the reduced vitamin requirements at minimum cost.

We recall, furthermore, that the differential cost in row 1 was computed as

$$D_1 = 10y_1 + 50y_3 + 40y_7 - 1,000 \tag{13}$$

therefore

$$\bar{w}_1 = D_1 + 1,000 \tag{14}$$

This means, in fact, that in Table 12, in the last column D in row 1, we have the cost of V_1, i.e., $\bar{w}_1$. (Because of inaccuracies in the computations, we find in Table 12 the number 3.60 instead of the more accurate number of 3.578.) Similarly the cost of V_2 is given by the number in row 3:

$$w_2 = D_3 + 1,000 \tag{15}$$

and the cost of V_3 is given by the number in row 7:

$$w_3 = D_7 + 1,000 \tag{16}$$

(Both of these numbers are inaccurate in Table 12; we find 5.89 and 4.49 instead of the more accurate numbers of 5.872 and 4.495.)

We have made, then, the important observation that the proper differential cost in the final family of solutions in the simplex method automatically gives the costs of the units of vitamins.

We can proceed now to impute a *value* to each vitamin pill. By this imputed value we mean the combined cost of the vitamin content of each pill. Let us denote these imputed values by v_1, v_2, etc. Then:

$$5\bar{w}_1 + 3\bar{w}_2 + \bar{w}_3 = v_1 = 40.00$$

$$\bar{w}_2 \qquad\qquad = v_2 = 5.87$$

$$2\bar{w}_1 + 5\bar{w}_2 + 3\bar{w}_3 = v_3 = 50.00$$

$$\bar{w}_3 = v_4 = 4.50 \qquad\qquad (17)$$

$$3\bar{w}_1 + 2\bar{w}_2 + 2\bar{w}_3 = v_5 = 31.47$$

$$\bar{w}_1 \qquad\qquad = v_6 = 3.58$$

$$2\bar{w}_1 + \bar{w}_2 + 6\bar{w}_3 = v_7 = 40.00$$

We observe that P_1, P_3, and P_7 have the same imputed values as the actual cost. However, P_2 has an imputed value of only 5.87 cents, which is smaller than its cost of 10 cents. This explains why we do not buy any P_2's: a pill P_2 is worth only 5.87 cents to us, and so we are not willing to pay 10 cents for it. Pill P_4 has the imputed value of 4.5 cents, whereas its cost is 6 cents. P_5 has the imputed value of 31.46 cents, which is again less than its cost of 35 cents. Finally, the imputed value of P_6 is 3.58 cents, whereas its cost is 7 cents. Notice that the imputed value of a pill is less than, or equal to, its cost, and that the imputed value reaches the actual cost only when that particular vitamin pill enters in the cheapest combination of pills. When the imputed value of a pill is less than its cost, it is not worth while to buy this pill; when the imputed value equals the cost, then we do buy the pill.

One further remark here: suppose the cost of P_5 is lowered. As long as this cost is more than 31.47 cents we do not buy this pill and the optimal solution is unchanged. However, if the cost drops below 31.47 cents, we have to reconsider the problem in order to determine the cheapest combination of pills.

2. THE DUAL PROBLEM

Let us look at the nutrition problem from the point of view of price imputations. We forget for the moment that we know the minimal combination of pills, and the corresponding prices of the various vitamins. Starting fresh, we ask the question, what should the imputed value be of each unit of vitamin V_1, V_2, and V_3? Let us denote these unknown imputed values by w_1, w_2, and w_3. (We will ignore, for the moment, the fact that in the last section we did determine these values as $\bar{w}_1$, $\bar{w}_2$, and $\bar{w}_3$.)   Let us, furthermore, denote by v_1, v_2, $\cdots$, v_7, the imputed values of pills P_1, P_2, $\cdots$, P_7.   Then we have

$$5w_1 + 3w_2 + \; w_3 = v_1$$

$$w_2 \qquad\qquad = v_2$$

$$2w_1 + 5w_2 + 3w_3 = v_3$$

$$w_3 = v_4 \qquad\qquad (18)$$

$$3w_1 + 2w_2 + 2w_3 = v_5$$

$$w_1 \qquad\qquad = v_6$$

$$2w_1 + \; w_2 + 6w_3 = v_7$$

These imputed values make sense only if these values are less than, or equal to, the actual cost of the pills.   Therefore, w_1, w_2, and w_3 will form a "sensible" set of imputed values only if the following inequalities hold:

$$5w_1 + 3w_2 + \; w_3 \leq 40 \qquad\qquad (19a)$$

$$w_2 \qquad\quad \leq 10 \qquad\qquad (19b)$$

$$2w_1 + 5w_2 + 3w_3 \leq 50 \qquad\qquad (19c)$$

$$w_3 \leq \; 6 \qquad\qquad (19d)$$

$$3w_1 + 2w_2 + 2w_3 \leq 35 \qquad\qquad (19e)$$

$$w_1 \qquad\qquad \leq \; 7 \qquad\qquad (19f)$$

$$2w_1 + \; w_2 + 6w_3 \leq 40 \qquad\qquad (19g)$$

Now we proceed to perform a little arithmetic.   Multiply equation (19a) by x_1, equation (19c) by x_3, and equation (19g) by x_7.   Add the right-hand sides to each other, and the left-hand sides to each other. We get:

$$w_1(5x_1 + 2x_3 + 2x_7) + w_2(3x_1 + 5x_3 + x_7)w_3$$
$$+ \; w_3(x_1 + 3x_3 + 6x_7) \leq 40x_1 + 50x_3 + 40x_7 \quad (20)$$

We compare this with equation (5).   We observe that the first expression in parantheses on the left-hand side is 100, the second 80, and the third 120, so we get:

$$100w_1 + 80w_2 + 120w_3 \leq z_{\min} \qquad\qquad (21)$$

Notice that the left-hand side is the total imputed cost of the vitamins meeting the requirements.   Let us denote by Z this total imputed cost.

Then

$$Z = 100w_1 + 80w_2 + 120w_3 \qquad (22)$$

We observe, therefore, that, according to equation (21), *any "sensible" total imputed cost is less than or equal to the minimal cost $z_{\min}$.* When we select the imputed cost $\bar{w}_1$, $\bar{w}_2$, $\bar{w}_3$, the total imputed cost becomes exactly $z_{\min}$. It is seen then that the cheapest combination of pills leads to the largest "sensible" imputed cost. Therefore, the solution to equations (19) which *maximizes* the function given by equation (22) is the solution to our nutrition problem. This is the so-called dual formulation of our linear programming problem. We proceed now to state the dual theorem in its general form.

3. GENERAL STATEMENT OF THE DUAL THEOREM

Let us consider two linear programming problems.

Problem 1. Determine the nonnegative solution to the system of inequalities:

$$a_{1,1}x_1 + a_{1,2}x_2 + \cdots + a_{1,n}x_n \geq b_1$$
$$a_{2,1}x_1 + a_{2,2}x_2 + \cdots + a_{2,n}x_n \geq b_2$$

$$\vdots \qquad (23)$$

$$a_{m,1}x_1 + a_{m,2}x_2 + \cdots + a_{m,n}x_n \geq b_m$$

which minimizes:

$$c_1x_1 + c_2x_2 + \cdots + c_nx_n \qquad (24)$$

Problem 2. Determine the nonnegative solution to the system of inequalities:

$$a_{1,1}w_1 + a_{2,1}w_1 + \cdots + a_{m,1}w_m \leq c_1$$
$$a_{1,2}w_1 + a_{2,2}w_2 + \cdots + a_{m,2}w_m \leq c_2$$

$$\vdots \qquad (25)$$

$$a_{1,n}w_1 + a_{2,n}w_2 + \cdots + a_{m,n}w_m \leq c_n$$

which maximizes:

$$b_1 w_1 + b_2 w_2 + \cdots + b_m w_m \tag{26}$$

These two linear programming problems are called duals to each other. Problem 1 has n unknowns and m equations. Problem 2 has m unknowns and n equations. The relationship between the two problems can be made clearer by showing the table of detached coefficients:

	x_1	x_2	$\cdots$	x_n	
w_1	$a_{1,1}$	$a_{1,2}$	$\cdots$	$a_{1,n}$	b_1
w_2	$a_{2,1}$	$a_{2,2}$	$\cdots$	$a_{2,n}$	b_2
.	.	.	.	.	.
.	.	.	.	.	.
.	.	.	.	.	.
w_m	$a_{m,1}$	$a_{m,2}$	$\cdots$	$a_{m,n}$	b_m
	c_1	c_2	$\cdots$	c_n	

Problems 1 and 2 can now be stated in shorthand notation.

Problem 1. Determine $x_1, x_2, \cdots, x_n$, so that

$$\left. \begin{array}{l} x_i \geq 0 \\ \sum_j a_{i,j} x_j \geq b_i \end{array} \right\} \quad i = 1, 2, \cdots, n$$

Minimize $\sum_j c_j x_j$.

Problem 2. Determine $w_1, w_2, \cdots, w_m$ so that

$$\left. \begin{array}{l} w_i \geq 0 \\ \sum_i a_{i,j} w_i \leq c_j \end{array} \right\} \quad j = 1, 2, \cdots, m$$

Maximize $\sum_i b_i w_i$.

Now that we have developed the concept of duality, let us turn our attention to the dual theorem of linear programming.

Denote by $z_{\min}$ the minimum value associated with the solution of Problem 1 and by $z_{\max}$ the maximum value associated with the solution of Problem 2. *The dual theorem of linear programming asserts that*

$$z_{\min} = z_{\max} \tag{27}$$

Proof of the theorem is omitted here, but the argument runs very close to the one we have given for the nutrition problem.

The advantage of the dual theorem is that we can choose which of the two problems to solve; often one of the problems can be solved more easily than the other. We will now proceed to show as an illustration how the dual theorem can be applied to the transportation problem.

4. APPLICATION TO TRANSPORTATION ALLOCATION

We propose to consider the combined production and transportation problem described in Chapter 2, Section 7. The firm operates four factories and five warehouses as shown in Table 22 of Chapter 2. (One of the warehouses is hypothetical to take care of excess capacities.) It will be convenient to use the following notation for the unknowns:

	W_1	W_2	W_3	W_4	W_5
F_1	x_1	x_2	x_3	x_4	x_5
F_2	x_6	x_7	x_8	x_9	x_{10}
F_3	x_{11}	x_{12}	x_{13}	x_{14}	x_{15}
F_4	x_{16}	x_{17}	x_{18}	x_{19}	x_{20}

For instance, the number of units sent from factory 3 to warehouse 3 is x_{13}. We proceed now to develop a system of inequalities between these unknowns. First of all, we write

$$x_1 + x_2 + x_3 + x_4 + x_5 \leq 140 \tag{28}$$

$$x_6 + x_7 + x_8 + x_9 + x_{10} \leq 260 \tag{29}$$

$$x_{11} + x_{12} + x_{13} + x_{14} + x_{15} \leq 360 \tag{30}$$

$$x_{16} + x_{17} + x_{18} + x_{19} + x_{20} \leq 220 \tag{31}$$

We are certain that these relations hold as, in fact, we know that production plus unused capacity must equal total capacity in each factory. As far as the warehouses are concerned, we write

$$x_1 + x_6 + x_{11} + x_{16} \geq 180 \tag{32}$$

$$x_2 + x_7 + x_{12} + x_{17} \geq 280 \tag{33}$$

$$x_3 + x_8 + x_{13} + x_{18} \geq 150 \tag{34}$$

$$x_4 + x_9 + x_{14} + x_{19} \geq 200 \tag{35}$$

$$x_5 + x_{10} + x_{15} + x_{20} \geq 170 \tag{36}$$

Again, these relations must hold as, in fact, we know that the shipments to each warehouse must equal the requirements. The problem is to minimize the transportation cost. We realize that the solution with the minimum transportation cost will turn all these inequality signs into equation signs.

The fact of the matter is that we could have written equations everywhere instead of inequalities. The only reason we wrote inequalities is that this facilitates development of the dual equations. Now we prepare the table of coefficients as shown in Table 1. We denote the unknowns in the dual problem by u_1, u_2, u_3, u_4, v_1, v_2, v_3, v_4, and v_5, as shown in the first column of Table 1. The dual equations can be written as

$$-u_1 + v_1 \leq 88 \tag{37}$$

and

$$-u_1 + v_2 \leq 100 \tag{38}$$

and so on, a total of 20 equations. The function to be maximized is the following:

$$z = -140u_1 - 260u_2 - 360u_3 - 220u_4 + 180v_1 + 280v_2$$
$$+ 150v_3 + 200v_4 + 170v_5 \tag{39}$$

Let us stop here for a moment and state the dual equations for the transportation problem in a more general form. The equations of the transportation problem can be replaced by the following system of inequalities:

$$\sum_j x_{i,j} \leq a_i \qquad i = 1, 2, \qquad , m \tag{40}$$

$$\sum_i x_{i,j} \geq b_j \qquad j = 1, 2, \cdots, n \tag{41}$$

The transportation cost to be minimized is the following:

$$z = \sum_i \sum_j c_{i,j} x_{i,j} \tag{42}$$

The dual theorem can be expressed by the following system of inequalities

$$-u_i + v_j \leq c_{i,j} \tag{43}$$

The function to be maximized is given by

$$z = -\sum_i a_i u_i + \sum_j b_j v_j \tag{44}$$

Now let us review the interpretation of the dual problem as given by the imputed costs. If we decrease the capacity of factory F_i by a

TABLE 1. Table of Coefficients for Combined Production and Transportation Problem

	x_1	x_2	x_3	x_4	x_5	x_6	x_7	x_8	x_9	x_{10}	x_{11}	x_{12}	x_{13}	x_{14}	x_{15}	x_{16}	x_{17}	x_{18}	x_{19}	x_{20}	
u_1	-1	-1	-1	-1	-1																-140
u_2						-1	-1	-1	-1	-1											-260
u_3											-1	-1	-1	-1	-1						-360
u_4																-1	-1	-1	-1	-1	-220
v_1	$+1$					$+1$					$+1$					$+1$					180
v_2		$+1$					$+1$					$+1$					$+1$				280
v_3			$+1$					$+1$					$+1$					$+1$			150
v_4				$+1$					$+1$					$+1$					$+1$		200
v_5					$+1$					$+1$					$+1$					$+1$	170
	88	100	96	98	0	90	100	96	102	0	90	102	100	102	0	96	108	100	106	0	

single unit, how much does the total cost change? The imputed cost here is u_i dollars, and, therefore, the total cost goes up by u_i dollars. Suppose requirements at warehouse W_j go up by a single unit. How does the cost change? The imputed cost is v_j dollars here, and so cost goes up by v_j dollars. Furthermore, if we increase the capacity of factory F_i by a single unit and simultaneously increase the requirement at warehouse W_j by a single unit, then the combined production and transportation cost goes up by an amount $v_j - u_i$. We recognize that this cost increase must be less than, or equal to, the transportation cost $c_{i,j}$ as expressed by equation (43).

Let us assume for the moment that we do know the solution of the transportation problem, that is, we know the numbers as shown in Table 23 of Chapter 2. How do we get the solution to the dual problem? Suppose we decrease the capacity of F_4 from 220 to 219. We know that the total combined production and transportation cost does not change as there is idle capacity in factory 4. Consequently, $u_4 = 0$ (see Table 2). Suppose requirements increase by a single unit in W_5. How does the combined cost change? We know that W_5 represents a hypothetical warehouse to take care of unused capacities in the factories, and therefore we know that an increase in the capacity of W_5 does not involve a change in the combined cost. Consequently, $v_5 = 0$.

Let us now increase the capacity of F_4 by a single unit and simultaneously increase the requirement at W_3 by a single unit. We observe in Table 22 of Chapter 2 that the combined production and transportation cost from F_4 to W_3 is \$100, or $c_{4,3} = 100$. As this transportation route is being used in the solution, this is the cheapest way to send goods from F_4 to W_3, and therefore we must have

$$-u_4 + v_3 = 100 \tag{45}$$

We know that $u_4 = 0$, and so we get

$$v_3 = 100 \tag{46}$$

Let us repeat the same argument for F_2 and W_3. We note from Table 22 that there is a cost of \$96 here, and therefore we must have

$$-u_2 + v_3 - 96 \tag{47}$$

We already know v_3, and so we get

$$-u_2 + 100 = 96 \tag{48a}$$

or

$$u_2 = +4 \tag{48b}$$

TABLE 2. Price Imputation for Combined Production and Transportation Problem

Legend for each cell:

$$
\begin{array}{cc}
c' & c \\
 & x \\
(c-c') &
\end{array}
$$

			Warehouses			
Factories	W_1	W_2	W_3	W_4	W_5	Row Numbers
F_1	86, 88; +2	98, 100; +2	94, 96; +2	98, 98; **140**; *	−6, 0; +6	$u_1 = +6$
F_2	88, 90; +2	100, 100; **160**; *	96, 96; **100**; *	100, 102; +2	−4, 0; +4	$u_2 = +4$
F_3	90, 90; **180**; *	102, 102; **120**; *	98, 100; +2	102, 102; **60**; *	−2, 0; +2	$u_3 = +2$
F_4	92, 96; +4	104, 108; +4	100, 100; **50**; *	104, 106; +2	0, 0; **170**; *	$u_4 = 0$
Column numbers	$v_1 = 92$	$v_2 = 104$	$v_3 = 100$	$v_4 = 104$	$v_5 = 0$	

x = unknown.

We can proceed, step by step, and get the solution to the dual problem. We list here the equations to be used and the results obtained.

$$-u_2 + v_2 = 100 \qquad v_2 = 104 \qquad\qquad (49)$$

$$-u_3 + v_2 = 102 \qquad u_3 = +2 \qquad\qquad (50)$$

$$-u_3 + v_1 = 90 \qquad v_1 = 92 \qquad\qquad (51)$$

$$-u_3 + v_4 = 102 \qquad v_4 = 104 \qquad\qquad (52)$$

$$-u_1 + v_4 = 98 \qquad u_1 = -10 \qquad\qquad (53)$$

The solution to the dual problem is shown in the last column of Table 2 under the heading "row numbers," and in the bottom row of the same table under the heading "column numbers." For instance, we observe in Table 2 that, if the capacity of F_1 is decreased by a single unit, then the combined production and transportation cost goes up by \$6. If requirements in W_1 go up by a single unit, the cost goes up by \$92.

We see, then, that if we do have the solution to our transportation problem it is easy to construct the solution to the dual problem. Therefore, the imputed costs (or prices) can also be computed. However, we also wish to show now that such row and column numbers can be used to carry out the square evaluation technique described in Chapter 2, Section 4.

In Table 3 we show the first solution to the transportation problem, which was obtained with the aid of the north-west rule. Let us compute row and column numbers associated with this first solution. We recognize that $v_5 = 0$ and then write the equation

$$-u_4 + v_5 = c_{4,5} \qquad\qquad (54a)$$

However, $c_{4,5} = 0$ and, consequently,

$$u_4 = 0 \qquad\qquad (54b)$$

We continue, step by step, and get all the row and column numbers as shown below:

$$-u_4 + v_4 = 106 \qquad v_4 = 106 \qquad\qquad (55)$$

$$-u_3 + v_4 = 102 \qquad u_3 = 4 \qquad\qquad (56)$$

$$-u_3 + v_3 = 100 \qquad v_3 = 104 \qquad\qquad (57)$$

$$-u_3 + v_2 = 102 \qquad v_2 = 106 \qquad\qquad (58)$$

$$-u_2 + v_2 = 100 \qquad u_2 = 6 \qquad\qquad (59)$$

$$-u_2 + v_1 = 90 \qquad v_1 = 96 \qquad\qquad (60)$$

$$-u_1 + v_1 = 88 \qquad u_1 = 8 \qquad\qquad (61)$$

TABLE 3. First Solution to Combined Production and Transportation Problem

(Square evaluation with row and column numbers)

Factories	W1	W2	W3	W4	W5	Row Numbers
F1	88 88 * **140**	100 98 +2	96 96 0	98 98 0 −8	0 +8 0	$u_1 = 8$
F2	90 90 * **40**	100 100 **220** *	98 96 −2	102 102 +6 −6	0 +6 0	$u_2 = 6$
F3	92 90 −2	102 102 **60** *	100 100 **150** *	102 102 **150** * −4	0 +4 0	$u_3 = 4$
F4	96 96 0	108 106 +2	104 100 −4	106 106 **50** * 0	0 **170** *	$u_4 = 0$
Column numbers	$v_1 = 96$	$v_2 = 106$	$v_3 = 104$	$v_4 = 106$	$v_5 = 0$	

These row and column numbers are shown in the last column and the bottom row of Table 3.

Suppose, now that we wish to evaluate the square showing transporting costs from F_4 to W_3. If the capacity of F_4 increases by a single unit, and if simultaneously requirements at W_3 increase by a single unit, then the combined cost increases by an amount:

$$c'_{4,3} = -u_4 + v_3 = 0 + 104 = 104 \qquad (62)$$

We show this number in the upper left-hand corner of the square. The number in the right-hand upper corner shows that the direct cost of producing and transporting from F_4 to W_3 is \$100. This means, then, that the direct route from F_4 to W_3 is \$4 cheaper than the indirect one, and therefore we list the \$4 saving as a -4 in the lower right-hand corner. We see, then, that with the aid of the row and column numbers, we can directly evaluate each square in Table 3.

The method described here is a slight modification of our method of solving the transportation problem. We start with the north-west rule as before, but then, instead of doing the square evaluation with a diagram similar to Table 11 in Chapter 2, we compute the row and column numbers and thereby obtain the proper square evaluations. We modify the solution exactly the same way as indicated in Chapter 2 and so proceed to the second solution. Again we compute row and column numbers to get the square evaluations and determine which square offers the greatest potential saving.

This method is somewhat more straightforward then the one introduced in Chapter 2, and it is easier to program it on an electronic computer. We recognize, however, that this alternate method of solution is essentially the same as the old one.

5. THE GENERALIZED TRANSPORTATION ALLOCATION PROBLEM

In Sections 3, 4, and 5 of Chapter 3, we described various linear programming problems that we called the generalized transportation problem. These problems could be solved with the aid of the simplex method, but fortunately there is an important short-cut method of solution. We wish to show now that the generalized transportation problem can be solved in a similar way to the transportation problem. We proceed to show our method of solution by solving the aircraft routing allocation problem described in Section 5 of Chapter 3.

We begin by repeating here, for convenience, equations (35) and (36) of Chapter 3:

$$\sum_{i=1}^{4} r_{i,j}x_{i,j} \leq b_j \qquad j = 1, 2, \cdots, 5 \qquad\qquad (63a)$$

$$\sum_{j=1}^{5} x_{i,j} = a_i \qquad\qquad i = 1, 2, \cdots, 4 \qquad\qquad (63b)$$

Then we introduce slack variables so that equation (63a) can be replaced by a relationship where the equality sign holds:

$$\sum_{i=1}^{4} r_{i,j}x_{i,j} + x_{5,j} = b_j \qquad j = 1, 2, \cdots, 5 \qquad (64)$$

Here, $x_{5,j}$ denotes the unfilled demand on route j. For instance, if we carried 24,000 passengers on route 1 (New York to Los Angeles, one stop), then there is an unfilled demand of 1,000 as the total potential is 25,000 and, consequently, we have $x_{5,1} = 1,000$. The profit to be maximized is given by equation (37) of Chapter 3, which we repeat here for convenience

$$z = \sum_{j=1}^{5} p_j \left(\sum_{i=1}^{4} r_{i,j}x_{i,j} \right) - \sum_{i=1}^{4} \sum_{j=1}^{5} c_{i,j}x_{i,j} \qquad (65)$$

With the aid of the slack variables this can be written as

$$z = \sum_{j=1}^{5} p_j(b_j - x_{5,j}) - \sum_{i=1}^{4} \sum_{j=1}^{5} c_{i,j}r_{i,j} \qquad (66)$$

Let us introduce now a new set of costs defined by the following equation

$$c_{5,j} = p_j \qquad j = 1, 2, 3, 4, 5 \qquad\qquad (67)$$

Then the profit can be expressed as

$$z = \sum_{j=1}^{5} p_j b_j - \sum_{i=1}^{5} \sum_{j=1}^{5} c_{i,j}x_{i,j} \qquad\qquad (68)$$

and we can say that the problem is to minimize the "variable cost" given by

$$z' = \sum_{i=1}^{5} \sum_{j=1}^{5} c_{i,j}x_{i,j} \qquad\qquad (69)$$

For the sake of uniformity we rewrite equation (64) in the form

$$\sum_{i=1}^{5} r_{i,j}x_{i,j} = b_j \qquad j = 1, 2, 3, 4, 5 \qquad\qquad (70)$$

where we used the notation

$$r_{5,j} = 1 \qquad j = 1, 2, 3, 4, 5 \qquad\qquad (71)$$

In order to be able to write the dual equations, we have to write the equation in the form of inequalities. We write

$$\sum_{j=1}^{5} - x_{i,j} \geq -a_i \quad i = 1, 2, 3, 4 \tag{72a}$$

$$\sum_{i=1}^{5} r_{i,j} x_{i,j} \geq b_j \quad j = 1, 2, 3, 4, 5 \tag{72b}$$

Our problem is to obtain a solution to the above two relations which minimizes the variable cost as given by equation (69). (We recognize that the solution will be such that in (72a) and (72b) the equality signs will hold.) We can write the dual equations as

$$-u_i + r_{i,j} v_j \leq c_{i,j} \quad \begin{aligned} j &= 1, 2, 3, 4 \\ i &= 1, 2, 3, 4, 5 \end{aligned} \tag{73}$$

We propose to solve these inequalities in a similar fashion to the one used in the transportation problem. Let us try to obtain a first solution to the problem by allocating the various aircraft to different routes. Utilizing the cost information in Table 5 of Chapter 3 we can easily discover that type 1 aircraft has the lowest cost per passenger on all routes. Therefore, we begin by allocating this type of aircraft. As this type of aircraft is also long range, we assign 10 of aircraft type 1 to route 1 as shown by the upper left-hand corner (cell 1-1) in Table 4. However, these 10 aircraft can only carry a total of 16,000 passengers, as each one can carry 1,600 passengers per month in route 1 (New York to Los Angeles, one stop). (The left-hand lower corner in cell 1-1 in Table 4 shows the number 1,600 indicating that each aircraft can carry 1,600 passengers.) We see, then, that there is a deficit of 9,000 passengers in route 1, and we also assign some type 4 aircraft to route 1. We need to assign 10 of these aircraft to make up the deficit of 9,000 passengers. We then list this number 10, in bold face in cell 4-1. Route 1 is taken care of, and we proceed now to examine route 2. On the basis of the lowest operating cost per passenger we assign type 4 to route 2. We still have 5 type 4 aircraft, and these we assign to route 2. (See cell 4-2.) We also assign 6.5 aircraft type 2 to route 2. (See cell 2-2.) (These aircraft assignments need not be whole numbers, since it is permissible to operate an aircraft, say, half of the time.) We proceed now to route 3. There is no aircraft of type 1 or type 4 available, but we have 12.5 of aircraft type 2. These we assign to route 3. (See cell 2-3.) There is still an unfilled demand of 500 passengers in route 3. The only aircraft available are type 3, and we allocate these to the fourth and fifth routes (cells 3-4 and 3-5.) We

TABLE 4. First Solution to Aircraft Allocation Problem[a]

(Total variable cost, $1,199,900)

Legend:

$$\begin{array}{ll} c'_{i,j} & c_{i,j} \\ & x \\ r_{i,j} & \boxed{c_{i,j} - c'_{i,j}} \end{array}$$

Aircraft Type	Routings 1	2	3	4	5	No. of Aircraft
1	18,000 **10.0** 1,600	−28,020 | 21,000 1,500 | +49,020	22,480 | 18,000 2,800 | −4,480	−68,410 | 16,000 2,300 | +84,410	−92,500 | 10,000 8,100 | +102,500	**10** $u_1 = 173{,}520$
2	X	15,000 **6.5** 1,000	16,000 **12.5** 1,400	−13,450 | 14,000 1,500 | +27,450	−25,000 | 9,000 5,700 | +34,000	**19** $u_2 = 82{,}000$
3	X	25,500 | 10,000 500	X	9,000 **12.8** 700	6,000 **12.2** 2,900	**25** $u_3 = 23{,}000$
4	17,000 **10.0** 900	16,000 **5.0** 400	63,300 | 17,000 2,200 | −46,300	−13,010 | 15,000 1,700 | +28,010	−35,700 | 10,000 5,500 | +45,700	**15** $u_4 = 90{,}700$
Passenger deficit	119.7 | 130 1 | +10.3	97 | 130 1	**500** 70 1	**40** 70 1	**24,620** 10 1	$u_5 = 0$
Passenger potential	25,000	12,000	18,000	9,000	60,000	
	$v_1 = 119.7$	$v_2 = 97$	$v_3 = 70$	$v_4 = 45.7$	$v_5 = 10$	

[a] Each cell is evaluated with the aid of row and column numbers.

x = unknown.

recognize that there is an unfilled demand of 500 passengers on route 3, 40 on route 4, and 24,600 on route 5.

This is, then, the first solution to our problem, shown in Table 4. In the first four rows in each cell the bold numbers show the number of aircraft allocated. In the fifth row the bold numbers show the deficit of passengers. In the first four rows the numbers in the lower left-hand corner of each cell show the capacity of each aircraft. For the sake of uniformity, the number 1 is listed in the lower left-hand corner of each cell in the fifth row. Also in the first four rows, in the upper right-hand corner of each cell, the operating costs of the aircraft are shown. In the fifth row, in the upper right-hand corner of each cell, the revenue per passenger is listed. The total variable cost for the first solution can be obtained with the aid of equation (69). We get $1,199,000.

Let us remember now that we have no reason to believe that this first solution is the best solution. The important thing is that we do have a solution, and now we may proceed to compute row and column numbers to determine whether this solution can be improved. We set $u_5 = 0$ and write the equation for cell 5-5

$$-u_5 + r_{5,5}v_5 = c_{5,5} \tag{74}$$

According to equation (67), $c_{5,5} = p_5$, as this is the revenue ($10) per passenger in route 5 (upper right-hand corner in cell 5-5). Furthermore, according to equation (71), $r_{5,5} = 1$. (This is shown in the lower left-hand corner in cell 5-5.) Consequently, we have

$$-u_5 + v_5 = 10 \tag{75}$$

from which it follows that $v_5 = 10$. We can now continue this process and determine the row and column numbers as follows:

$$-u_3 + r_{3,5}v_5 = c_{3,5} \qquad u_3 = 23{,}000 \tag{76}$$

$$-u_3 + r_{3,4}v_4 = c_{3,4} \qquad v_4 = 45.7 \tag{77}$$

$$-u_5 + r_{5,3}v_3 = c_{5,3} \qquad v_3 = 70 \tag{78}$$

$$-u_2 + r_{2,3}v_3 = c_{2,3} \qquad u_2 = 82{,}000 \tag{79}$$

$$-u_2 + r_{2,2}v_2 = c_{2,2} \qquad v_2 = 97 \tag{80}$$

$$-u_4 + r_{4,2}v_2 = c_{4,2} \qquad u_4 = 90{,}700 \tag{81}$$

$$-u_4 + r_{4,1}v_1 = c_{4,1} \qquad v_1 = 119.7 \tag{82}$$

$$-u_1 + r_{1,1}v_1 = c_{1,1} \qquad u_1 = 173{,}520 \tag{83}$$

Now we can evaluate each of the cells with the aid of the formula

$$c'_{i,j} = -u_i + r_{i,j}v_j \tag{84}$$

Applying this formula as an illustration to cell 1-2 (first row, second column), we get

$$c'_{1,2} = -173,520 + 1500(97) = -28,020 \tag{85}$$

We show these evaluations in the upper left-hand corner of each cell. The differential saving, $c - c'$, can be computed as

$$c_{1,2} - c'_{1,2} = 21,000 + 28,020 = 49,020 \tag{86}$$

This evaluation of cell 1-2 is shown in the lower right-hand corner of the cell.

We show the evaluation of every cell in Table 4, and we conclude that the greatest potential saving is $46,300, shown in cell 4-3. Consequently, we decide to modify our first solution by allocating some of the aircraft type 4 to route 3. Suppose we allocate one of aircraft type 4 to route 3. What would happen? We would have a deficit of aircraft type 4, and to make up for this we would have to take off one of aircraft type 4 from route 2. In order to take care of passengers on route 2, we need to add 1.1 of aircraft type 2 to route 2. Again we have a deficit, in aircraft type 2, and therefore we take off 1.1 aircraft of type 2 from route 3. Now we have a new allocation of aircraft as shown in Table 5. However, we now have, in cell 5-3, a passenger deficit of -160. This would mean that we are transporting more than the potential of 18,000. As this is not possible, we conclude that we cannot allocate on entire aircraft type 4 to route 3. The maximum number of aircraft type 4 that can be allocated to route 3 is given by $500/660 = 0.76$. This would make the deficit in cell 5-3 zero. Let us, therefore, allocate 0.76 aircraft of type 4 to route 3. We must remove this aircraft from route 2. We also allocate 1.1 (0.76) = 0.84 aircraft type 2 to route 2 and remove these aircraft from route 3. So we get the second solution to our problem shown in Table 6. The total variable cost for the second solution is $1,164,303, which represents a $34,698 saving compared to the first solution.

Now we check to see whether the second solution is the best one. We need to compute the row and column numbers again, and to evaluate every cell and see if the solution can be improved. This procedure is similar to the one used in evaluating the first solution. Then we proceed to the third solution, and so forth. We will omit the details of these computations and show only the fifth, or optimum, solution in Table 7. The total variable cost here is $1,014,400, representing a

TABLE 5. A Modification to the First Solution of the Aircraft Allocation Problem

Legend:

$c'_{i,j}$	$c_{i,j}$
	x
$r_{i,j}$	$c_{i,j} - c'_{i,j}$

Aircraft Type	Routings 1	2	3	4	5	No. of Aircraft
1	18,000 **10.0** 1,600	2,000 1,500	18,000 2,500	16,000 2,300	10,000 8,100	**10**
2		15,000 **6.5 + 1.1** 1,000	16,000 **12.5 − 1.1** 1,500	14,000 1,500	9,000 5,700	**19**
3		16,000 500		9,000 **12.8** 700	6,000 **12.2** 2,900	**25**
4	17,000 **10.0** 900	16,000 **5.0 − 1.0** 1,100	17,000 **0 + 1.0** 2,200	15,000 1,700	10,000 5,500	**15**
Passenger deficit	130 1	130 1	70 **500 − 660** 1	70 **40** 1	10 **24,620** 1	
Passenger potential	25,000	12,000	18,000	9,000	60,000	

x = unknown.

TABLE 6. Second Solution to Aircraft Allocation Problem

(Total variable cost, $1,164,303)

$$\begin{array}{c c}
c'_{i,j} & c_{i,j} \\
& x \\
r_{i,j} & c_{i,j} - c'_{i,j}
\end{array}$$

	\multicolumn{5}{c	}{Routings}	No. of Aircraft	
	1	2	3	4	5		
Aircraft Type 1	18,000 **10.0** 1,600	21,000 1,500	18,000 2,800	16,000 2,300	10,000 8,100	10	$u_1 = 238{,}000$
Aircraft Type 2	X	15,000 **7.34** 1,000	16,000 **11.66** 1,400	14,000 1,500	9,000 5,700	19	$u_2 = 115{,}000$
Aircraft Type 3	X	10,000 500	X	9,000 **12.8** 700	6,000 **12.2** 2,900	25	$u_3 = 23{,}000$
Aircraft Type 4	17,000 **10.0** 900	16,000 **4.24** 1,100	17,000 **0.76** 2,200	15,000 1,700	10,000 5,500	15	$u_4 = 127{,}000$
Passenger deficit	130 1	**−4** 130 1	**4** 70 1	**40** 70 1	**24,620** 10 1		$u_5 = 0$
Passenger potential	25,000	12,000	18,000	9,000	60,000		
	$v_1 = 160$	$v_2 = 130$	$v_3 = 70$	$v_4 = 45.7$	$v_5 = 10$		

x = unknown.

$c'_{i,j}$	$c_{i,j}$
	x
$r_{i,j}$	$c_{i,j} - c'_{i,j}$

TABLE 7. Fifth, or Optimum, Solution to Aircraft Allocation Problem
(Total variable cost, $1,014,400)

	Routings					No. of Aircraft	
	1	2	3	4	5		
Aircraft Type 1	18,000 **10.0** 1,600	21,000 −70,360 1,500	18,000 2,800	16,000 2,300	10,000 8,100	10	$u_1 = 169,360$
Aircraft Type 2		15,000 **8.0** 1,000	16,000 **5.0** 1,400	14,000 **6.0** 1,500	9,000 +6,000 5,700	19	$u_2 = 51,000$
Aircraft Type 3		10,000 **7.8** 500		9,000 +7,310 700	6,000 **17.2** 2,900	25	$u_3 = 23,000$
Aircraft Type 4	17,000 **10.0** 900	16,000 −16,780 1,100	17,000 **5.0** 2,200	15,000 1,700	10,000 5,500	15	$u_4 = 88,380$
Passenger deficit	130	130 **100** 1	70 1	70 1	10 **10,120** 1		$u_5 = 0$
Passenger potential	25,000	12,000	18,000	9,000	60,000		
	$v_1 = 117.1$	$v_2 = 66$	$v_3 = 47.9$	$v_4 = 43.3$	$v_5 = 10$		

x = unknown.

saving of $185,500 compared with the first solution. When the row and column numbers are computed for this solution, and every cell is evaluated, each evaluation turns out to be negative and no further improvement can be made. In fact, it can be proven vigorously that this solution is an optimum one. (See the paper by Ferguson and Dantzig, p. 67.)

It is seen, then, that a generalized transportation problem can be solved in a very similar way to the original transportation problem. We used the aircraft allocation problem only as an illustration. For the reader who is interested in the details of this problem, we refer to the original paper of Ferguson and Dantzig.

CHAPTER 6

THE GEOMETRY
OF
LINEAR PROGRAMMING

1. THE REQUIREMENT SPACE

In order to present a geometrical representation of linear programming, we return to study our original nutrition problem, from a different point of view. We begin by investigating all combinations of pills that can be purchased for $1.

Let us first consider combinations of pills P_6 and P_2 that can be purchased for $1. We propose to represent these combinations by the straight line between points P_2 and P_6 in Fig. 1. Each pill P_6 costs $0.07 and contains 1 unit of V_1. Consequently 14.3 units of V_1 can be obtained for $1 when purchasing P_6. This pill is represented by the point P_6 in Fig. 1. We now consider pill P_2. Each of them costs $0.10 and contains 1 unit of V_2. Consequently a dollar's worth of P_2 gives 10 units of V_2. This pill is represented by point P_2 in Fig. 1. The horizontal axis Q_1 indicates quantities of V_1; the vertical axis Q_2 indicates quantities of V_2. This geometrical representation only takes care of the two vitamins V_1 and V_2. Later we will develop a representation that will take care also of vitamin V_3.

Suppose we take $0.50 worth of P_6 and $0.50 worth of P_2 (shown in Fig. 1 by point A). This combination of pills contains:

$$Q_1 = 0.50 \times (14.3) = 7.15 \qquad (1a)$$

units of V_1, and

$$Q_2 = 0.50 \times 10 = 5 \qquad (1b)$$

171

units of V_2. This can be read directly in Fig. 1 by taking the projections of point A on the Q_1 and Q_2 axis.

We see that each point on the line P_2P_6 represents a combination of vitamins with a combined cost of $1. Suppose we take u_6 dollar's

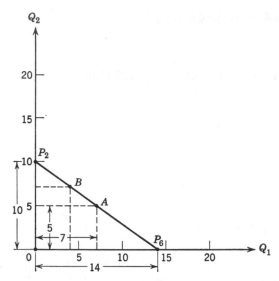

FIG. 1. Geometrical representation of combinations of pills P_2 and P_6. Point P_2 represents pill P_2; point P_6 represents pill P_6. Points on the line P_2P_6 represent combinations of these two pills. The combined cost of P_2 and P_6 is always $1. Q_1 and Q_2 denote the quantity of vitamins of type V_1 and V_2 contained in the two pills.

worth of P_6 and u_2 dollar's worth of P_2 where the total cost is $1, or

$$u_6 + u_2 = 1 \tag{2}$$

Suppose this pill is represented by point B in Fig. 1. The vitamin contents are given then by:

$$Q_1 = 14.3u_6 \tag{3}$$

and

$$Q_2 = 10u_2 \tag{4}$$

We compare this type of representation with weights at the end of a dumbbell. If we have equal proportions of P_2 and P_6, we have equal weights at the end of the dumbbell and the center of gravity (or point of balance) is halfway between (point A). If we have u_2 of P_2 and u_6 of P_6, then we place a weight u_2 at P_2 and u_6 at P_6 and the center of gravity is the point B. By varying the proportions of the weights at the end of the dumbbells, we can get all possible combinations of the two pills.

A further geometrical representation is shown in Fig. 2. Here pills P_1 and P_3 are again compared to the ends of a dumbbell. Each P_1 contains 5 units of V_1 and 3 units of V_2. Each P_1 costs \$0.40, and consequently a dollar's worth of P_1 contains 12.5 units of V_1 and 7.5 units of V_2. These values are shown by the projections of the point P_1 on the two axes. Each pill P_3 contains 2 units of V_1 and 5 units of

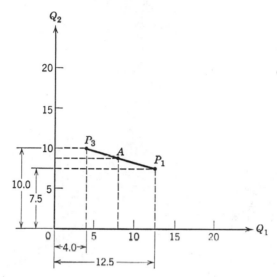

FIG. 2. Geometrical representation of combinations of pills P_1 and P_3.

V_2. Each P_3 costs \$0.50, and therefore a dollar's worth of P_3 contains 4 units of V_1 and 10 units of V_2, as shown by the projections. We now consider u_1 dollars worth of P_1 and u_3 dollar's worth of P_3, where the sum of the u's is \$1. How much V_1 and V_2 do we have in this combination? Clearly the quantity of the first vitamin is given by

$$Q_1 = 12.5u_1 + 4u_3 \qquad (5)$$

and the quantity of second vitamin by

$$Q_2 = 7.5u_1 + 10u_3 \qquad (6)$$

Consequently this combination can be represented by, say, point A between P_1 and P_2 (Fig. 2.) It is recognized again that all possible combinations of P_1 and P_3 which cost \$1 can be represented as points on the line P_1P_3, and the corresponding vitamin contents are shown by the appropriate projections.

So far we have considered only two vitamins. We may consider all three vitamins, by the representation shown in Fig. 3. P_1 and P_3 are points in a three-dimensional space. The projections of these points on the axes give the vitamin contents of a dollar's worth of

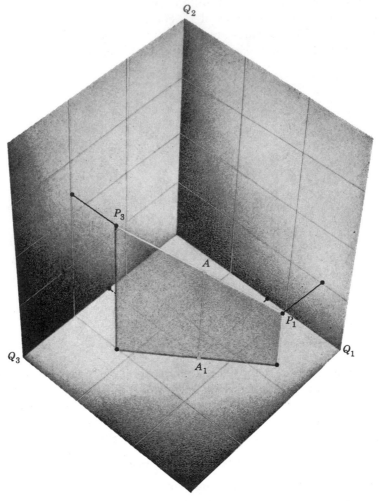

FIG. 3. Geometrical representation of combinations of pills P_1 and P_3. All three vitamin contents, Q_1, Q_2, and Q_3, are shown. (Each grid represents 5 units.)

each of these pills. How do we represent a combination, say, of \$0.50 worth of P_1 and \$0.50 worth of P_3? Obviously the halfway point A represents such a combination.

More generally, if we take u_1 dollar's worth of P_1 and u_3 dollar's

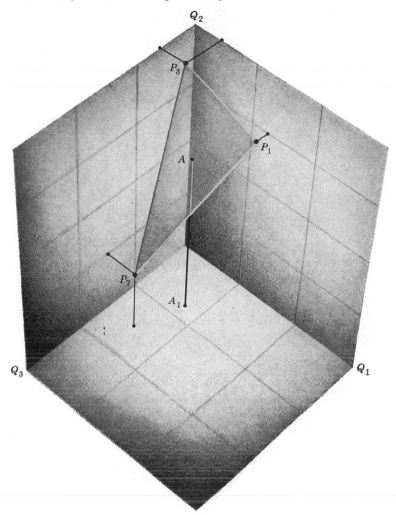

FIG. 4. Geometrical representation of combinations of pills Γ_1, Γ_3, and Γ_7. (Each grid represents 5 units.)

worth of P_3, we get a point between P_1 and P_3 which has the vitamin contents and projections

$$Q_1 = 12.5u_1 + 4u_3 \tag{7}$$

$$Q_2 = 7.5u_1 + 10u_3 \tag{8}$$

$$Q_3 = 2.5u_1 + 6u_3 \tag{9}$$

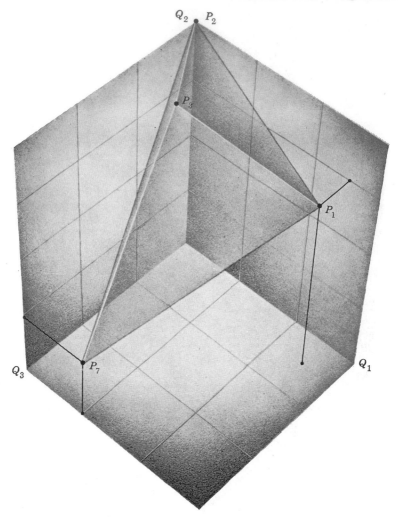

FIG. 5. Geometrical representation of combinations of pills P_1, P_2, P_3, and P_7. (Each grid represents 5 units.)

In summary, then, we see that the line P_1P_3 in three-dimensional space represents geometrically all possible combinations of vitamins that can be obtained by purchasing a dollar's worth of P_1's and P_3's.

In Fig. 4 we represent combinations of pills P_1, P_3, and P_7 that can be purchased for \$1. For instance, if the dollar is equally distributed between pills P_1, P_3, and P_7, we get a combination that can be represented by point A (the center of gravity) of the triangle $P_1P_3P_7$. If we distribute a dollar between the three pills in proportions u_1, u_3, and

u_7, we get vitamins in quantities of:

$$Q_1 = 12.5u_1 + 4u_3 + 5u_7 \tag{10}$$

$$Q_2 = 7.5u_1 + 10u_3 + 2.5u_7 \tag{11}$$

$$Q_3 = 2.5u_1 + 6u_3 + 15u_7 \tag{12}$$

This combination can be represented as the center of gravity of the weights u_1, u_3, and u_7 placed at points P_1, P_3, and P_7. The quantities of vitamins can be represented by the appropriate projections of this center of gravity.

In Fig. 5 we represent combinations of pills P_1, P_2, P_3, and P_7 that can be purchased for $1. Combinations of pills P_1, P_3, and P_7 are represented by the surface of the triangle $P_1P_3P_7$; combinations of pills P_1, P_2, and P_3 are represented by the surface of the triangle $P_1P_2P_3$. The other triangles represent the remaining combinations of these three pills. On the other hand, if we purchase a dollar's worth of all four pills, we get a point *interior* of the tetrahedron $P_1P_2P_3P_7$. These points can be interpreted as the center of gravity of the proper weights placed at the vertices of the tetrahedron.

In Fig. 6 finally we have a geometrical representation of all seven pills. As an example, any combination of pills P_1, P_2, and P_3 that can be purchased for $1 can be represented by a point on the triangle $P_1P_2P_3$. Furthermore, it can be seen, then, that any point on the surface of the polyhedron represents a combination of pills with a total price of $1. But these points do not represent all the possible combinations. If we purchase a dollar's worth of pills P_1, P_3, P_6, and P_7, we get a point inside the tetrahedron defined by the four corners P_1, P_3, P_6, and P_7. The fact of the matter is that any point inside the polyhedron shown in Fig. 6 represents a combination of pills. To be more specific, suppose that we purchase u_1 dollar's worth of P_1, u_2 dollar's worth of P_2, etc., where the total cost is $1,

$$u_1 + u_2 + u_3 + u_4 + u_5 + u_6 + u_7 = 1 \tag{13}$$

This combination is represented by the center of gravity of weights u_1, $u_2, \cdots$, etc., placed at points P_1, $P_2, \cdots$. The projections of this center of gravity give the vitamin contents:

$$Q_1 = 12.5u_1 + 4u_3 + 8.6u_5 + 14.3u_6 + 5u_7 \tag{14}$$

$$Q_2 = 7.5u_1 + 10u_2 + 10u_3 + 5.7u_5 + 2.5u_7 \tag{15}$$

$$Q_3 = 2.5u_1 + 6u_3 + 16.7u_4 + 5.7u_5 + 15u_7 \tag{16}$$

We see, then, that in Fig. 6 we have a geometrical representation of

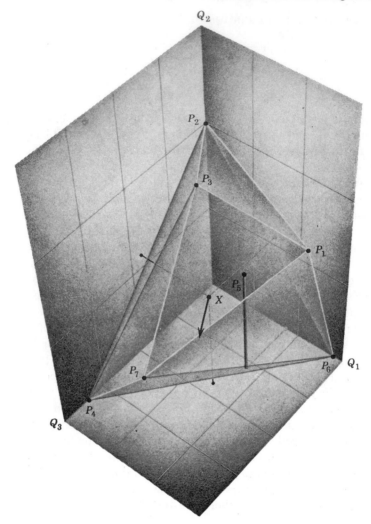

FIG. 6.   Geometrical representation of combinations of all seven pills.   Combined cost of these pills is $1.   (Each grid represents 5 units.)

all the combinations of pills that we can purchase for $1.   Now, let us remind ourselves that originally we were only interested in combinations of pills which have the three vitamins in proportions of 100:80: 120.   In a geometrical representation these points are such that the projections on the three axes have the ratio 100:80:120.   It is easy to see that these points in our space form a straight line as shown in Fig. 7 by the "requirement arrow."   Now we can ask: "Which is the combination of pills that solves our problem?" If we think in terms of purchasing vitamins for $1 our original question of the cheapest combination of vitamin pills is translated into the question of getting the most vitamins for $1 while keeping the proper proportions of vitamins.

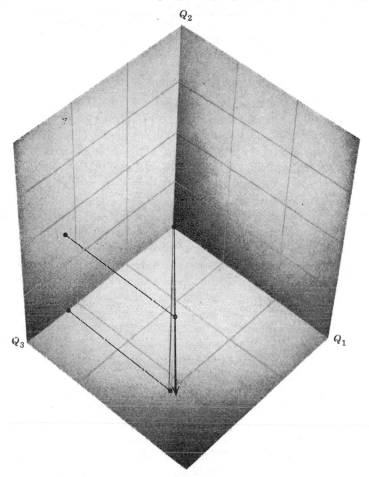

FIG. 7. Geometrical representation of requirement arrow. Points on arrow represent combination of pills with proper ratio of vitamin content. (Each grid represents 5 units.)

This means, then, that we seek the point on the requirement arrow in Fig. 7 which is farthest away from the center of the figure. However, this point must not lie outside of the polyhedron in Fig. 6, as all combinations of pills can be represented by the interior and the surface of the polyhedron. Therefore we can see that the point we seek can be identified as the intersection between the requirement arrow and the surface of the polyhedron as shown by point X in Fig. 6. This intersection represents, in fact, the solution to our linear programming problem.

In summary, then, our problem is to (1) determine the polyhedron defined by the various pills, and (2) determine the intersection of this polyhedron with the requirement arrow. It can be verified from Fig. 16 that the point of intersection has the projections:

$$Q_1 = 7.32, \quad Q_2 = 5.85, \quad Q_3 = 8.8$$

this is then the most vitamins we can get for $1 if it is required that the vitamins be in proportions 100:80:120. In order to get 100 units of V_1, 80 units of V_2, and 120 units of V_3, we need 13.67 times as many vitamins as we can get for $1. The cheapest combination of pills, then, that meet the vitamin requirements costs $13.67, which is in agreement with our original result.

Suppose now that we want vitamins in proportions of 60:100:70. How do we represent a solution to this problem? We draw a new requirement arrow to represent these new proportions. The intersection of this requirement arrow with the surface of the polyhedron yields the proper representation of the solution to this new problem.

The geometrical representation gives an easy interpretation to some of the theorems of linear programming. For instance, consider the fundamental theorem, which says that the cheapest combination of pills cannot contain more than three pills. There are three equations describing the problem. We consider Fig. 6 again. The requirement arrow intersects the surface of the polyhedron at point X, representing the optimum solution. As the surface is made up of triangles, the intersection will lie on one of the triangles, and so only those three pills can enter into the optimum combination that are represented by the vertices of the triangle. However, it might happen that the requirement arrow intersects an edge of the polyhedron. In this case only two vitamin pills are required. If the requirement arrow goes through one of the vertices of the polyhedron, then of course only the pill it represents will meet the requirements. These cases are described in the theory of linear programming by the word *degeneracy*.

One further remark in connection with P_5: this pill is represented by a point inside of the polyhedron. This means, then, that whatever requirements are imposed, pill P_5 will never enter into any of the solutions. The price of this pill is too high. Let us suppose, on the other hand, that the price of this pill begins to drop. Then the point corresponding to this pill would move out towards the surface of the polyhedron and would finally reach it.   Say that P_5 reaches triangle $P_1 P_6 P_7$.   Say, also, that the requirement arrow intersects the triangle $P_1 P_6 P_7$.   In such a case, the requirements can be met either by a combination of P_1, P_5, and P_7, or of P_1, P_6, and P_7, indicating that there is an alternate optimum solution to the problem.   In fact, in such a case there are infinitely many optimum solutions to the problem.

2.   THE SOLUTION SPACE

We will now proceed to a different type of geometrical representation.   If we deal with n unknowns and m equations, the requirement space must be m dimensional and the representation requires n points.

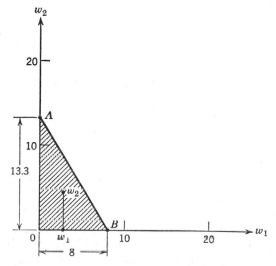

FIG. 8.   Geometrical representation of an inequality.   The shaded area represents the inequality (18): $\frac{w_1}{8} + \frac{w_2}{13.3} \leq 1$.

On the other hand, we can develop a geometrical representation in the solution space that requires n dimensional space and m planes.   If we tried to represent our original nutrition problem in this new requirement space, we would need a seven-dimensional space, as the nutrition problem has seven unknowns.   We prefer, therefore, as an illustration, to use the dual of the nutrition problem as described in Chapter 5.   The dual problem has three unknowns and seven equations, and, consequently, a geometrical representation in the solution space will require a three-dimensional space.

To start, we will present an exercise on representing geometrical inequalities. Let us consider the inequality:

$$5w_1 + 3w_2 \leq 40 \tag{17}$$

which can be written as

$$\frac{w_1}{8} + \frac{w_2}{13.3} \leq 1 \tag{18}$$

The shaded area in Fig. 8 is a geometrical representation of this inequality. There are two axes showing w_1 and w_2. If any point is selected in the shaded area, the coordinates (i.e., the projections of this point) will be such that the inequality is satisfied. The boundary line (i.e., the line AB) is given by

$$\frac{w_1}{8} + \frac{w_2}{13.3} = 1 \tag{19}$$

Point A is defined by $w_1 = 0$ and $w_2 = 13.3$. Point B is defined by $w_1 = 8$ and $w_2 = 0$.

In Fig. 9 we have a three-dimensional representation of the inequality:

$$\frac{w_1}{8} + \frac{w_2}{13.3} + \frac{w_3}{40} \leq 1 \tag{20}$$

Points inside of the tetrahedron in Fig. 9 (that is, points below the triangle in the "corner,") represent points defined by (20). The triangle can be defined by the equation that is obtained from (20) when the inequality is replaced by an equation sign.

Notice now that, if equation (20) is multiplied by the factor 40, the inequality (19a) of Chapter 5 is obtained, showing that these two inequalities are the same. Let us also recall that this inequality was used to determine the imputed value of P_1. To remind ourselves of this, we call the triangle in Fig. 9 the triangle P_1. We proceed now to rewrite inequalities (19c), (19e), and (19g) of Chapter 5 in the form:

$$\frac{w_1}{52} + \frac{w_2}{10} + \frac{w_3}{16.7} \leq 1 \tag{21}$$

$$\frac{w_1}{11.7} + \frac{w_2}{17.5} + \frac{w_3}{17.5} \leq 1 \tag{22}$$

$$\frac{w_1}{20} + \frac{w_2}{40} + \frac{w_3}{6.7} \leq 1 \tag{23}$$

Each of these inequalities leads to a tetrahedron similar to the one

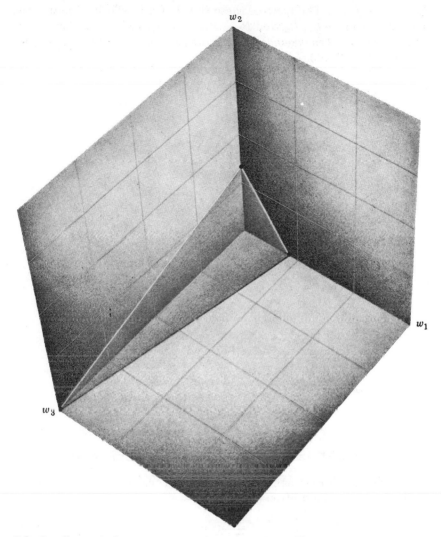

FIG. 9. *Geometrical representation of an inequality.* The interior of the tetrahedron represents the inequality (20): $\dfrac{w_1}{8} + \dfrac{w_2}{13.3} + \dfrac{w_3}{40} \leq 1$. (Each grid represents 10 units.)

shown in Fig. 9.   The faces of these tetrahedrons will be different, as they relate to pills P_3, P_5, and P_7.   Points lying inside of all these four tetrahedrons are the geometrical representation of the inequalities described by (20)–(23).

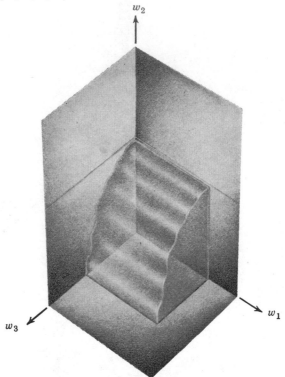

FIG. 10.   The slice represents the inequality (24): $w_1/7 \leq 1$.

We still have three further inequalities to consider.   Equation (19f) of Chapter 5 can be written as:

$$\frac{w_1}{7} \leq 1 \qquad\qquad (24)$$

This inequality was used to determine the imputed value of pill P_6. A geometrical representation is shown in Fig. 10.   The points between the two parallel planes, limiting the slice in the figure, represent geometrically equation (24).   The remaining two inequalities (19b) and (19d) of Chapter 5 can be written as:

$$\frac{w_2}{10} \leq 1 \qquad\qquad (25)$$

and

$$\frac{w_3}{6} \leq 1 \qquad (26)$$

Each of these can be represented by a slice similar to the one shown in Fig. 10 but oriented in a different fashion.

The combination of the inequalities (24), (25), and (26) can be represented by the points in the interior of the parallelepipedon shown in

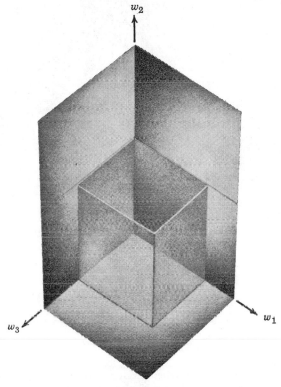

FIG. 11. The interior of the parallelepipedon represents inequalities (24), (25), and (26). (Each unit represents 10 unit.)

Fig. 11. If this figure is combined with the interior of the four other tetrahedrons representing equations (20) through (23), we obtain the polyhedron shown in Fig. 12. In summary, then, we can say that solutions to our seven inequalities can be represented in a three-dimensional space as the interior (and surface) points of the polyhedron shown in Fig. 12.

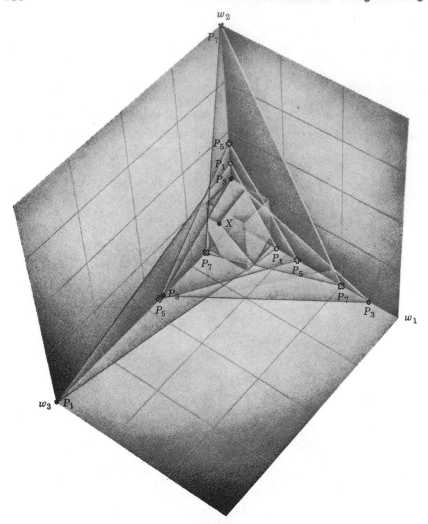

FIG. 12. The interior of the polyhedron represents all the inequalities of the problem of the vitamin pills. (Each grid represents 10 units.)

We now need to know which of the points in the interior (or on the surface) of the polyhedron is the point that represents the solution to our problem? In order to answer this question, we recall that we seek the solution that maximizes the payoff function:

$$z = 100w_1 + 80w_2 + 120w_3 \qquad (27)$$

Let us consider for the moment points in our three-dimensional space,

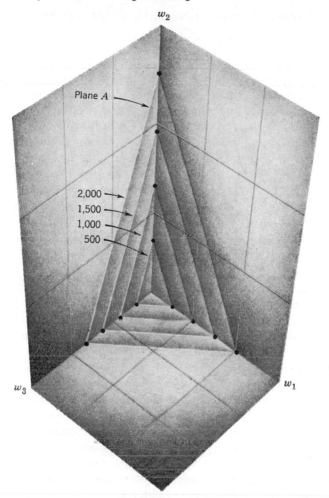

FIG. 13. Geometrical representation of payoff function. On each plane the payoff function is constant. The plane closest to the center has the smallest payoff. (Each grid represents 10 units.)

for which:

$$100w_1 + 80w_2 + 120w_3 = \text{Constant} \qquad (28)$$

Such points will lie in a plane. In Fig. 13, some of these planes are shown graphically. For instance, if we make the constant in equation (28) equal to 2,000, we get:

$$100w_1 + 80w_2 + 120w_3 = 2,000 \qquad (29)$$

This is plane A in Fig. 13. The position of this plane can be determined by dividing both sides of equation (29) by 2,000:

$$\frac{w_1}{20} + \frac{w_2}{25} + \frac{w_3}{16.7} = 1 \qquad (30)$$

If $w_2 = 0$ and $w_3 = 0$, then $w_1 = 20$; this means that the plane A cuts the w_1 axis at the distance 20.   The same plane cuts the w_2 axis at the distance 25 and the w_3 axis at the distance 16.7.

We see, then, that our payoff function (27) takes a constant value on each of these planes, and, as we are interested in maximizing our payoff function, that we are seeking the plane that is farthest away from the center of Fig. 13.   We remember now that solutions to our inequalities are represented by points in the interior (or on the surface) of the polyhedron in Fig. 12.   By combining Figs. 12 and 13, we conclude that we seek the point in Fig. 12 which is in the interior (or on the surface) of the polyhedron, and which lies in one of the planes of Fig. 13. In particular, we want this point to lie on the plane in Fig. 13 that lies the farthest from the center of the figure.   Let us imagine that these parallel planes slice parts off the polyhedron in Fig. 12, and consider the planes moving away from the center.   At a certain instant a point is reached on the polyhedron beyond which the planes do not intersect the polyhedron any more.   This point is designated in Fig. 12 by X, and is the solution to our problem.

We note that the plane representing P_5 does not form any of the sides of the polyhedron in Fig. 12, as the polyhedron lies completely below this plane.   Therefore pill P_5 does not enter into the solution of the problem at all.   This confirms what we have discovered previously when using the representation in the requirement space.   The reason is again, of course, that pill P_5 is priced too high.

Let us now suppose that the payoff function to be maximized, as given in equation (27), is changed.   The inequalities being the same, the polyhedron in Fig. 12 remains unchanged.   However, the parallel planes in Fig. 13 must be changed to slant in accordance with the new payoff function.   The solution to the problem will always be a point on the surface of the polyhedron, but it might shift from one vertex to another.

3. THE GRAVITY SPACE

Geometrical representation with the aid of a gravity space is somewhat similar to the representation in the requirement space.   Before going into this representation we introduce some new hypothetical pills.

We take $\frac{1}{3}$ of P_1 and call that pill $P_1{}^*$.   We take three of P_2 and call it $P_2{}^*$, etc., as shown by the table.   Using these pills does not alter the

Take	$\frac{1}{3}$ of	P_1	and call it	$P_1{}^*$
	3	P_2		$P_2{}^*$
	$\frac{3}{10}$	P_3		$P_3{}^*$
	3	P_4		$P_4{}^*$
	$\frac{3}{7}$	P_5		$P_5{}^*$
	3	P_6		$P_6{}^*$
	$\frac{1}{3}$	P_7		$P_7{}^*$

problem as we can simply say that our original table of vitamin contents, requirements, and costs is replaced by a new table.

	$P_1{}^*$	$P_2{}^*$	$P_3{}^*$	$P_4{}^*$	$P_5{}^*$	$P_6{}^*$	$P_7{}^*$	
V_1	$\frac{5}{3}$	0	$\frac{3}{5}$	0	$\frac{9}{7}$	3	$\frac{2}{3}$	100
V_2	1	3	$\frac{3}{2}$	0	$\frac{6}{7}$	0	$\frac{1}{3}$	80
V_3	$\frac{1}{3}$	0	$\frac{9}{10}$	3	$\frac{6}{7}$	0	2	120
\$	$\frac{40}{3}$	30	15	18	15	21	$\frac{40}{3}$	

Let us now study combinations of these new pills.   We assume that we are considering a total number of 100 pills.   Denoting by u_1 the number of $P_1{}^*$'s, by u_2 the number of $P_2{}^*$'s, etc., we have then the relationship:

$$u_1 + u_2 + u_3 + u_4 + u_5 + u_6 + u_7 = 100 \qquad (31)$$

Now we pose the question, "By taking these 100 pills, how many units of vitamins V_1, V_2, and V_3 do we get?"   Let us denote these quantities by Q_1, Q_2, and Q_3.   Then

$$
\begin{aligned}
\tfrac{5}{3}u_1 \quad\quad + \tfrac{3}{5}u_3 \quad\quad\quad + \tfrac{9}{7}u_5 + 3u_6 + \tfrac{2}{3}u_7 &= Q_1 \\
u_1 + 3u_2 + \tfrac{3}{2}u_3 \quad\quad\quad + \tfrac{6}{7}u_5 \quad\quad + \tfrac{1}{3}u_7 &= Q_2 \qquad (32)\\
\tfrac{1}{3}u_1 \quad\quad + \tfrac{9}{10}u_3 + 3u_4 + \tfrac{6}{7}u_5 \quad\quad + 2u_7 &= Q_3
\end{aligned}
$$

What will be the cost of such a combination of pills?   The cost is given by:

$$\tfrac{40}{3}u_1 + 30u_2 + 15u_3 + 18u_4 + 15u_5 + 21u_6 + \tfrac{40}{3}u_7 = z \quad (33)$$

So far there appears to be no reason why we introduced these new hypothetical pills.   There is, however, something interesting about the total quantity of vitamins involved when buying these 100 pills.   We get this quantity by adding the three equations given by (32):

$$3u_1 + 3u_2 + 3u_3 + 3u_4 + 3u_5 + 3u_6 + 3u_7 = Q_1 + Q_2 + Q_3 \qquad (34)$$

If (34) is compared with (31) we realize that:

$$Q_1 + Q_2 + Q_3 = 300 \qquad (35)$$

This means that, whatever combination of these 100 new pills is purchased, the total units of vitamins contained in these pills will be exactly 300. This property of the new pills allows us to formulate our original nutrition problem in a way which is useful for our geometrical representation.

We can say that we need to combine 100 new pills in such a fashion that we get 80 units of V_2 and 120 units of V_3. We need not concern ourselves with the quantity of V_1, as this will automatically be 100. We seek the combination of these 100 new pills that gives the proper amount of V_2 and the proper amount of V_3 required, and that has the lowest total cost. To formulate the problem mathematically, we say that we need to determine the unknowns u_1, u_2, etc., such that

$$u_1 + 3u_2 + \tfrac{3}{2}u_3 \qquad + \tfrac{6}{7}u_5 + \tfrac{1}{3}u_7 = Q_2 \qquad (36a)$$

$$\tfrac{1}{3}u_1 \qquad + \tfrac{9}{10}u_3 + 3u_4 + \tfrac{6}{7}u_5 + 2u_7 = Q_3 \qquad (36b)$$

where $Q_2 = 80$ and $Q_3 = 120$. Furthermore, the cost function:

$$\tfrac{40}{3}u_1 + 30u_2 + 15u_3 + 18u_4 + 15u_5 + 21u_6 + \tfrac{40}{3}u_7 = z \qquad (37)$$

must become a minimum

We are ready now to give a geometrical representation of our problem. In Fig. 14, each combination of 100 pills is represented by coordinates which show the vitamin contents Q_2 and Q_3. For instance, the coordinates of point $P_3{}^*$ are 150 and 90, as 100 of $P_3{}^*$ contain 150 units of V_2 and 90 units of V_3.

How do we represent combinations of these pills? Say we want to represent 50 of $P_1{}^*$ and 50 of $P_3{}^*$. Recalling our representation of putting weights at points, we can see that the halfway point between the points $P_1{}^*$ and $P_3{}^*$, the point A, represents such a combination. In general we can say that any combination of these 100 pills can be represented by putting weights proportional to the quantity of pills at the representative points and taking the center of gravity of these weights.

We have succeeded, then, in finding a geometrical representation of our problem, but we have not considered costs yet. Costs can be handled by adding an additional vertical dimension, as shown in Fig.

15. In this representation, we must distribute 100 units of weights
at the points shown in Fig. 15.   The center of gravity of these weights
represents the particular combination of pills.   Projections on the
horizontal axes give the units of V_2 and V_3 contained in the combination.   (We recall that the total amount of vitamins is always 300
units).   The vertical coordinate of the center of gravity indicates the
price of this particular combination of pills.   We observe that all
these centers of gravities are *above* or *on* the bowl-shaped surface shown
in Fig. 15.

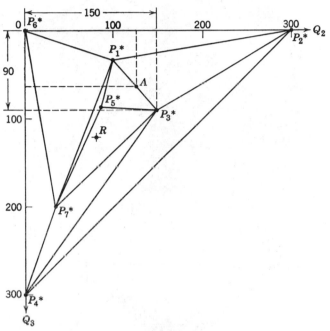

FIG. 14. Any combination of 100 hypothetical pills can be represented as the
center of gravity of weights placed at points P_1^*, P_2^*, $\cdots$, P_7^*. R represents
the required location of the center of gravity.

We have now a geometrical representation of the combination of
pills. We need to decide which combination (i.e., which of these
infinitely many centers of gravity) are we to select to solve our problem?
Let us remember that we want to get a combination that has
$Q_2 = 80$ units of V_2, and $Q_3 = 120$ units of V_3. This requirement is
shown by the dot R in Fig. 14. We must distribute weights in Fig.
14 so that the center of gravity lies at point R. Proceeding now to
Fig. 15, we see that the weights must be distributed so that the projec-
tion of the center of gravity is at point R. To put it another way, we

must distribute the weights so that the center of gravity is on the "requirement line," represented by the vertical rod in Fig. 15.

Where should the center of gravity lie on the requirement line? We want the lowest point, as the vertical distance shows the combined

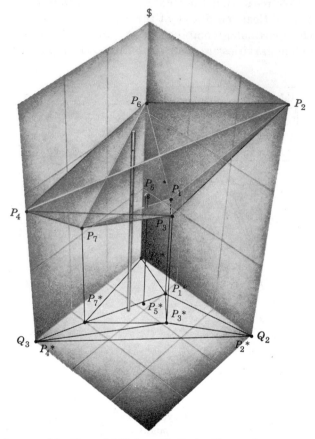

FIG. 15. Any combination of 100 hypothetical pills can be represented as the center of gravity of weights placed at points P_1, P_2, $\cdots$, P_7. The vertical coordinate of the center of gravity gives the cost. The vertical rod shows where the center of gravity must lie. (Each horizontal grid represents 100 units of vitamins. Each vertical grid represents $10.)

cost of the pills. Obviously, then, the solution is given by the intersection of the requirement line with the bowl-shaped surface in Fig. 15. This point is obtained as the intersection of the requirement line with the triangle $P_1P_3P_7$.

The advantage of this new representation is that the simplex method can be interpreted geometrically. The first solution we obtained was a combination of pills P_2, P_4, and P_6. In Fig. 16 the intersection of the top triangle with the requirement line represents this solution. The next solution combines pills P_3, P_4, and P_6. This solution is represented by the intersection of the requirement line with triangle $P_3P_4P_6$. The third solution is the intersection of the requirement

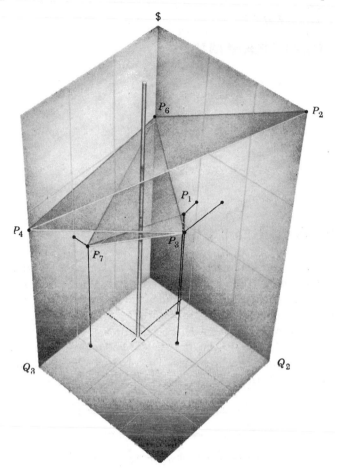

Fig. 16. Geometrical representation of the simplex method. The triangles $P_2P_4P_6$, $P_3P_4P_6$, $P_3P_6P_7$, and $P_1P_3P_7$ represent the first, second, third, and fourth (or optimum) solutions. (Each horizontal grid represents 100 units of vitamins. Each vertical grid represents \$10.)

line with triangle $P_3P_6P_7$, and finally the optimum solution is represented by the intersection of the requirement line with the lowest triangle $P_1P_3P_7$.

The simplex method is a technique to survey the various triangles in Fig. 16 and to select the triangle that intersects the requirement line in the lowest point.

CHAPTER 7

CONVEX PROGRAMMING

1. WHAT IS CONVEX PROGRAMMING?

Let us return our attention to Section 7 of Chapter 2, where we discussed a combined transportation and production problem. Let us focus our attention on the case which includes overtime production. We propose to look at this problem in a different way in order to introduce some new mathematical techniques.

We denote again by $x_{i,j}$ the quantity of goods produced in factory F_i that is to be shipped to warehouse W_j. Let us denote the production at each of the factories by y_1, y_2, y_3, and y_4. Then

$$y_1 = x_{1,1} + x_{1,2} + x_{1,3} + x_{1,4} \qquad (1a)$$

$$y_2 = x_{2,1} + x_{2,2} + x_{2,3} + x_{2,4} \qquad (1b)$$

$$y_3 = x_{3,1} + x_{3,2} + x_{3,3} + x_{3,4} \qquad (1c)$$

and

$$y_4 = x_{4,1} + x_{4,2} + x_{4,3} + x_{4,4} \qquad (1d)$$

In each of these factories, capacity is limited by the given combined straight and overtime. We can put this into mathematical form with the aid of the following inequalities:

$$y_1 \leq 140 + 50 = 190 \qquad (2)$$

$$y_2 \leq 260 + 80 = 340 \qquad (3)$$

$$y_3 \leq 360 + 120 = 480 \tag{4}$$

$$y_4 \leq 220 + 60 = 280 \tag{5}$$

Requirements at each warehouse can be expressed by the following equations:

$$x_{1,1} + x_{2,1} + x_{3,1} + x_{4,1} = 180 \tag{6}$$

$$x_{1,2} + x_{2,2} + x_{3,2} + x_{4,2} = 280 \tag{7}$$

$$x_{1,3} + x_{2,3} + x_{3,3} + x_{4,3} = 150 \tag{8}$$

$$x_{1,4} + x_{2,4} + x_{3,4} + x_{4,4} = 200 \tag{9}$$

Let us compute the combined production and transportation costs. Transportations costs can be computed with the aid of the formula

$$z = \sum_{i=1}^{4} \sum_{j=1}^{4} c_{i,j} x_{i,j} \tag{10}$$

However, the production costs are more complicated to compute. Let us, say, consider the first factory.   If production in this factory is less than 140 or

$$0 \leq y_1 \leq 140 \tag{11}$$

then the cost is given by

$$z_1 = 60 y_1 \tag{12}$$

However, if production is between 140 and 190 units, that is, if

$$140 \leq y_1 \leq 190 \tag{13}$$

then production costs are given by

$$z_1 = 60(140) + 90(y_1 - 140) \tag{14}$$

These production costs are shown graphically in the top part of Fig. 1. Let the mathematical notation for this graph be:

$$z_1 = f_1(y_1) \tag{15}$$

Similarly, the production cost in the other factories can be expressed by the equations

$$z_2 = f_2(y_2) \tag{16}$$

$$z_3 = f_3(y_3) \tag{17}$$

$$z_4 = f_4(y_4) \tag{18}$$

These are shown in Fig. 1.   The total cost, then, is given by

$$z = \sum_{i=1}^{4} \sum_{j=1}^{4} c_{i,j} x_{i,j} + \sum_{i=1}^{4} f_i(y_i) \tag{19}$$

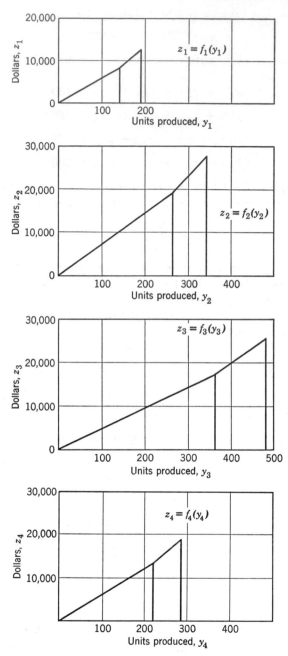

FIG. 1. Illustration of convex cost functions. Production costs are shown as functions of number of units produced.

where the first term is the transportation cost and the second term is the production cost. The problem is, then, to minimize the cost function as given by equation (19), under the restrictions expressed by equations (1) through (9).

This is a problem where the cost function is not a straight-line function, and, therefore, this is not a problem in linear programming, at least not as it is formulated here. However, we recall that we solved this problem in Chapter 2 where we formulated it in a somewhat different way. This is not a coincidence, as *any* problem in "convex" programming can be reduced to a problem in linear programming.

One particular method of reduction consists of "partitioning" the variables of the problem into auxiliary variables. In our particular case, this partitioning is done in the following fashion:

$$y_1 = y_{1,1} + y_{1,2} \tag{20a}$$

$$y_2 = y_{2,1} + y_{2,2} \tag{20b}$$

$$y_3 = y_{3,1} + y_{3,2} \tag{20c}$$

$$y_4 = y_{4,1} + y_{4,2} \tag{20d}$$

where

$$0 \le y_{1,1} \le 140 \tag{21}$$

$$0 \le y_{1,2} \le 50 \tag{22}$$

$$0 \le y_{2,1} \le 260 \tag{23}$$

$$0 \le y_{2,2} \le 80 \tag{24}$$

$$0 \le y_{3,1} \le 360 \tag{25}$$

$$0 \le y_{3,2} \le 120 \tag{26}$$

$$0 \le y_{4,1} \le 220 \tag{27}$$

$$0 \le y_{4,2} \le 60 \tag{28}$$

Now, our equation (19), which expresses cost, becomes

$$z = \left(\sum_{i=1}^{4} \sum_{j=1}^{4} c_{i,j} x_{i,j} \right) + 60y_{1,1} + 90y_{1,2} + 72y_{2,1} + 108y_{2,2}$$
$$+ 48y_{3,1} + 72y_{3,2} + 60y_{4,1} + 90y_{4,2} \tag{29}$$

The problem is now to minimize (29) under the restrictions of equations (1) through (9) and also (20) through (26). This is a problem in linear programming as all the restrictions and the payoff are linear functions. It can be seen, then, that the "convex" programming problem is transformed into a linear programming problem by partitioning the variables into a new set of variables, and by introducing a new set of linear restrictions.

So far, we have not explained what a convex function is, and we defer elaboration on this point to the next section. However, one point should be made clear. Suppose we are dealing with the situation where the overtime cost is *smaller* than the regular time cost. What would happen in this case? We might obtain a solution which involves

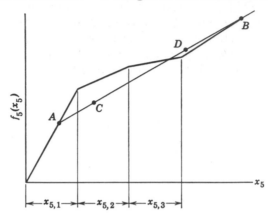

FIG. 2. Illustration of nonconvex payoff function. Point C is *below* and point D is *above* the curve.

overtime but no regular time, (or at least no regular time up to capacity). Now, obviously such a solution makes no sense as it is impossible to operate exclusively on overtime. Our method works only if the cost function as shown in Fig. 1 gets steeper as production goes up. On the other hand, if the cost function looks something like the one in Fig. 2, our method of partitioning the variables into different parts would not work.

2. GENERAL STATEMENT OF THE PROBLEM OF CONVEX PROGRAMMING

Figure 3 shows a function that is called a convex function from below. The reason that this curve is called convex from below is the following: Let us select two arbitrary points, A and B, on the curve, connect the two points A and B by a straight line, and select a point C on the straight line between A and B. In Fig. 3 this point C will always be *below* the curve. On the other hand, Fig. 4 shows a convex function from *above*, because the same point C is always above the curve. The dotted lines in Figs. 3 and 4 are convex polygons (the first one is a convex polygon from below; the second one is a convex polygon from above), and these polygons are approximations to the convex curves shown. By the word approximation we mean that for computational purposes it is accurate enough to consider the values

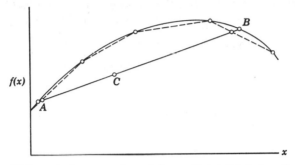

FIG. 3. This curve is convex from below. Point C is below the curve.

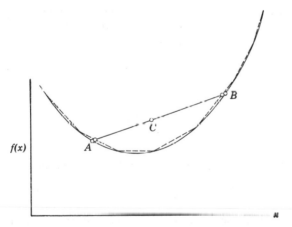

FIG. 4. This curve is convex from above. Point C is *above* the curve.

along the polygons instead of the actual curved lines. Now the curve shown in Fig. 2 is a nonconvex curve. If we select a point C or D on the line between A and B, this point may or may not lie above the curve.

Now we are ready to discuss convex programming. Consider the programming problem where the restrictions are given by the equations

$$\sum_{j=1}^{n} a_{i,j} x_j = b_i \qquad (30)$$

These are linear restrictions. However, let us assume that the cost function is given by

$$z = f_1(x_1) + f_2(x_2) + \cdots + f_n(x_n) \tag{31}$$

where all the functions are convex from above.

This is a problem in convex programming. The general method of solution of a problem of this type consists of partitioning the variables into proper auxiliary variables according to the following equation:

$$x_1 = x_{1,1} + x_{1,2} + x_{1,3} + \cdots$$
$$x_2 = x_{2,1} + x_{2,2} + x_{2,3} + \cdots \tag{32}$$
$$x_3 = x_{3,1} + x_{3,2} + x_{3,3} + \cdots$$

where for each of the auxiliary variables there is a constraint introduced:

$$\alpha_{i,k} < x_{i,k} < \alpha_{i,k+1} \tag{33}$$

This partitioning must be carried out according to the breaks in the convex polygons. As an illustration, consider the cost function in Fig. 5. In this particular case the partitioning into the auxiliary variables is given by the following inequalities:

$$\alpha_{3,1} < x_{3,1} < \alpha_{3,2} \qquad \alpha_{3,1} = 0 \qquad \alpha_{3,2} = 1 \tag{34}$$

$$\alpha_{3,2} < x_{3,2} < \alpha_{3,3} \qquad \alpha_{3,3} = 3 \tag{35}$$

$$\alpha_{3,3} < x_{3,3} < \alpha_{3,4} \qquad \alpha_{3,4} = 7 \tag{36}$$

$$\alpha_{3,4} < x_{3,4} < \alpha_{3,5} \qquad \alpha_{3,5} = 10 \tag{37}$$

With the aid of these auxiliary variables the payoff function $f_3(x_3)$ is replaced by

$$f_3(x_3) = \tfrac{1}{2}x_{3,2} + \tfrac{7}{8}x_{3,3} + \tfrac{3}{2}x_{3,4} \tag{38}$$

By this method, we can replace the convex cost function with a linear cost function, and then we can use the simplex method to solve the linear programming problem. However, the introduction of the additional constraints makes the problem more complicated, and, therefore, the numerical solution of the problem becomes more laborious. Fortunately, there is a short-cut method of solving problems of this type, though we do not propose to discuss it here. The reader who is particularly interested in this problem is referred to the original literature.*

* A. Charnes and C. E. Lemke, *Minimization of Non-Linear Convex Functionals*, Carnegie Institute of Technology, May 27, 1954.

Let us now elaborate further on the point of why the cost function must be convex (from above) in order to be able to get the solution. The argument is very similar to the one we used in our example of overtime production. If the curve is of the type shown in Fig. 2, we might get a solution that requires a certain amont of $x_{5,2}$, but no amount of $x_{5,1}$ or insufficient amount of $x_{5,1}$. In such a case, the partitioning of the variable into the auxiliary variables makes no sense, or the auxiliary variables do not "fit" one after the other. On the other hand, if the function is convex (form above) as shown in Fig. 4, this sort of thing cannot happen.

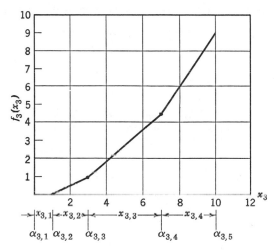

FIG. 5.   Method of solution for a convex programming problem.   Each variable must be partitioned into auxiliary variables.

We discussed convex programming when the payoff is of a cost type, and when this payoff has to be minimized. On the other hand, if the problem is to maximize a payoff function (say, to maximize profit), then the payoff function still has to be convex, but in this case it has to be convex from below. The same sort of an argument as we used before can be applied here, and it is easy to deduce that the method will work only when the function is convex from below.

So far, we have assumed that the payoff function is a polygon. In case these functions are curved, we can approximate them by polygons and solve the problem using these polygons as payoff functions. For any practical purpose, it is accurate enough to consider the straight-line polygon instead of the curved payoff functions.

The reader can readily see that the potential applications of convex programming are great. There are many problems where costs and

profits follow a convex curve instead of a straight line. These problems can be handled with the general method developed here. We proceed now to show a few illustrative examples of convex programming.

3. THE PROBLEM OF THE DISTRIBUTION OF EFFORT

A certain corporation is producing and marketing three different
products, all utilizing the same type of resource. ("Resource" may
cover labor resources, the land required in a farm enterprise, warehouse space, or any other commodity that goes into the production of

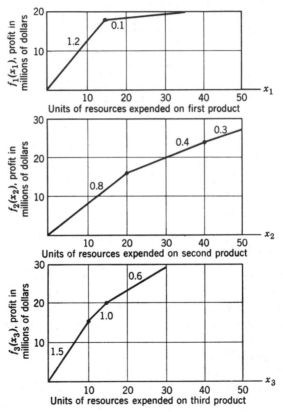

FIG. 6. The problem of the distribution of effort as an illustration in convex
programming. The curves show the profitability of each product.

the three products.) Figure 6 shows the profit for each of these products, and it is assumed that any quantity of them can be sold. For
instance, the top graph in Fig. 6 shows that, if on Product 1 resources
in quantities of fewer than 15 units are expended, then the profit is

1.2 millions for each unit of resource expended. (The million is omitted from the graph in order to save space.) However, if more than 15 of these units are expended, then the profit drops down to \$100,000 for each unit of resource. The other graphs in Fig. 6 have similar meanings. The problem we propose to examine now is the following: The total resources available to the corporation are given. How can we best allocate these resources to the three products?

Let us denote by A the total resources available, and let us denote by x_1, x_2, and x_3 the quantities of these resources allocated to the first, second, and third product. The mathematical expression of these facts can be written as

$$x_1 + x_2 + x_3 = A \tag{39}$$

The profit associated with this allocation of products can be written as

$$z = f_1(x_1) + f_2(x_2) + f_3(x_3) \tag{40}$$

where each of these functions is shown in Fig. 6. Mathematically speaking, then, the problem is to maximize the profit as expressed by equation (40) under the restriction of equation (39). Such a problem is often referred to as the problem of the distribution of effort since the resources are considered as efforts expended in producing the different products. Note that this is not a problem in linear programming, as the profit function is not a linear function. It is a problem in convex programming as each of the profit functions are convex polygons.

Following our general method of partitioning the variables into the auxiliary variables, we introduce the following system of equations:

$$x_1 = x_{1,1} + x_{1,2} \tag{41}$$

$$x_2 = x_{2,1} + x_{2,2} + x_{2,3} \tag{42}$$

$$x_3 = x_{3,1} + x_{3,2} + x_{3,3} \tag{43}$$

where

$$0 \leq x_{1,1} \leq 15 \tag{44}$$

$$0 \leq x_{1,2} \leq 20 \tag{45}$$

$$0 \leq x_{2,1} \leq 20 \tag{46}$$

$$0 \leq x_{2,2} \leq 20 \tag{47}$$

$$0 \leq x_{2,3} \leq 10 \tag{48}$$

$$0 \leq x_{3,1} \leq 10 \tag{49}$$

$$0 \leq x_{3,2} \leq 5 \tag{50}$$

$$0 \leq x_{3,3} \leq 15 \tag{51}$$

With the aid of these auxiliary variables, the profit can be expressed as

$$z = 1.2x_{1,1} + 0.1x_{1,2} + 0.8x_{2,1} + 0.4x_{2,2} + 0.3x_{2,3} + 1.5x_{3,1}$$
$$+ 1.0x_{3,2} + 0.6x_{3,3} \quad (52)$$

The constraint (we are distributing a given amount of resources) can be expressed as

$$x_{1,1} + x_{1,2} + x_{2,1} + x_{2,2} + x_{2,3} + x_{3,1} + x_{3,2} + x_{3,3} = A \quad (53)$$

We could solve this problem by using the simplex method. Fortunately, however, there is a much simpler way to get an answer, namely, we can set up a sequence of priorities of the auxiliary variables as shown in the table. If our total resources are fewer than 10 units,

Auxiliary Variable	Profit per Unit of Resource	Maximum Number of Units That May Be Allocated	Cumulative Number Units Allocated
$x_{3,1}$	1.5	10	10
$x_{1,1}$	1.2	15	25
$x_{3,2}$	1.0	5	30
$x_{2,1}$	0.8	20	50
$x_{3,3}$	0.6	15	65
$x_{2,2}$	0.4	20	85
$x_{2,3}$	0.3	10	95
$x_{1,2}$	0.1	20	115

we "use" $x_{3,1}$ or produce product 3. This is due to the fact that product 3, up to 10 units of resources, yields a profit of 1.5 million dollars per unit of resource, and this is the highest profit rate that can

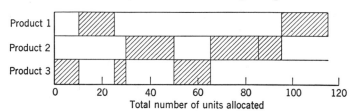

FIG. 7. Optimum allocation of resources to three products. The shaded area shows units of resources allocated to each product.

be obtained. If we have between 10 and 25 units of resources available, then we allocate 10 units to product 3 and the rest of the resources to product 1. This is what we mean by listing $x_{1,1}$ in the second row of the table.

With the aid of these priorities we can prepare the chart shown in Fig. 7. For instance, as long as the resources are available in units

fewer than 10, we produce only product 3. When resources are available up to 25 units, we will produce some of product 1 and some of
product 3 as shown by Fig. 7. In fact, even if the resources go up to
30 units, we will still produce product 1 and product 3. However, if
our resources go up from 30 to 50, then the thing to do is produce all
three products in the quantities shown by Fig. 7.

We can determine, with the aid of the graph shown in Fig. 7, how
much of each resource should be allocated to each product depending
on the quantity of resources available. The graph in Fig. 8 shows the

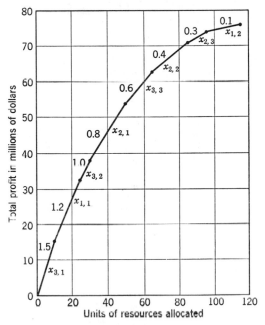

FIG. 8. Solution to the problem of the distribution of effort. Profit is shown
when resources are allocated the best.

profit that can be realized as a function of the various units of resources
that are available. This graph was prepared by taking the straight-
line segments from Fig. 6 and putting them, one after the other, in
the order of the priorities, that is, in the order of decreasing returns.

It can be seen, then, that the problem of the distribution of effort,
when the profit functions are convex polygons (from below), can be
solved with a very simple graphical (or numerical) method.

Let us turn our attention now to a further application of the problem on the distribution of effort. Let us study the problem of the
oil corporation described in Section 8 of Chapter 3. First, we simplify

the problem by assuming that the capacities in the secondary stages of refinery are quite high, and that both of the intermediate products can be put through the secondary stages of refining.   Mathematically speaking, this means that equations (66) and (68) in Chapter 3 hold automatically, as both B and C are very large.   In the profit function, as described by equation (69) in Chapter 3, we can neglect the terms referring to N_1 and M_1, as both of these quantities are zeros.   The profit function simplifies to

$$z = \nu_2 N + \mu_2 M - \sum_1^6 c_i y_i \tag{54}$$

which can be written as

$$z = \nu_2 \sum_1^6 n_i x_i + \mu_2 \sum_1^6 m_i x_i - \sum_1^6 c_i y_i \tag{55}$$

or as

$$z = \sum_1^6 [(\nu_2 n_i + \mu_2 m_i) x_i - c_i y_i] \tag{56}$$

Let us introduce, now, the notation

$$\nu_2 n_i + \mu_2 m_i = p_i \tag{57}$$

With the aid of this we can write the profit function as

$$z = \sum_1^6 (p_i x_i - c_i y_i) \tag{58}$$

or

$$z = (p_1 x_1 - c_1 y_1) + (p_2 x_2 - c_2 y_2) + (p_3 x_3 - c_3 y_3) \\ + (p_4 x_4 - c_4 y_4) + (p_5 x_5 - c_5 y_5) + (p_6 x_6 - c_6 y_6) \tag{59}$$

Our problem is now to maximize the profit function as expressed by (58) or (59), under the restriction that

$$x_1 + x_2 + x_3 + x_4 + x_5 + x_6 \leq A \tag{60}$$

(This last equation expresses the fact that the capacity in the first stage of refining is given by A.   See equation (62) of Chapter 3.)

The quantity of oil y_i that is to be purchased is above the minimum a_i as set by policy, or

$$y_i \geq a_i \qquad i = 1, 2, \cdots, 6 \tag{61}$$

As we can refine only the oil that has been purchased,

$$x_i \leq y_i \qquad i = 1, 2, \cdots, 6 \tag{62}$$

Furthermore, we must have

$$0 \le x_i \qquad i = 1, 2, \cdots, 6 \tag{63}$$

The problem is, then, maximize the profit as expressed by equations (58) or (59), under the restrictions of equations (60), (61), (62), and (63).

In order to develop a solution to this problem, let us consider first the first term in equation (59).

$$z_1 = p_1 x_1 - c_1 y_1 \tag{64}$$

Let us suppose that the quantity of the first crude that is to be refined is zero; we must still buy the quantity a_1 of the first crude. Obviously, we would not purchase more than a_1 of this first crude, as we are refining nothing. What is the profit in this particular situation?

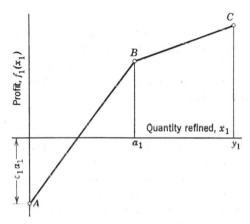

FIG. 9. Study of an oil corporation. The profit function for first crude is a convex polygon from below

According to equation (64) (or just by simple reasoning), there is a loss of $c_1 a_1$ dollars.

To continue our argument, suppose that the quantity refined is more than zero but less than a_1, or, in mathematical terms,

$$0 \le x_1 \le a_1 \tag{65}$$

What is the profit in this case? We still must buy the quantity a_1 as set by the policy, and so the profit becomes

$$z_1 = p_1 x_1 - c_1 a_1 \tag{66}$$

The situation we have described here with mathematics is shown graphically in Fig. 9. As long as we are refining an amount between 0 and a_1, the profit is given by the line AB. Let us suppose, now, that x_1 is more than the a_1 but less than y_1, or

$$a_1 \leq x_1 \leq y_1 \tag{67}$$

In this case, we should buy sufficient quantities of crude, that is, we should have

$$y_1 = x_1 \tag{68}$$

The profit in this particular case is given by the formula

$$z_1 = (p_1 - c_1)x_1 \tag{69}$$

This is shown graphically in Fig. 9 by the line BC. We can summarize this state of affairs by saying that the profit is given by

$$z_1 = f_1(x_1) \tag{70}$$

where $f_1(x)$ is the convex (from below) polygon shown in Fig. 9.

Similarly, we can form profit functions for the second, third, fourth, fifth, and sixth crude. For each of these crudes the profit can be expressed as a polygon, convex from below. The total profit can be expressed by the formula

$$z = f_1(x_1) + f_2(x_2) + f_3(x_3) + f_4(x_4) + f_5(x_5) + f_6(x_6) \tag{71}$$

where each of the functions corresponds to a graph, and each of them represents a polygon convex from below.

We see, in summary, that the simplified problem can be solved by maximizing the profit as expressed by equation (71) under the restriction of equation (60). This is, however, the problem of the distribution of effort, and we have already shown a simple method of solving this problem.

Before we proceed to the solution of the original problem, when the secondary stages of refining are limited, we want to make one further point. We have assumed so far that the capacity limitation A in the first stage is given and cannot be changed. Let us suppose, however, the question is asked: How much would the profit increase if the capacity in the first stage of refining is increased? If we have solved the problem for *any* value A, then we can answer this question by comparing the profit for different values of A. Therefore, our solution in fact evalutes in dollars the availability of capacity or the lack of capacity. Such information is of great use when a manager is faced with the question of enlarging the capacity of a refinery.

We proceed now to solve our original problem.

4. THE STUDY OF AN OIL CORPORATION

Let us now consider the problem with the condition that capacities in the secondary stages of refining are limited. We propose to show that this more general problem can be reduced to the simplified problem, that is, to the problem of the secondary stages having large capacities. We will investigate this general problem under four different hypotheses, and we will show that we can reduce the general problem under each of these hypotheses to the simplified problem. It will be obvious that one of the hypotheses must be true; therefore by solving the simplified problem at most four times, we will solve the general problem. Let us now consider each of these hypotheses.

First Hypothesis

This is the simplified problem when capacities in the secondary refinery stages are large. Under this hypothesis, we know that

$$N_1 = 0 \tag{72}$$

$$M_1 = 0 \tag{73}$$

and with these equations we have already solved the problem. We can proceed now to our next hypothesis.

Second Hypothesis

Let us now assume that B is large, but that C, the secondary stage of refining for the second product, is a limiting factor. Under this condition, the first crude will be all processed through both stages, therefore none of the first intermediate product is sold or

$$N_1 = 0 \tag{74}$$

On the other hand, C is a limiting factor, and therefore some of the second intermediate product is sold, without being processed through the secondary stage of refinery. This means, then, that the quantity of second intermediate product sold does not equal zero, or:

$$M_1 \neq 0 \tag{75}$$

Because none of the first intermediate product is sold, we have

$$N_2 = N = \sum_1^6 n_i x_i \tag{76}$$

Furthermore, as C is a limiting factor, we know that C gives the quantity of the second intermediary product to be processed through the secondary stage or

$$M_2 = C \tag{77}$$

From this it follows that

$$M_1 = M - M_2 = M - C = \sum_1^6 m_i x_i - C \tag{78}$$

We can now compute the profit with the aid of equation (69), Chapter 3. We recognize that

$$N_1 = 0$$
$$N_2 = \Sigma n_i x_i$$
$$M_1 = \Sigma m_i x_i - C$$
$$M_2 = C$$

and, therefore, the profit is given by

$$z = \mu_1 \left(\sum_1^6 m_i x_i - C \right) + \nu_2 \left(\sum_1^6 n_i x_i \right) + \mu_2 C - \sum_1^6 c_i y_i \tag{79a}$$

By carrying out the multiplications and collecting terms, we get

$$z = \sum_1^6 (\nu_2 n_i + \mu_1 m_i) x_i - \sum_1^6 c_i y_i + C(\mu_2 - \mu_1) \tag{79b}$$

Let us compare this profit function with the profit function given by equation (58). If we put

$$p_i = \nu_2 n_i + \mu_1 m_i \tag{80}$$

we get back the form of equation (58), except that there is a constant added at the end of the equation, which makes no difference from the point of view of maximization. We can see, then, that we can solve the problem under the second hypothesis the same way as we solved the problem when there was no limitation in the secondary stages, except that we have to replace equation (57) by equation (80). Let us proceed now to the third hypothesis.

Third Hypothesis

Let us assume now that B is a limiting factor, but that C is sufficiently large. Under this condition, some of the first intermediate product will be sold, and so we have

$$N_1 \neq 0 \tag{81}$$

On the other hand, none of the second intermediate product will be sold, and so we have

$$M_1 = 0 \tag{82}$$

Finally, because of the fact that B is a limiting factor, we have

$$N_2 = B \tag{83}$$

From this, it follows that

$$N_1 = N - N_2 = N - B = \sum_1^6 n_i x_i - B \tag{84}$$

and

$$M_2 = M = \sum_1^6 m_i x_i \tag{85}$$

Under these conditions the profit function can be expressed the following way:

$$z = \sum_1^6 (\nu_1 n_i + \mu_2 m_i) x_i - \sum_1^6 c_i y_i + B(\nu_2 - \nu_1) \tag{86}$$

We recognize now that if we put

$$p_i = \nu_1 n_i + \mu_2 m_i \tag{87}$$

we again find ourselves facing a problem like the simplified problem. Therefore, we can see that we can solve the problem under the third hypothesis. Let us now proceed to our fourth hypothesis.

Fourth Hypothesis

Let us assume, finally, that both B and C are limiting factors. We are going to sell both of the intermediate products on the market, and we have

$$N_1 \neq 0 \tag{88}$$

$$M_1 \neq 0 \tag{89}$$

Furthermore, as both B and C are limiting factors, we must have

$$N_2 = B \tag{90}$$

$$M_2 = C \tag{91}$$

From this, follows that

$$N_1 = N - N_2 = N - B = \Sigma n_i x_i - B \tag{92}$$

$$M_1 = M - M_2 = M - C = \Sigma m_i x_i - C \tag{93}$$

The profit function can be expressed in the form

$$z = \sum_1^6 (\nu_1 n_i + \mu_1 m_i)x_i - \sum_1^6 c_i y_i + B(\nu_2 - \nu_1) + C(\mu_2 - \mu_1) \quad (94)$$

We see again that by putting

$$p_i = \nu_1 n_i + \mu_1 m_i \quad (95)$$

we can reduce the problem to the simplified problem. In summary, then, we see that we can solve the general problem, by reducing it to the simplified problem, under any of four hypotheses. *However, one of the hypotheses must be true.* Therefore, if we solve the general problem under each of the four hypotheses, one of the solutions gives the solution to the general problem. Thus the method of solution is the following:

First, we solve the problem under the first hypothesis. If it is found that there is sufficient capacity in the secondary stages, then we are through with the problem. On the other hand, if we find that there is insufficient capacity, we must solve the problem under the second

TABLE 1.   Study of an Oil Corporation [a]

			N_1	N_2	M_1	M_2
H_1:	$N_1 = 0$	$M_1 = 0$	0	$\Sigma n_i x_i$	0	$\Sigma m_i x_i$
H_2:	$N_1 = 0$	$M_1 \neq 0$	0	$\Sigma n_i x_i$	$\Sigma m_i x_i - C$	C
H_3:	$N_1 \neq 0$	$M_1 = 0$	$\Sigma n_i x_i - B$	B	0	$\Sigma m_i x_i$
H_4:	$N_1 \neq 0$	$M_1 \neq 0$	$\Sigma n_i x_i - B$	B	$\Sigma m_i x_i - C$	C

[a] H_1, H_2, H_3, and H_4 refer to the four hypotheses used in the method of analysis.

hypothesis. If this does not run into contradiction, we have the solution; if it does run into contradiction, we solve the problem under the third hypothesis. If this does not lead to contradiction, we have the solution. On the other hand, if even the third hypothesis gets us into a contradiction, we solve the problem under the fourth hypothesis, and this finally must give a solution to the general problem. We can see, then, that in the worst case we need to solve the simplified problem four times.

For convenience, the four hypotheses and the mathematics involved in each hypothesis are summarized in Table 1.

5. A PROBLEM IN PRODUCTION AND INVENTORY CONTROL

As a further application of convex programming, we return to the problem treated in Section 9 of Chapter 3. When introducing this problem we assumed that the initial inventory is zero; now we allow more generally that the initial inventory, u_0 is not zero. Let us look at Fig. 4, Chapter 3. Our problem is to determine a production plan represented as in Fig. 4 by a broken line lying above the requirement line. On the left-hand side, the line representing the proper production plan is anchored at the level of the initial inventory, and at the right-hand side at the level of the requirements (108 units).

In order to solve this problem, we begin by partitioning the production in each period into day and night shifts. We put

$$x_i = v_i + w_i \tag{96}$$

where v_i is day shift and w_i is night shift production. Each of these is limited:

$$0 \le v_i \le 15 \tag{97}$$
$$0 \le w_i \le 15 \tag{98}$$

Using these auxiliary variables, production costs can be expressed as

$$z = 100(v_1 + v_2 + v_3 + v_4 + v_5 + v_6)$$
$$+ 120(w_1 + w_2 + w_3 + w_4 + w_5 + w_6) \tag{99}$$

The inventory levels at the end of each production period can be expressed with the aid of equation (81) in Chapter 3. We get

$$u_1 = u_0 + X_1 - R_1 = u_0 + x_1 - R_1$$
$$u_2 = u_0 + X_2 - R_2 = u_0 + x_1 + x_2 - R_2 \tag{100}$$
$$u_3 = u_0 + X_3 - R_3 = u_0 + x_1 + x_2 + x_3 - R_3$$

$$\dots \dots \dots \dots \dots \dots \dots \dots \dots \dots$$

$$u_6 = u_0 + X_6 - R_6 = u_0 + x_1 + x_2 + x_3 + x_4 + x_5 + x_6 - R_6 \tag{101}$$

The inventory cost associated with this production program can be determined with the aid of equation (91) of Chapter 3. We get

$$z_I = \tfrac{1}{2}q[u_0 + 2u_1 + 2u_2 + 2u_3 + 2u_4 + 2u_5 + u_6] \tag{102}$$

or, by substituting in the values of the inventory levels, we get

$$z_I = \tfrac{1}{2}q[u_0 + 2(u_0 + x_1 - R_1)$$
$$+ 2(u_0 + x_1 + x_2 - R_2)$$
$$+ 2(u_0 + x_1 + x_2 + x_3 - R_3)$$
$$+ 2(u_0 + x_1 + x_2 + x_3 + x_4 - R_4) \qquad (103)$$
$$+ 2(u_0 + x_1 + x_2 + x_3 + x_4 + x_5 - R_5)$$
$$+ (u_0 + x_1 + x_2 + x_3 + x_4 + x_5 + x_6 - R_6)]$$

This last equation can be written in the form

$$z_I = \tfrac{1}{2}q[12u_0 + 11x_1 + 9x_2 + 7x_3 + 5x_4 + 3x_5 + x_6 - C] \quad (104)$$

where the constant C is given by

$$C = 2R_1 + 2R_2 + 2R_3 + 2R_4 + 2R_5 + R_6 \qquad (105)$$

In order to get the cost function in terms of the auxiliary variables, we substitute into equation (104) the auxiliary variables as given by equation (96). In order to simplify matters further, we use the actual numerical values for the inventory costs and replace q by 16. We also replace the constant C by its value of 478. With the aid of these values, we get for the inventory carrying cost the following formula:

$$z_I = 88v_1 + 88w_1 + 72v_2 + 72w_2 + 56v_3 + 56w_3 + 40v_4$$
$$+ 40w_4 + 24v_5 + 24w_5 + 8v_6 + 8w_6 + 96u_0 - 3824 \quad (106)$$

In order to get the combined production and inventory cost, we have to add together equations (99) and (106). Their sum is given by the following formula:

$$z = 188v_1 + 208w_1 + 172v_2 + 192w_2 + 156v_3 + 176w_3 + 140v_4$$
$$+ 160w_4 + 124v_5 + 144w_5 + 108v_6 + 128w_6 + 96u_0 - 3824 \quad (107)$$

Next we propose to use a sequence of priorities by arranging the terms in order of increasing costs. For this reason, we write equation (107) in the following form:

$$z = 108v_6 + 124v_5 + 128w_6 + 140v_4 + 144w_5 + 156v_3 + 160w_4$$
$$+ 172v_2 + 176w_3 + 188v_1 + 192w_2 + 208w_1 + 96u_0 - 3824 \quad (108)$$

We can express this sequence of priorities by saying that combined production and inventory costs progressively increase according to the following sequence:

Day shift in production period 6
Day shift in production period 5
Night shift in production period 6
Day shift in production period 4
Night shift in production period 5
Day shift in production period 3
Night shift in production period 4
Day shift in production period
Night shift in production period 3
Day shift in production period 1
Night shift in production period 2
Night shift in production period 1

Now we propose to solve our problem through a step by step process by steadily decreasing the initial inventory u_0. Let us first assume that the initial inventory level is 108 units. Under this condition, of course, we do not have to produce anything, and our costs are exclusively inventory carrying costs. These costs can be computed as

$$z = 96(108) - 3824 = 6544 \qquad (109)$$

Let us suppose now that the initial inventory level is between 100 and 108 units. The cheapest way to make these 8 units available, according to our priority list, is to produce these 8 units during the day shift in the sixth production period. Using equation (108) to express the combined production and inventory cost, we get for the total cost

$$z = 108v_6 + 96u_0 - 3824 \qquad (110)$$

However, v_6, the quantity of units to be produced, is given by the difference between the total requirements of 108 and the initial inventory level of u_0, or

$$v_6 = 108 - u_0 \qquad (111)$$

Consequently, combined production and inventory costs are given by

$$z = 108(108 - u_0) + 96u_0 - 3824 = 7840 - 12u_0 \qquad (112)$$

We see, then, that we have the solution to the problem as long as the initial inventory level is between 100 and 108.

Let us assume now that the initial inventory is between 85 and 100 units or

$$85 \leq u_0 \leq 100 \qquad (113)$$

Under this condition we should produce 8 units during the day shift in the sixth production period. The rest of the units (fewer than 15)

TABLE 2. A Problem in Production and Inventory Control[a]

	v_1	w_1	v_2	w_2	v_3	w_3	v_4	w_4	v_5	w_5	v_6	w_6	z
$100 \le u_0 \le 108$										0	$108-u_0$	0	$7{,}840-12u_0$
$85 \le u_0 \le 100$									$100-u_0$	0	8	0	$9{,}440-28u_0$
$70 \le u_0 \le 85$							$85-u_0$	0	15	0	8	0	$10{,}800-44u_0$
$55 \le u_0 \le 70$							15	0	15	$70-u_0$	8	0	$11{,}080-48u_0$
$40 \le u_0 \le 55$					$55-u_0$	0	15	0	15	15	8	0	$11{,}740-60u_0$
$25 \le u_0 \le 40$					15	0	15	$40-u_0$	15	15	8	0	$11{,}900-64u_0$
$10 \le u_0 \le 25$			$25-u_0$	0	15	0	15	15	15	15	8	0	$12{,}200-76u_0$
$5 \le u_0 \le 10$			15	0	15	$10-u_0$	15	15	15	15	8	0	$12{,}240-80u_0$
$0 \le u_0 \le 5$	$5-u_0$	0	15	0		5					8	0	$12{,}300-92u_0$

[a] The left-hand column shows the initial inventory level. The following 12 columns show production in each production period. The last column shows combined production and inventory cost.

we should produce during the day shift in the fifth production period, as this is the second cheapest method according to our priority list. Therefore, we get

$$v_5 = 100 - u_0 \tag{114}$$

Using our formula for combined production and inventory costs, we get the total cost under this condition as

$$z = 108(8) + 124(100 - u_0) + 96u_0 - 3824 = 9440 - 28u_0 \tag{115}$$

We see, then, that we can solve the problem as long as initial inventory level is more than 85 units.

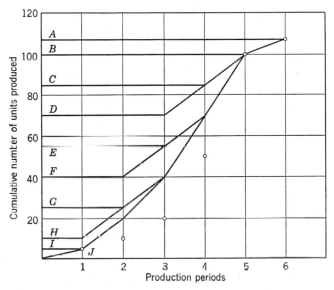

FIG. 10. A problem in production and inventory control. To each level of initial inventory the corresponding optimum production plan is shown.

The next step is to solve the problem when the initial inventory is between 70 and 85 units. As the method of solution is exactly the same, we leave the details to the reader. In Table 2 we show a summary of what the various steps are, and what the combined production and inventory costs are, in each of these cases. A graphical representation of the allocation of production for each of the initial inventory levels is shown in Fig. 10. Figure 11 shows the combined production and inventory costs as functions of the various initial inventory levels.

We note that the combined production and inventory cost for the optimum solution is \$12,300 when we start with no initial inventory. We recall (Chapter 3, Section 9) that the minimum night shift plan has a cost of $12,500, whereas the minimum inventory plan has a cost of $12,340. It is seen, then, that our new solution is better by $40 than the minimum inventory plan.

Let us compare our new plan shown by the bottom line in Fig. 10, with the minimum inventory plan shown in Fig. 4 of Chapter 3. The difference between the two plans is that in the best plan we produce 15 units in the second period and 20 units in the third period, whereas in the minimum inventory plan we produce 5 units in the second period

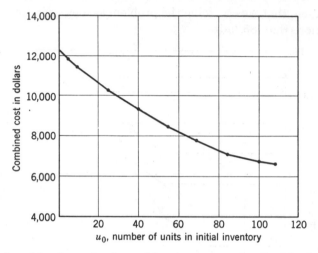

FIG. 11. A problem in production and inventory control. Combined production and inventory costs for various initial inventory levels are shown.

and 30 units in the third period. The best plan involves less cost, because it is cheaper to produce the additional 10 units in the second period and carry it in inventory than to produce these 10 units in the third period during the night shift.

It is obvious, then, that this problem in production and inventory can be solved with the methods developed in this chapter. It is interesting to note that we had to solve the problem for various initial inventory levels in order to obtain the solution for the case when there is no initial inventory.

CHAPTER 8

DYNAMIC PROGRAMMING

1. DISTRIBUTION OF SALES EFFORT BETWEEN VARIOUS MARKETING AREAS

In Section 3 of Chapter 7 we developed a method to solve the problem of distribution of effort, provided the payoff functions were convex. We propose now to develop a general method which is independent of the nature of the payoff functions.

In order to simplify matters let us start with a simple problem, where our firm has only two marketing areas to consider and the problem is to distribute a given number of salesmen between these two marketing areas. The profit for each of these marketing areas is given as a function of the sales effort expended, as shown in Fig. 1 and Fig. 2. For instance, it can be seen in Fig. 1 that if 7 salesmen are assigned to the first marketing area a profit of \$96,000 results. Figure 1 also shows that, if more than 8 salesmen are assigned to this marketing area, then profits will actually go down. This is so because if more than 8 salesmen work in the area they do not get more sales, but they all have to be paid, and so the net profit for the corporation will go down. As a matter of fact, the situation could conceivably arise where too many salesmen antagonize the customers and sales even drop.

The problem here is to distribute a given number of salesmen between the two marketing areas so that the profit will become maximum. We will use $f_1(x)$ to denote profit in the first marketing area if x number of salesmen are employed in this area, and $f_2(x)$ to denote profit in the second marketing area if x number of salesmen are employed there.

As an illustration, let us suppose that the corporation has 6 salesmen, and the problem is to allocate these 6 salesmen so that profit will

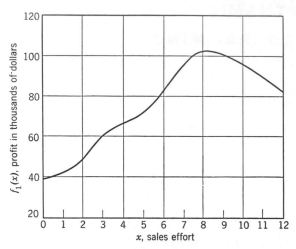

FIG. 1.   Profit for first marketing area as function of sales effort.

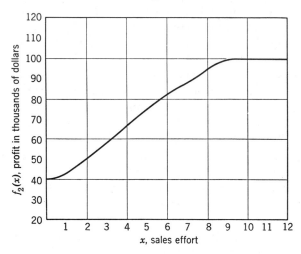

FIG. 2.   Profit for second marketing area as function of sales effort.

be maximum.   There are only seven possibilities: we can allocate no salesmen to area 1 and 6 salesmen to area 2; we can allocate 1 salesman to area 1 and 5 salesmen to area 2; etc.   Therefore, we can prepare the table shown.

x_1	0	1	2	3	4	5	6	
x_2	6	5	4	3	2	1	0	
$f(x_1)$	38	41	48	58	66	72	83	In thousands
$f(x_2)$	82	75	66	60	50	42	40	of dollars
z	120	116	114	118	116	114	123	

The last row shows the profit realized corresponding to each of the seven allocation schemes. It can be seen that the best allocation is to assign all of the 6 salesmen to the first area and no salesmen to the second area, because this results in maximum profit of $123,000. To use our mathematical notation, we can say that the method of obtaining the best allocation is the selection of the largest of the following seven numbers:

$$[f_1(0) + f_2(6)], [f_1(1) + f_2(5)], [f_1(2) + f_2(4)], [f_1(3) + f_2(3)],$$

$$[f_1(4) + f_2(2)], [f_1(5) + f_2(1)], [f_1(6) + f_2(0)]$$

A simpler way to express this maximum profit z is

$$z = \max_{0 \le x \le 6} [f_1(x) + f_2(6 - x)] \qquad (1)$$

Let us now denote by $F(A)$ the maximum profit that can be realized if A salesmen are allocated (the optimum fashion) between the two marketing areas. Then we can write equation (1) as

$$F(6) = \max_{0 \le x \le 6} [f_1(x) + f_2(6 - x)] \qquad (2)$$

We can proceed now to determine the maximum profit for 1, 2, 3, · · · 12 salesmen; in fact we can determine the profit $F(A)$ for any number of salesmen. A somewhat simpler procedure is shown in Table 1, where the profit is computed by assuming that a certain number of salesmen are assigned to the first area, and that a certain number are assigned to the second area. For instance, it can be seen that, if 3 salesmen are assigned to the first area and 2 salesmen to the second area, then the profit realized will be $110,000. Now observe the diagonals (Table 1), as along these diagonals the combined number of salesmen assigned to the two areas is the same. For instance, if we assign 4 salesmen between the two areas we read along the diagonal the following numbers: 104, 99, 98, 102, 106. We see, then, that the best way to allocate these 4 salesmen is to allocate them all to the first marketing area; the profit in this case is $106,000. Therefore,

TABLE 1. Optimum Distribution of Sales Effort Between Two Marketing Areas[a]

Profit in thousands of dollars

Number of Salesmen in Second Area	Profit	Number of Salesmen in First Area → 0	1	2	3	4	5	6	7	8	9	10	11	12
		38	41	48	60	66	72	83	96	102	100	95	89	82
0	40	78*	81*	88*	100*	106*	112	123*	136*	142*	140	135	129	122
1	42	80	83	90	102	108	114	125	138	144	142	137	131	
2	50	88	91	98	110	116	122	133	146*	152	150	145		
3	58	96	99	106	118	124	130	141	154*	160	158			
4	66	104	107	114	126	132	138	149	162*	168				
5	75	113*	116	123	135	141	147	158	171*					
6	82	120	123	130	142	148	154	165						
7	88	126	129	136	148	154	160							
8	95	133	136	143	155	161								
9	99	137	140	147	159									
10	100	138	141	148										
11	100	138	141											
12	100	138												

[a] The numbers marked with asterisks are the maxima along each diagonal.

by using a table of this kind we can determine $F(A)$, which is the maximum profit realizable if a combined number of A salesmen are assigned to the two marketing areas. Mathematically speaking, we have described here a method of determining $F(A)$ from the equation

$$F(A) = \max_{0 \le x \le A} [f_1(x) + f_2(A - x)] \tag{3}$$

$F(A)$ can be represented either in a tabular form or can be plotted as shown in Fig. 3.

Thus, as long as we deal with two marketing areas, we can solve the distribution of effort problem, irrespective of the shape of profit functions.   Let us suppose, now that there are three marketing areas

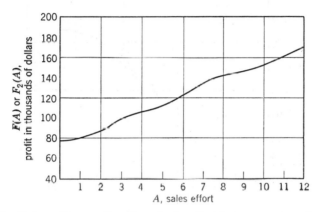

FIG. 3.   Profit for optimum allocation of sales effort between two marketing areas.

to consider.   The profit as a function of sales effort for the third marketing area is shown in Fig. 4.   How should we solve the problem in this more complicated case?   A simple trial and error computation shows that 6 salesmen can be allocated 21 different ways and 12 salesmen can be allocated 78 ways.   As we are trying to develop a general method of solving the problem, so that not only three or four but any number of marketing areas can be considered, it is obvious that the method of preparing tables for all possible cases leads to an enormous amount of computation.

Mathematically speaking, the problem is to obtain the maximum profit as represented by

$$z = \max [f_1(x_1) + f_2(x_2) + f_3(x_3) + \cdots f_N(x_N)] \tag{4}$$

where N, the number of terms on the right-hand side, relates to the number of marketing areas to be considered.

In order to obtain a solution to this problem, we propose to consider the situation from a somewhat different point of view. Suppose we want to solve the problem of allocating 6 salesmen to three marketing areas, with the proviso *that we are allocating 2 salesmen to the first two areas and the rest (that is, the 4 salesmen that remain) to the third marketing area.* What is the best possible profit that can be realized in this special problem?

The best profit that can be obtained by using 2 salesmen in the first and second marketing area is given by $F(2)$, and the profit from allocating 4 salesmen to the third area is, of course, $f_3(4)$. Therefore, we

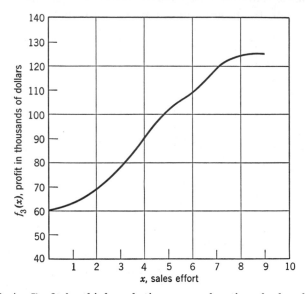

FIG. 4.   Profit for third marketing area as function of sales effort.

can say that the best profit for this particular problem is given by

$$z = F(2) + f_3(4) \tag{5}$$

However, there is no good reason to allocate exactly 2 salesmen to the first two areas, and so we abandon this assumption. We should try to allocate 0 salesman, 1 salesman, 2 salesmen, etc., to the first two marketing areas. Therefore it can be seen that our problem is to select the largest of the following seven numbers:

$$[F(0) + f_3(6)], [F(1) + f_3(5)], [F(2) + f_3(4)], [F(3) + f_3(3)],$$
$$[F(4) + f_3(2)], [F(5) + f_3(1)], [F(6) + f_3(0)] \tag{6}$$

Mathematically speaking, we see that we can solve the problem of the three marketing areas by evaluating the right-hand side of the following equation:

$$z = \max_{0 \leq x \leq A} [F(x) + f_3(A - x)] \tag{7}$$

Now we propose to introduce a new notation.   Let us denote by $F_2(A)$ the best profit that can be realized by allocating A number of salesmen between the first two marketing areas.   (The subscript 2 reminds us that we are dealing with *two* marketing areas.)   This is the same function that we denoted by $F(A)$ before, and we recall that, according to equation (3), this function is given by the following equation:

$$F_2(A) = \max_{0 \leq x \leq A} [f_1(x) + f_2(A - x)] \tag{8}$$

Let us now denote by $F_3(A)$ the best profit that can be realized by allocating A number of salesmen between the three marketing areas. With this notation, then, equation (7) changes into the following:

$$F_3(A) = \max_{0 \leq x \leq A} [F_2(A) + f_3(A - x)] \tag{9}$$

It can be seen, then, that the problem with three marketing areas can be solved in exactly the same fashion as the problem for the two marketing areas.   We present Table 2 to show the method of solution. The top row shows the combined number of salesmen that are allocated to the first and second area; the second row shows the maximum profit that can be realized by allocating the salesmen between the first two areas in the best possible fashion.   (In other words, the second row is $F_2(A)$.   The first column on the left-hand side shows the number of salesmen allocated to the third marketing area, and the next column shows the profit that can be realized by allocating these salesmen to the third area.   The table itself shows the combined profit.   What we have to do again is to follow the diagonals and select the maximum value.   In Table 2 these maxima are shown by asterisks.   Figure 5 shows a graphical representation of $F_3(A)$, or the best profit that can be realized when considering three marketing areas.

The problem of four marketing areas represents nothing new as we can simply write

$$F_4(A) = \max_{0 \leq x \leq A} [F_3(A) + f_4(A - x)] \tag{10}$$

This problem can be solved again by preparing an appropriate table.

Mathematically speaking, the problem is to solve the following equation:

$$z = \max_{x_1 + x_2 + \cdots + x_N = A} [f_1(x_1) + f_2(x_2) + \cdots + f_N(x_N)] \tag{11}$$

TABLE 2. Optimum Distribution of Sales Effort for Three Marketing Areas[a]

		Combined Number of Salesmen in First and Second Area												
		0	1	2	3	4	5	6	7	8	9	10	11	12
		78	81	88	100	106	113	123	136	142	146	154	162	171
0	60	138	141	148*	160*	166	173	183	196	202*	206	214	222	231
1	64	142*	145	152	164	170	177	187	200	206	210	218	226	
2	68	146	149	156	168	174	181	191	204	210	214	222		
3	78	156	159	166	178	184	191	201	214	220	224			
4	90	168*	171	178	190	196	203	213	226*	232				
5	102	180*	183	190	202*	208	215*	225	238*					
6	109	187*	190	197	209*	215*	222	232						
7	119	197*	200	207	219	225	232							
8	124	202*	205	212	224	230								
9	125	203	206	113	225									
10	125	203	206	113										
11	125	203	206											
12	125	203												

Number of Salesmen in Third Area

Profit in thousands of dollars

[a] The numbers marked with asterisks are the maxima along each diagonal.

which is the same as (4) but the side condition is stated explicitly here. The method of solution is to obtain $F_2(A)$ from equation (8), $F_3(A)$ from equation (9), $F_4(A)$ from equation (10), etc. In general, for any number of marketing areas, we obtain the solution from

$$F_n(A) = \max_{0 \leq x \leq A} [F_{n-1}(A) + f_n(A - x)] \qquad n = 2, 3, \cdots \quad (12)$$

In the mathematical literature such a method of solution is called an *algorithm*. Solution with the aid of an algorithm means that the solution is not obtained at once, but is obtained step by step, and in each

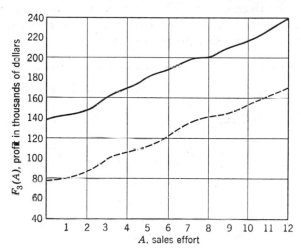

FIG. 5. Profit for optimum allocation of sales effort for three marketing areas. (The dotted line shows the maximum profit when the salesmen are allocated to the first two areas.)

step the results obtained in the preceding steps are utilized. The first step is to obtain the solution when there are two marketing areas; this solution can be obtained with the aid of a table. Then step by step more tables are built up and the solutions successively obtained.

2. A WAREHOUSING PROBLEM

A hypothetical firm is operating a single warehouse and distributes a single product from this warehouse. We will assume that this product can be purchased and sold in any quantity, but that there are fluctuations in its purchasing cost and selling price. We will further assume that the cost and profit structure is complicated by matters of discount and competition.   Let us suppose that the firm is making plans for the next five months, and trying to decide how much to purchase and sell in each month.   We will assume that both the cost and sales price for each of these five months is known in advance.

We will represent the purchase and sales policy in a graphical fashion as shown in Fig. 6.   The inventory level at the beginning of the first period is u_0.   A certain quantity at the beginning of the month is bought (B.) and then a certain quantity is sold (S.).   This leads us to an inventory level of u_1 at the beginning of the second period.   The policy at the beginning of the second period is "not to buy" which is denoted in the diagram by N.B.   The further policy is the "sell" in the second period, which is denoted by S.   This leads to the inventory level of u_2 at the beginning of the third period.

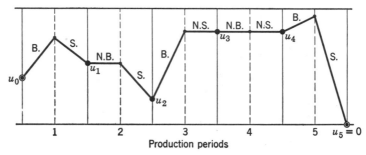

FIG. 6.   Warehousing problem.   The vertical coordinate shows quantities bought (B.) and sold (S.). u_i denotes the inventory level at the end of the ith production period.

We assume that the initial inventory level u_0 is given, and that, at the end of the fifth period (that is, at the end of the planning horizon), everything will be sold and the inventory level will be zero.   We can visualize the problem, then, by imagining a string placed between the point u_0 at the beginning and the zero point at the end of the fifth period.   The string must lie between the two parallel lines, as we cannot purchase more than the capacity of the warehouse, and, of course, we cannot sell below the zero level.   The problem we propose to solve is what is the best way to place the string between the two end anchors such that a maximum total profit for the five periods results.

Let us proceed to put this problem into mathematical form.   For simplicity, let us assume that the capacity of the warehouse is unity. To put it another way, we assume that the quantity of goods stored in the warehouse is measured in units of the capacity of the warehouse. Let us denote by x_1 the quantity of goods purchased in the first month.

Then we must have

$$u_0 + x_1 \leq 1 \qquad (13)$$

or otherwise the goods purchased could not be stored.   Let us denote by y_1 the quantity sold in the first month.   The inventory at the end of the first period (or at the beginning of the second period) is given by

$$u_1 = u_0 + x_1 - y_1 \qquad (14)$$

This, of course, must be a positive number as we cannot sell more than we have at hand.   We can put this into mathematical form by writing

$$u_0 + x_1 - y_1 \geq 0 \qquad (15)$$

The next thing is to introduce the cost and price function: we denote by $f_1(x_1)$ the cost of purchasing x_1 units of goods in the first month, and by $g_1(y_1)$ the revenue obtained by selling y_1 quantity of goods.   With this notation, the profit for the first month is given by

$$z_1 = g_1(y_1) - f_1(x_1) \qquad (16)$$

Similar equations can be developed for each of the five months. We can never buy more than the capacity of the warehouse allows, so

$$u_{n-1} + x_n \leq 1 \qquad n = 1, 2, \cdots, 5 \qquad (17)$$

which is the generalization of equation (13).   Furthermore, we cannot sell more goods than we have; that is, we must always have a positive inventory, and so we have

$$u_n = u_{n-1} + x_n - y_n \geq 0 \qquad n = 1, 2, \cdots, 5 \qquad (18)$$

which is a generalization of equations (14) and (15).   The profit for the five months can be written in the form

$$z = \sum_1^5 [g_n(y_n) - f_n(x_n)] \qquad (19)$$

The problem, mathematically speaking, is to maximize the profit as given by equation (19) under the restrictions of equations (17) and (18).   We also have to assume that the initial and final inventories are given; and, in particular, we will assume that the initial inventory u_0 is given, but that the final inventory u_5 is zero.

Before we solve this problem for any general cost functions $f(x)$ and price functions $g(y)$, we are going to solve the problem for a simple case when each of these functions can be represented by straight lines. More specifically, we will assume that in the first month the purchase price for each unit of goods is \$8, and that the sales price is \$12.

Furthermore, in the second month the purchase price is assumed to be $20 and the sales price $14, and so on, as shown in the table.

Month	1	2	3	4	5
Purchase price	8	20	6	9	13
Sales price	12	14	10	6	11

Mathematically speaking, we can say that the profit function as shown in equation (19) is replaced by the following:

$$z = 12y_1 + 14y_2 + 10y_3 + 6y_4 + 11y_5$$
$$- 8x_1 - 20x_2 - 6x_3 - 9x_4 - 13x_5 \qquad (20)$$

The problem of maximizing the profit as given by equation (20) under the restrictions of (17) and (18) is a problem in linear programming and, therefore, could be solved with the simplex method. However, our general problem, as expressed by the profit function of equation (19), is not a problem of linear programming. As we are to develop a general method of solution, we shall not use the simplex method, even in the linear case, but develop a direct method of solution of the problem.

We solve this problem by working backwards, starting from the fifth production period. We assume that the inventory level at the beginning of the fifth month u_4 is given. Then we ask the question, "what is the best policy that will result in the maximum profit?" We recognize that the purchase price is $13 for each unit, whereas the sales price is $11. Therefore, the best thing to do is not to buy any new units but to sell whatever is at hand. As we have u_4 number of units and we get $11 for each unit, the best profit that can be realized is given by

$$z = 11u_4 \qquad (21)$$

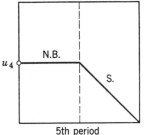

5th period

We call $F_1(u_4)$ the maximum profit that can be realized during the last month, provided the inventory level at the beginning of the last month is u_4. Then, we have

$$F_1(u_4) = 11u_4 \qquad (22)$$

From the point of view of our string analogy, we can see that the string is anchored on the left-hand side on the level of u_4, then stretched horizontally to the middle of the diagram where the sales representation starts, and finally stretched to the bottom of the right-hand side.

Let us now suppose that we restrict ourselves to the last two months, the fourth and fifth months. For the moment let us assume that the inventory levels at the beginning of both the fourth and fifth periods are given, which means that both u_3 and u_4 are given. What is the best policy that we can follow? In the fourth period the purchase price is \$9 and the sales price is \$6, which means that purchasing and selling in the fourth period is a losing proposition. In other words, we should buy only if we have to, and should sell as much as possible. In order to get an answer to our problem, we need to consider two cases.

First Hypothesis (Fourth Period)

Let us assume that u_3 is less than (or equal to) u_4 as shown by the lower line on the diagram. The best thing to do here is to buy up to the level of u_4 and then not sell anything. If we bought more than necessary and sold it, we would suffer an avoidable loss in the trans-actions. Therefore, we can say that the profit in the fourth period is given by

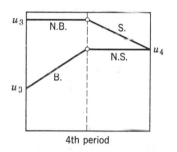

4th period

$$z = -9(u_4 - u_3) \qquad (23)$$

(It is recognized that u_3 is less u_4. There-fore, this is a loss or a negative profit.) We have now an inventory level of u_4 at the beginning of the fifth period. The best profit that can be realized from this inventory level is $F_1(u_4)$, according to our previous discussion. Therefore, we can say that the best profit that can be realized in the fourth and fifth period is given by the equation

$$z = -9(u_4 - u_3) + F_1(u_4) \qquad (24)$$

or by

$$z = 2u_4 + 9u_3 \qquad (25)$$

where it is again assumed that both u_3 and u_4 are given. Let us sup-pose, however, that only u_3 is given, but that u_4 can be varied; what would be the maximum profit then? Inspecting equation (25) we see that we should make u_4 just as large as possible. As we cannot make it more than the capacity of the warehouse, which is assumed to be unity, we conclude that u_4 should be made equal to 1, and then we get the highest profit possibility as

$$z = 2 + 9u_3 \qquad (26)$$

Second Hypothesis (Fourth Period)

Let us assume now that u_3 is larger (or equal to) u_4, as shown by the upper line in the preceding diagram. In this case, the best policy is not to buy anything but sell out so that the inventory gets down to the level of u_4 as specified. Under this condition, the profit in the fourth period is given by

$$z = 6(u_3 - u_4) \tag{27}$$

The maximum profit that can be realized in the fourth and fifth period is given by the formula

$$z = 6(u_3 - u_4) + F_1(u_4) = 5u_4 + 6u_3 \tag{28}$$

Let us assume, now, that only u_3 is given, but that u_4 can be changed. What is the value of u_4 that gives the maximum profit? Obviously, we should make u_4 as large as possible. However, according to our second hypothesis, u_4 cannot be more than u_3. Therefore, the maximum profit is obtained when u_4 equals u_3, in which case equation (28) becomes

$$z = 11u_3 \tag{29}$$

We see, then, that under the first hypothesis the best profit is given by equation (26), whereas under the second hypothesis the best profit is given by equation (29). Let us recognize now that u_3 is always less than the capacity, which means that u_3 is always less than unity. This means that the maximum profit under the first hypothesis is higher than the maximum profit under the second hypothesis. Consequently, if we assume that the inventory level at the beginning of the fourth month, that is, u_3, is given and that we are at liberty to select u_4, we should always select the first hypothesis.

In order to put our result into a mathematical form, let us denote by $F_2(u_3)$ the maximum profit that can be realized during the last two months of our planning horizon, under the assumption that the initial inventory at the beginning of the fourth month is given by u_3. (The subscript 2 reminds us that we are dealing with two months.) Then, we have shown that this maximum profit is given by

$$F_2(u_3) = 2 + 9u_3 \tag{30}$$

We can summarize matters, then, as shown in Fig. 7 in row B. The best policy, if only the last two months are considered, is to buy up to capacity and not sell anything in the fourth month, and not buy anything but sell everything in the fifth month.

Let us proceed now to the case where the last three months, that is, the third, fourth, and fifth months, are considered. We again assume that the inventory level u_3, at the beginning of the fourth month, is given. It is recognized that the third month is a profitable one as the

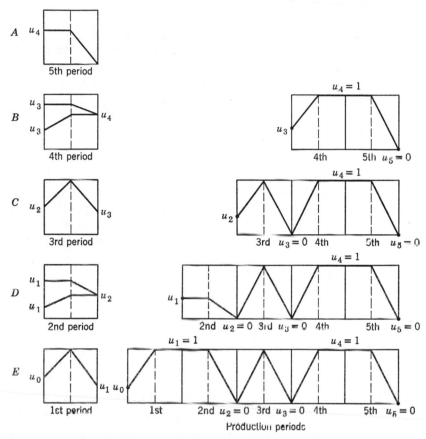

FIG. 7. Development of optimum policy for warehousing problem. Row E shows that the optimum policy is: buy and not sell; not buy and sell; buy and sell; buy and not sell; not buy and sell.

purchase price is $6, but the sales price is $10. Consequently, the best policy is to purchase up to the capacity of the warehouse and then sell down to the specified inventory level of u_3. The profit under these conditions in the third month is given by

$$z = -6(1 - u_2) + 10(1 - u_3) \tag{31}$$

Now we assume that we start at the fourth month with the inventory level of u_3, and that we follow the best possible policy. Under this condition, the combined profit for the third, fourth, and fifth months is given by

$$z = 4 + 6u_2 - 10u_3 + F_2(u_3) = 4 + 6u_2 - 10u_3 + 2 + 9u_3$$
$$= 6 + 6u_2 - u_3 \quad (32)$$

Let us assume that u_2, the inventory level at the beginning of the third month, is given, and that we are at liberty to change u_3. What value of u_3 gives the maximum profit? As u_3 appears with a negative sign in equation (32), we should make u_3 as small as possible, that is, we should sell everything in the third month and so make $u_3 = 0$. Putting this value into equation (32) we get the profit when the last three months are considered:

$$F_3(u_2) = 6 + 6u_2 \quad (33)$$

In Fig. 7, row C, shows graphically the best policy.

Let us consider now the last four months, that is, the second, third, fourth, and fifth months. During the second month the purchase price is $20 and the sales price is $14, so this month represents a losing proposition. Let us now consider the problem under two hypothesis.

First Hypothesis (Second Period)

We will assume that u_1 is larger than (or equal to) u_2, (Fig. 7, row D, left-hand side.) The best policy under these conditions is not to buy any goods but to sell down to the level of u_2. Under this policy, the profit in the second month is given by

$$z = 14(u_1 - u_2) \quad (34)$$

Again we assume that, in the last three months, the best policy is used. Then we get for the combined profit in the four months

$$z = 14(u_1 - u_2) + F_3(u_2) = 14u_1 - 8u_2 + 6 \quad (35)$$

What value of u_2 should we select to get the maximum profit? As u_2 again appears with a negative sign, the best thing is to make it equal zero, in which case we get the profit

$$z = 14u_1 + 6 \quad (36)$$

Second Hypothesis (Second Period)

Let us assume that u_1 is less than (or equal to) u_2 (Fig. 7, row D, the lower line on the left-hand side.) Following the method we used previously, we can develop the profit for the last four periods as

$$z = -20(u_2 - u_1) + F_3(u_2) = 20u_1 - 14u_2 + 6 \qquad (37)$$

This becomes the largest when u_2 becomes the smallest.   However, u_2 cannot be less than u_1, under this hypothesis, and so we get for the best profit the expression

$$z = 6u_1 + 6 \qquad (38)$$

When comparing the profit as expressed by equation (38) with the profit expressed by equation (36), we conclude that the first hypothesis results in a higher profit.   This means, then, that the best policy in the second period is not to buy any goods.   The combined profit of the last four months is given by

$$F_4(u_1) = 14u_1 + 6 \qquad (39)$$

Let us finally consider all five months of the planning horizon.   The first month is profitable, and, therefore, the best policy is to buy up to capacity and then sell down to the specified inventory level of u_1. Consequently, the profit in the first months is given by

$$z = -8(1 - u_0) + 12(1 - u_1)$$
$$= 4 + 8u_0 - 12u_1 \qquad (40)$$

In order to get the combined profit from all five months, we have to utilize the inventory of u_1 at the beginning of the second period, according to the best policy.   This results in a combined profit of

$$z = 4 + 8u_0 - 12u_1 + F_4(u_1) = 10 + 8u_0 + 2u_1 \qquad (41)$$

What value of u_1 should be select to make this profit the highest? Clearly, we should make u_1 as large as possible, which means that we should buy up the capacity; that is, we should make u_1 equal to one. This results in the formula

$$F_5(u_0) = 12 + 8u_0 \qquad (42)$$

which is, then, the best profit that can be realized in all the five months, providing that the initial inventory of u_0 is given at the beginning of the planning horizon.

In Fig. 7, row F, this final policy of obtaining maximum profit is represented graphically.   It can be seen that the best policy is the following: During the first period we should purchase to capacity and not sell anything; during the second period we should not buy but sell out everything; during the third period we should buy up to capacity and sell everything; during the fourth period we should buy up to capacity and not sell anything; and, finally, during the fifth period we should not buy anything but sell out everything at hand.

Let us return now to our general problem when the cost and price functions are not straight lines but are expressed by equation (19). How should we go about solving this problem? First of all, we introduce an additional mathematical notation. Let us denote by v_1, v_2, $\cdot$ $\cdot$ $\cdot$, v_5 the inventory level in the first, second, third, fourth, and fifth months *after* a purchase is made. In our geometrical representation this means that these symbols represent the middle points of the string that is stretched across between the parallel lines. The inventory level in the middle of a month is given by taking the initial inventory level and adding to it the purchased quantity or

$$v_n = u_{n-1} + x_n \qquad (43)$$

We must again work backwards. Let us denote again by $F_1(u_1)$, $F_2(u_2)$, $\cdot$ $\cdot$ $\cdot$, $F_5(u_5)$ the maximum profit that can be realized during the last month; during the last two months; during the last three months, etc. Furthemore, we introduce a new series of functions $G_1(v_1)$, $G_2(v_2)$, $\cdot$ $\cdot$ $\cdot$, $G_5(v_5)$, where each of these represent the maximum profit that can be realized, provided we start our study after the purchase in the particular month is already effected. This means that $G_1(v_5)$ is the maximum profit that can be realized in the fifth month by selling the quantity of v_5 units of goods. This is given by

$$G_1(v_5) = g_5(v_5) \qquad (44)$$

as the highest profit is obtained when everything is sold. Similarly, $G_2(v_4)$ denotes the maximum profit that can be realized during the fourth and fifth months provided that in the middle of the fourth month we have an inventory level of v_4.

Let us now ask the question, "What is the best profit that can be realized in the fifth month if we start this month with an initial inventory of u_4?" Suppose we buy a quantity of x_5 and then we sell everything. The profit in this last month is

$$z = G_1(u_4 + x_5) - f_5(x_5) \qquad (45)$$

We can now compute a table on the basis of equation (45) for various values of the initial inventory u_4 and purchase quantity x_5, and we can select the maximum profit that is obtained by the best selection of x_5. This way, then, we can obtain the maximum profit that is realizable in the fifth month, if the initial inventory of u_4 is specified. Mathematically speaking, we say that the maximum profit in the fifth month is given by

$$F_1(u_4) = \max_{0 \le x_5 \le 1 - u_4} [G_1(u_4 + x_5) - f_5(x_5)] \qquad (46)$$

It is seen, then, that the optimum profit for the fifth month can be determined by developing a table similar to the one used in Section 1 in relation to the sales distribution problem.

Let us proceed now to determine $G_2(v_4)$, that is, the maximum profit that can be realized using the fourth and fifth months, but assuming that a purchase has already been made in the fourth month and that we have an inventory of v_4. We have to make a decision of how much to sell in the fourth month. Let this quantity be denoted by y_4. Then, the combined profit is given by

$$z = g_4(y_4) + F_1(v_4 - y_4) \qquad (47)$$

where it is assumed that the inventory of $(v_4 - y_4)$ at the beginning of the fifth month is followed by the best possible policy in the fifth month. We are to select y_4, the quantity sold in the fourth period, such that this combined profit becomes a maximum. Mathematically speaking, we get this maximum profit with the aid of the formula

$$G_2(v_4) = \max_{0 \le y_4 \le v_4} [g_4(y_4) + F_1(v_4 - y_4)] \qquad (48)$$

We can see, then, that $G_2(v_4)$ can be determined by developing an appropriate table, just the same way as done previously.

The function $F_2(u_3)$ is determined again by developing a table on the basis of the formula

$$F_2(u_3) = \max_{0 \le x_4 \le 1 - u_3} [G_2(u_3 + x_4) - f_4(x_4)] \qquad (49)$$

Similarly, $G_3(v_3)$, $F_3(u_2)$ are both obtained from the equations

$$G_3(v_3) = \max_{0 \le y_3 \le v_3} [g_3(y_3) + F_2(v_3 - y_3)] \qquad (50)$$

$$F_3(u_2) = \max_{0 \le x_3 \le 1 - u_2} [G_3(u_2 + x_3) - f_3(x_3)] \qquad (51)$$

We see, then, that in just the same way as we did in the sales distribution problem we can develop here a step by step process, or an algorithm.

Finally we wish to mention that, if the cost functions $f(x)$ are convex from above and the price functions $g(y)$ are convex from below, then this profit expression (19) becomes a convex function from below and the problem becomes a convex programming problem. As we have seen in Chapter 7, such a problem can be transformed into a linear programming problem and solved as such. However, we believe that the direct solution outlined here is less laborious from the computational point of view.

3. A PROBLEM IN PRODUCTION AND INVENTORY CONTROL

We return now to the problem introduced in Section 9 of Chapter 3 (p. 79) and recall that we developed a solution in Section 5, Chapter 7 (p. 213), that was satisfactory provided the cost functions were convex from below. We will now develop a general method which gives a solution irrespective of whether the cost function is convex or not.

We develop our solution to this problem by working backwards in the production periods. Let us first consider only the fifth and six production periods, and let the inventory at the beginning of the fifth production period be denoted by u_4. Let us answer the question, "What is the best production plan in the fifth and sixth production period?   Let us assume that we produce x_5 units in the fifth production period and x_6 units in the sixth or final production period.   In order to meet the requirement of 50 in the fifth production period, we must have

$$u_4 + x_5 \geq 50 \qquad (52)$$

In order to meet the combined requirements of 58 units, we must have

$$x_6 = 58 - x_5 - u_4 \qquad (53)$$

The combined production cost for these two periods is given by

$$z_P = f(x_5) + f(58 - x_5 - u_4) \qquad (54)$$

and the combined inventory cost is given by

$$z_I = \tfrac{1}{2}q[u_4 + (u_4 + x_5 - 50)] + \tfrac{1}{2}q[(u_4 + x_5 - 50) + 0] \qquad (55)$$

The combined production and inventory cost for the last two production periods is given now by adding equations (54) and (55):

$$z = f(x_5) + f(58 - x_5 - u_4) + \tfrac{1}{2}q(3u_4 + 2x_5 - 100) \qquad (56)$$

Assuming that u_4, the initial inventory at the beginning of the fifth production period, is given, what is the best value of x_5, the quantity produced in the fifth production period?   We can develop a table that shows the values of the combined cost, as shown by equation (56), for various values of u_4 and x_5.   Then we can select for each value of u_4 the value of x_5 which gives the minimum cost.   Let us denote this minimum cost (considering only the last two periods) by $F_2(u_4)$, for any value of the initial inventory u_4. (The subscript 2 reminds us that we are considering only two periods.) Mathematically speaking, this function is determined by

$$F_2(u_4) = \min \left[f(x_5) + f(58 - x_5 - u_4) + \tfrac{1}{2}q(3u_4 + 2x_5 - 100) \right] \quad (57)$$

where

$$30 \geq x_5 \geq 50 - u_4 \qquad 50 \geq u_4 \geq 20$$

We will develop this table for only those values of u_4 and x_5 that make sense. If the production capacity for each production period is 30, then we will use values of x_5 that are less than 30. The initial inventory in this case must be more than 20, as otherwise the requirements cannot be met; therefore the table should be prepared only for values of u_4 that are more than 20 but less than 50.

The next step is to consider the last three production periods. We will assume that the initial inventory at the fourth period is u_3. Let us denote the minimum production cost by $F_3(u_3)$. The question is how to determine this $F_3(u_3)$ function. Let us assume that we produce x_4 units in the fourth production period. Then the combined production and inventory costs in the fourth production period are given by

$$z = f(x_4) + \tfrac{1}{2}q[u_3 + (u_3 + x_4 - 30)] \quad (58)$$

as the requirement in the fourth production period is 30 units. We recognize that the inventory level at the beginning of the fifth period is given by $u_3 + x_4 - 30$. We assume, of course, that we will follow an optimum policy in the fifth and sixth period, and we know that the minimum cost in these two production periods will be $F_2(u_3 + x_4 - 30)$. Therefore, we can see that the combined production and inventory costs for these three production periods will be given by

$$z = f(x_4) + \tfrac{1}{2}q(2u_3 + x_4 - 30) + F_2(u_3 + x_4 - 30) \quad (59)$$

Assuming that u_3 is given, what value of x_4 should we select to minimize this cost? The thing to do is to prepare a table representing equation (59) that gives the cost values for various values of x_4 and u_3, then select the minimum possible cost. This table gives us the minimum cost for the last three production periods, $F_3(u_3)$:

$$F_3(u_3) = \min_{x_4 \geq 0} \left[f(x_4) + \tfrac{1}{2}q(2u_3 + x_4 - 30) + F_2(u_3 + x_4 - 30) \right] \quad (60)$$

Using the same argument, we can determine the minimum cost for the last four production periods with the aid of the formula

$$F_4(u_2) = \min_{x_3 > 0} \left[f(x_3) + \tfrac{1}{2}q(2u_2 + x_3 - 10) + F_3(u_2 + x_3 - 10) \right] \quad (61)$$

where it is recognized that the requirement in the fourth period is ten units. Similarly, we get the minimum cost for the last five and the last six production periods as

$$F_5(u_1) = \min_{x_2 \geq 0} \ [f(x_2) + \tfrac{1}{2}q(2u_1 + x_2 - 5) + F_4(u_1 + x_2 - 5)] \quad (62)$$

$$F_6(u_0) = \min_{x_1 \geq 0} \ [f(x_1) + \tfrac{1}{2}q(2u_0 + x_1 - 5) + F_5(u_0 + x_1 - 5)] \quad (63)$$

We see, then, that we have a method which through a step by step sequence of solutions gives the answer to our problem.

In all the problems we have discussed so far, we started at the end of the planning horizon and worked backwards. In these problems this is convenient, but there is another way to work problems and that is to start at the beginning and work toward the end. Which of the two methods is used depends on individual taste and on the detailed nature of the problem. If, for instance, the study is to be continued as the planning horizon is extended into the future, then it is probably better to start at the beginning and work towards the end. On the other hand, with a definitive problem and a fixed period, it might be more convenient to follow the procedure we have used.

An important application of the problem we are discussing here is the consideration of setup costs in a production department. It is recognized that, when articles are produced in production lots, then the production cost is not proportionate to the number of units produced, as there is a certain cost involved in the mere fact that a lot is produced. For instance, the particular machine has to be set up, so the lot can be produced; also certain documents must be prepared to instruct the production department to manufacture the lot. Therefore, in many production situations, the cost of producing x number of units is given by a function $f(x)$, which looks like the graph in Fig. 8. Mathematically speaking, the production cost is zero when we produce nothing, |

$$f(x) = 0 \qquad \text{when } x = 0 \qquad , \qquad (64)$$

and the production cost for more than nothing is given by the function

$$f(x) = s + rx \qquad \text{when } x > 0 \qquad (65)$$

The letter s stands for the cost involved in setting up the machines and the other initial costs, whereas the letter r stands for the cost of producing each of these parts. (This is usually called the run cost.) This cost function $f(x)$ is not convex from above, and, as the problem is to minimize cost, it cannot be considered as a problem in convex programming. However, the method that we developed in this section works irrespective of the nature of the cost functions, and therefore we can develop the solution to the problem. Admittedly, it is quite laborious to obtain solutions by our method. In a manufacturing plant, where there might be thousands of articles produced, it would be

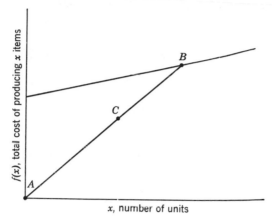

FIG. 8. Cost of production when setup cost is important. Point C does not lie above the line; this function is *not* convex from above.

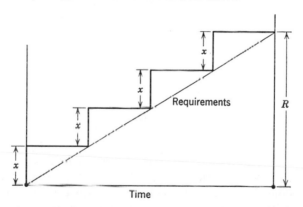

FIG. 9. Graphical representation of production in lots. In each production cycle x number of parts are manufactured. Average inventory level is $x/2$.

impractical to carry out calculations of this sort. Fortunately, there is a short-cut method of solution that works in many practical cases.

We are referring here to the conventional economic lot size study that can be found in many books on production and inventory control. In this case it is assumed, as shown in Fig. 9, that requirements form a straight line and that production is performed in equal lots. The question in this case is how large should these lots be or how many times should lots be produced in each year?   The answer can be found in books on production control, but for the convenience of the reader we will develop the solution for this simple problem.

Let us assume that we produce n times per year and that we produce to meet a total demand of D.   Then we can write

$$nx = D \tag{66}$$

where x denotes the quantity produced at each release.   Production costs are given by

$$z_p = ns + rD \tag{67}$$

From equation (66) we get the value of n

$$n = D/x \tag{68}$$

By substituting the value of n from equation (68) into equation (67), we get

$$z_p = \frac{Ds}{x} + rD \tag{69}$$

We determine now the inventory carrying costs.   Let q denote the yearly cost of carrying a single unit.   The inventory level will vary between a maximum level of x and a minimum level of zero (see Fig. 9), and so the average inventory level is $x/2$.   Consequently the inventory cost is given by

$$z_I = \tfrac{1}{2}qx \tag{70}$$

and the combined production and inventory cost by

$$z = \tfrac{1}{2}qx + \frac{Ds}{x} + rD \tag{71}$$

A graphical representation of this sort of a cost function is given in Fig. 10.   As x, the lot size, goes up, the inventory costs go up according to the straight-line function.   On the other hand, as the lot size goes up, the number of lots go down, and, therefore, the setup costs go down as an inverse function.   The fixed production cost D is, of course, a straight horizontal line.   By adding these three curves, we get the combined production and inventory cost as shown in Fig. 10.   Our problem is to determine the lowest point on this curve.   This is a problem in calculus and can be solved by computing the slope of the curve.   The slope (or derivative) is given by the formula

$$\text{Slope} = \frac{dz}{dx} = \frac{q}{2} - \frac{Ds}{x^2} \tag{72}$$

The minimum cost is obtained when the slope of the curve is zero (or when the derivative is zero). The appropriate value of x can be computed by making equation (72) equal zero. We get for the economic lot size

$$x = \sqrt{2Ds/q} \qquad (73)$$

It is customary to express the inventory carrying cost as a percentage figure. If we denote the cost of the part by C, and the percentage

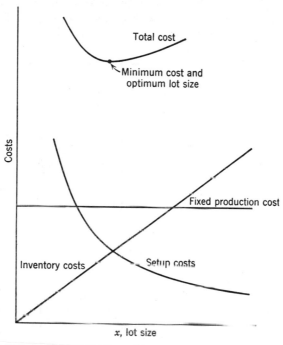

FIG. 10.   Combined production and inventory costs for various lot sizes.

carrying cost by p, then

$$q = pC$$

and so the economic lot size formula becomes

$$x = \sqrt{2Ds/pC} \qquad (74)$$

This is, then, the conventional economic lot size formula that is widely used in industry. It is very simple and can be computed rapidly, but let us remember that it applies only when the demand forms a straight line.

4. A PROBLEM RELATED TO STABLE EMPLOYMENT

We propose now to take a new look at our familiar production and inventory control problem.   There is an important drawback in each of the solutions we have proposed so far: rate of production and employment vary from production period to production period.   The labor market might be such that it is very difficult to hire, fire, or rehire workers.   Laying off people might promote such bad employee relations that production effectiveness is greatly impaired.   In fact, union rules might make this type of operation impossible.

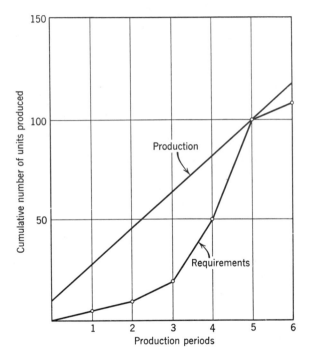

FIG. 11.   Meeting requirements with a steady employment.

Figure 11 shows a counterproposal to the production schedules we have considered so far.   It is proposed that at the beginning of each year there should be an inventory level of 10 units, and that in each production period 18 units be produced.   This will then result in a steady employment, though in each production period there is production during the night shift.   This solution does not minimize either inventory cost or production cost, but it provides stable employment.

The illustration we use here represents, of course, an extreme case. In real life situations a certain fluctuation in employment can always be tolerated. There is a certain amount of attrition: people leave jobs on their own, and also there is some amount of hiring that can be done. Therefore, we pose the problem of how to quantitatively evaluate the problem of variable employment, and how to. make a compromise between the three costs: the inventory cost, the production cost, and the cost involved in a variable employment level. In order to get quantitative answers in a problem of this type, we have to develop the cost associated with increasing or decreasing employment.

Let us assume that a production rate of 1 unit per production period requires 10 men. Let us furthermore assume that the hiring of each person costs the company $5. (This cost might be due to the initial cost of employing a person or to the cost of training.) Let us furthermore assume that people can be laid off at will and that there is no particular cost involved here.

Let us examine from this point of view our minimum night shift plan (Table 7, Chapter 3). We observe that in order to follow this plan we would have to hire 100 men for the fourth production period (as there is an increase of production from 15 to 25 units), hire another 50 for the fifth production period, then fire 220 in the sixth period, and finally hire 70 men so we have sufficient number of men to start production next year. The hiring of these people will cost the company

$$x_E = 5(100) + 5(50) + 5(70) = \$1,100 \qquad (75)$$

which $1,100 must be added to the $12,500 representing production and inventory costs. It can be seen, then, that the minimum night shift plan leads to a total cost of $13,600.

Similarly we can compute that the minimum inventory plan (Table 8, Chapter 3) involves the hiring of 250 men and a total cost of $13,590.

Finally, our new steady employment plan involves no hiring costs, but production and inventory costs can be computed to amount to $13,480.

How can we go about determining the production plan that results in minimum total cost? In order to be able to answer this question, we proceed now to develop a mathematical notation that is capable of dealing with this problem.

First let us introduce the following shorthand notation

$$a_+ = a \qquad \text{when } a \text{ is positive} \qquad (76)$$

$$a_+ = 0 \qquad \text{when } a \text{ is negative or zero} \qquad (77)$$

With this notation, then, we can say that the cost due to the change in the rate of production from the first to the second production period is given by

$$z = \alpha(x_2 - x_1)_+ \tag{78}$$

where α is the cost of increasing production by 1 unit. (In the present case, α is \$50, as we must hire 10 men to increase production by 1 unit per period.) This equation is just a shorthand expression of the fact that, when employment increases from x_1 to x_2, then, in order to get the cost, we have to take the difference of x_2 and x_1 and multiply the difference by the factor α. The formula also tells us with its shorthand notation that, when the employment does not change, or if the employment decreases, then there is no cost involved. The total cost due to changes in employment level for the whole planning period is given by

$$z_E = \alpha \sum_1^6 (x_{i+1} - x_i)_+ \tag{79}$$

The combined cost (that is, the production cost, inventory cost, and the cost due to changes in employment) can be obtained by taking equation (84) of Chapter 3 and adding these new terms that we have just developed.

Before we proceed to develop a solution to this type of problem, we want to formulate it for a somewhat more general condition. It is possible that laying off people involves a certain cost, and also that the cost involved in hiring people is not a straight-line function. Therefore, in order to allow for any contingency, we will simply say that the cost due to a change in production rate is given by

$$z = g(x_{i+1} - x_i) \tag{80}$$

and that the total cost due to changes in employment for the planning horizon is given by:

$$z_E = \sum_1^6 g(x_{i+1} - x_i) \tag{81}$$

The combination of all these types of costs for the planning horizon is given by

$$z = \sum_1^6 f(x_i) + \tfrac{1}{2}q \sum_1^6 (u_i + u_{i-1}) + \sum_1^6 g(x_{i+1} - x_i) \tag{82}$$

and this is the cost function that replaces the one given by equation (84) in Chapter 3. Previously, we have assumed that the initial and final inventories u_0 and u_6 are given. Now we assume in addition, that, the level of employment at the beginning of the planning horizon is given, and furthermore that x_7, employment at the beginning of the next planning horizon, is given too.

Mathematically speaking, the problem is to minimize the cost as expressed by equation (82) under the restriction given in Chapter 3 by equations (70) to (75). We can see that this is a programming problem, but it is neither a linear nor a convex programming problem. We can solve it by working backwards in the planning horizon and using a step by step process.

Let us first consider the last two stages, that is, the fifth and sixth production periods of the planning horizon. Let us start in the fifth production period with an inventory level of u_4 and a production level of x_4; and assume that we want to have no inventory at the end of the planning period but that we want a production rate of 15 units per production period in the seventh production period (which is the first production period in the next planning horizon). What will be the total cost involved in the fifth and sixth production periods? Using the notation developed previously, this cost can be expressed as

$$z = f(x_5) + f(x_6) + \tfrac{1}{2}q(u_4 + u_5) + \tfrac{1}{2}q(u_5 + 0)$$
$$+ g(x_5 - x_4) + g(x_6 - x_5) + g(15 - x_6) \quad (83)$$

We recognize furthermore that the inventory level at the end of the fifth period is given by taking the inventory level at the end of the fourth period and adding to it the surplus in the fifth period, or

$$u_4 + x_5 - 50 - u_5 \quad (84)$$

The combined production in the fifth and sixth periods is given by

$$x_5 + x_6 - 58 - u_4 \quad (85)$$

as the combined requirements in the two periods are 58 units. The problem, then, is the following: assuming that u_4 and x_4 are given, how should we select x_5, x_6, and u_5 such that the cost as expressed by equation (83) becomes a minimum? We can see that we do not need to vary independently all three of the variables x_5, x_6, and u_5, because as we assume a value of x_5 we can compute the value of x_6 from equation (85) and u_5 from equation (84). Therefore we can say that the cost function can be expressed by

$$z = f(x_5) + f(58 - u_4 - x_5) + \tfrac{1}{2}q(3u_4 + 2x_5 - 100)$$
$$+ g(x_5 - x_4) + g(58 - u_4 - 2x_5) + g(u_4 + x_5 - 43) \quad (86)$$

Now our problem is to assume a value of x_4 and u_5 and determine the value of x_5 that makes this cost the smallest. We recognize, however, that only those values of x_5 are permissible for which

$$x_5 \geq 50 - u_4 \qquad (87)$$

as otherwise the requirements of 50 units in the fifth period would not be met. Furthermore we recognize that only those values of x_5 are admissible for which

$$x_5 \leq 58 - u_4 \qquad (88)$$

as otherwise we would have to produce a negative quantity of units in the sixth production period to meet the condition of no inventory at the end of the sixth production period. Let us denote by $F_2(x_4, u_4)$ the minimum production cost for this problem. Then with mathematics we can say that this cost can be expressed with the aid of the complicated equation

$$F_2(x_4, u_4) = \min_{x_5} [f(x_5) + f(58 - u_4 - x_5) + \tfrac{1}{2}q(3u_4 + 2x_5 - 100)$$
$$+ g(x_5 - x_4) + g(58 - u_4 - 2x_5) + g(u_4 + x_5 - 43)] \quad (89)$$

where

$$50 - u \leq x_5 \leq 58 - u$$

A practical method of selecting this minimum cost is to assume a certain value of x_4 and then compute a table of numbers showing the cost function for various values of u_4 and x_5. Then we select a value of u_4, run through the various values of x_5, and select the x_5 which gives the lowest cost. Now we look up in the table another value of u_4 and again select the x_5 that gives the minimum cost. Repeating this and using the same table for various values of u_4, we can determine the minimum cost for the various values of u_4's, provided, however that initial production level of x_4 is unchanged. Now we repeat the whole process by starting with another value of the initial production level x_4. We again prepare a table, run through the various values of u_4, and determine the minimum cost. This way, then, we can prepare tables for various values of x_4 and finally get a table which shows the minimum cost for various values of x_4 and u_4. This is the function $F_2(x_4, u_4)$ that we need for our solution.

The next step in the method of solution is to consider the last three production periods. Again we assume that the initial production level is x_3 and that the initial inventory level is u_3. Assuming that we are going to use the optimum policy for the fifth and sixth production periods, we can then compute the combined cost associated with these last three production periods:

$$z = f(x_4) + \tfrac{1}{2}q(2u_3 + x_4 - 30) + g(x_4 - x_3)$$
$$+ F_2(x_4, u_3 + x_4 - 10) \quad (90)$$

In the last term on the right-hand side, we have taken into consideration the fact that, at the end of the fourth production period, the inventory level is $u_4 = u_3 + x_4 - 10$.

We can compute the costs as expressed by equation (90) by a series of tables, each using a fixed value of u_3 but different values of x_3 and x_4. For any value of u_3 and x_3, we can select the minimum cost and then prepare a table which gives the minimum cost as function of u_3 and x_3. We denote these minimum costs by $F_3(x_3, u_3)$, which is then the solution to the problem, provided only the three last production periods are considered.

We can proceed then to the four-stage, five-stage, and six-stage problem, and prepare tables for the functions $F_4(x_2, u_2)$, $F_5(x_1, u_1)$, and $F_6(x_0, u_0)$. Each of the steps involves the computation of a series of tables. We see, then, that this problem is much more complicated than the problems we dealt with in the first three sections of this chapter, because those problems involved the preparation of a single table of numbers for each step, whereas this problem involves the preparation of a series of tables for each step. This indicates that the amount of numerical work required to get a solution to the problem considered here is likely to be higher than the work required in the problems that we dealt with before.

In the method of solution described here, we start at the end of the planning horizon and work backwards. It would be possible to develop a method of solution starting at the beginning, and, of course, the solution obtained would be exactly the same.

We mentioned before that this problem in general is not a linear programming problem. However, there are important types of g functions for which the problem can be formulated as a problem in convex and linear programming.

Let us assume, that v_1, v_2, etc., denote the increase of production at the end of each production period, and that w_1, w_2, $\cdots$ denote the decrease at the end of each production period. (Clearly either v_1 or w_1 is zero and either v_2 or w_2 is zero, etc., but for the moment we ignore this fact.) Let $h(v)$ denote the cost of increasing the production by v and $k(w)$ denote the cost of decreasing the production by w. The cost due to the changes in production rates is given by

$$z_E = \sum_1^6 h(v_1) + \sum_1^6 k(w_i) \quad (91)$$

which replaces equation (80).   We also recognize that

$$x_{i+1} - x_i = v_i - w_i \tag{92}$$

though we recall that either v_i or w_i is zero.

The total cost for the planning horizon is given by

$$z = \sum_1^6 f(x_i) + \tfrac{1}{2}q \sum_1^6 (u_i + u_{i-1}) + \sum_1^6 h(v_i) + \sum_1^6 k(w_i) \tag{93}$$

(This replaces equation (82).)   If the functions f, h, and k are all convex from above, then we have a problem in convex programming and the problem can be solved as a problem in linear programming.   We also recognize that, when the problem is solved, either v_i or w_i will be automatically zero in the same production period, as no solution can have a minimal cost which implies a simultaneous increase and decrease in production within the same production period.

In particular we recognize, that, when there is a fixed cost associated with hiring or firing each person, the h and k functions become straight lines or

$$h(v_i) \equiv A v_i \tag{94}$$

$$k(w_i) \equiv B w_i \tag{95}$$

These may be considered as convex functions.   If in addition the f function is convex from above (as in the overtime and night shift case), then the problem can be solved as a problem in convex (or linear) programming.

Under such particular conditions, it might be less laborious to solve the problem with techniques of linear programming than by using the special programming technique developed here.

5.   A PROBLEM RELATED TO ATTRITION OF PRODUCTION FACILITIES

Let us return now to the problem we discussed in Section 10 of Chapter 3 and develop a method of solving this problem.

Let us first plan for a single year and assume that a total of A machines are available at the beginning of this year.   Let us assume that x of these production machines are allocated to the first product and y of the machines are allocated to the second product.   The profit associated with this method of allocation is given by

$$z = f(x) + g(y) \tag{96}$$

where
$$x + y = A \tag{97}$$

It is recognized, then, that if we plan only for one year we have the problem of the distribution of effort. We know how to solve this problem by preparing a table of numbers, showing the profits for the various values of x and y and by selecting the largest profit along the "diagonals." Let us denote by $F_1(A)$ the largest profit that can be realized in a single year if A number of machines are available at the beginning of the year. Then, mathematically speaking

$$F_1(A) = \max_{0 \le x \le A} [f(x) + g(A - x)] \tag{98}$$

Let us consider now a two-stage problem and assume again that we begin with A number of machines, and that we allocate x of these to the first product and y of these to the second product. Let A' denote the number of machines available for the second period. As 60% of the x and 80% of the y will be available, we have

$$A' = 0.6x_1 + 0.8y_1 \tag{99}$$

Now whatever way we allocate our machines in the first period we certainly will allocate our machines the best possible fashion in the second period. Therefore, we can say that our profit for the two years is given by

$$z = f(x) + g(y) + F_1(0.6x + 0.8y) \tag{100}$$

However, we recognize that

$$y = A - x \tag{101}$$

and, therefore,

$$A' = 0.6x + 0.8y = 0.6x + 0.8(A - x) = 0.8A - 0.2x \tag{102}$$

We can say that the combined profit for the two years is given by

$$z = f(x) + g(A - x) + F_1(0.8A - 0.2x) \tag{103}$$

The question is then, what value of x should we select to make this profit the largest possible? We see that by assuming various values of A and x, we can prepare a table showing the above costs. Then for each value of A we can select the value of x which gives the maximum profit. In mathematical notation we can say that the best profit that can be obtained in a two-year plan is given by

$$F_2(A) = \max_{0 \le x \le A} [f(x) + g(A - x) + F_1(0.8A - 0.2x)] \tag{104}$$

(The index 2 reminds us that we consider a two-year plan.) Similarly, if we denote by $F_3(A)$ the best possible profit that can be obtained in a three-year period, we can determine this $F_3(A)$ with the aid of the equation

$$F_3(A) = \max_{0 \le x \le A} [f(x) + g(A - x) + F_2(0.8A - 0.2x)] \quad (105)$$

This is again the mathematical statement describing the preparation of a table of numbers and the selection of the appropriate maximum values.

We can now proceed to solve the problem for the four-year period and in fact the whole problem can be solved by a step by step process. Each step involves the preparation of a table of numbers, and each step relies on the result of the previous step.

In this particular problem we are not concerned with whether we should start from the end of planning horizon and work towards the beginning or start at the beginning and work towards the end. The reason is that every year is the same from the point of view of attrition and costs, and therefore there is no distinction between the various years of the planning horizon. If we wanted to discount costs to the first year, a distinction would have to be made and the procedure would have to be modified.

6. GENERAL DESCRIPTION OF DYNAMIC PROGRAMMING PROBLEMS

The problems we discuss in this chapter have certain common features, and these make them problems in dynamic programming.* The definition of dynamic programming is somewhat vague, but we will describe the common features in the problems we have treated so far and the features that characterize dynamic programming problems.

A. Multistage processes are involved. In our warehousing problems, we considered a problem that consists of the five stages of purchasing and selling. Similarly, in the production and inventory problem we dealt with six different stages. In the problem relating to the attrition of machines, the situation was again the same. In all these cases, the stages referred to certain time intervals as usual in dynamic programming, but we have seen in the case of the distribution

---

* R. Bellman, "Some Applications of the Theory of Dynamic Programming: A Review," *Journal of the Operations Research Society of America,* Vol. 2, 1954, pp. 275.

of effort problem that the stages do not necessarily mean stages in time; they might be stages in some other sense.

B. At each stage the problem can be described by a small number of variables. In the problem of the distribution of effort, when we allocate a certain part of the effort to a zone, the profit in this particular zone depends only on the amount of effort allocated. In our warehousing problem, the profit depends in each period on (1) the initial inventory, (2) how much is purchased, (3) how much is sold. In our production and inventory problem, the cost depends in each period on (1) the initial inventory, (2) requirements, (3) the amount produced. The problem of the steady employment is somewhat more complicated because it is necessary to know the levels of production in the period prior to the one being considered. In the problem of the attrition of the machines, all we have to know at the beginning of the year is how many machines are available. Profits then depend on how these machines are allocated between the two products. Comparing these problems to other problems in mathematical programming we recognize that in these problems, at each stage, the number of variables involved is small.

C. The effect of a decision at any stage, is to transform this set of variables into a similar set of variables. Let us consider, for instance, the warehousing problem. The initial inventory at any period results from the initial inventory in the previous period and from how much was bought and how much sold in the previous period. In the production and inventory control problem the situation is similar. The initial inventory at each period results from the decisions made in the production period prior to the one considered, and in particular from how much was produced in that prior production period. In the case of the steady employment problem, the situation is similar but somewhat more complicated as production rates must be taken into account.

Finally, following the exposition of Bellman, we add to these features what he calls the principle of optimality:

An optimal policy has the property that, whatever the initial state and initial decision are, the remaining decisions must constitute an optimal policy with regard to the state resulting from the first decision.

To elaborate on this statement, let us consider our warehousing problem. Suppose we make the wrong decisions for the first and the second periods, that is, we buy or sell the wrong amount of goods. This will leave us with a certain inventory level at the beginning of the third period. Our method of solution of the problem was such that we can start with this initial inventory level at the beginning of the third period and apply an optimum policy to maximize our profit in the remaining three periods. In other words, it makes no difference what the prior decisions were; our method of solution still gives the optimum decisions. This is due to the fact that, even if we make the wrong decision in the first and second period, we can still go ahead and make right decisions in the third, fourth, and fifth period. The reader will easily convince himself that similar considerations hold in the other illustrations we used in this chapter.

CHAPTER 9

THE ELEMENTS
OF
THE THEORY OF GAMES

1. WHAT IS A TWO-PERSON ZERO-SUM GAME?

In Chapter 3, Section 11, we described a production problem in refinery operation, where the manager had to decide on a certain policy, in face of competition. We have shown that, in this case, the solution to the problem can be obtained with the aid of the theory of games. We will now develop the concepts involved. In order to fix ideas, we begin by describing a game that has been played in Italy since classical antiquity. This game, the so called two-finger morra, is played by two people, each of whom shows one or two fingers and simultaneously calls his guess as to the number of fingers his opponent will show. If just one player guesses correctly he wins an amount equal to the sum of the fingers shown by himself and his opponent. Otherwise, the game is a draw and no one pays anything. If I am to play this game, I can describe, with the aid of Table 1, the amount of money I have to pay under various conditions. For instance, if I show one finger and guess that my opponent is going to show two fingers, that is, if I play my strategy (2), and on the other hand my opponent shows two fingers and guesses that I am going to show two fingers, that is, if my opponent plays his strategy [4], then Table 1 shows that I am going to win $3. (I guessed correctly how many fingers my opponent is showing, and so I collect the sum of the fingers shown, that is the $3.) On the other hand, if I play my strategy (3), and my opponent plays his strategy [4], then he wins the amount of $4,

256

Mathematical Programming

which is shown on the table by the negative number -4. (I am to pay money in this case). Table 1 shows the payoff matrix for two-finger morra, which is a two-person rectangular game. It is called a two-person game because two persons play it. It is a rectangular game because the payoff matrix is a rectangular table of numbers. It is a zero-sum game, as money is exchanged and not added or withdrawn.

TABLE 1. Payoff Matrix for Two-Finger Morra[a]

	[1] (1,1)	[2] (1,2)	[3] (2,1)	[4] (2,2)
(1) (1,1)	0	2	-3	0
(2) (1,2)	-2	0	0	3
(3) (2,1)	3	0	0	-4
(4) (2,2)	0	-3	4	0

[a] If I play (2) and he plays [4] I get $3.

The question now is what is the best way to play this game? If the question makes sense, then there is a rational way to argue what is the best way to play the game. This is, then, the type of problem that the theory of games deals with.

In order to develop our approach, we will study a game for which the payoff matrix is simpler than for the morra game. We assume that there are only two strategies available to me, that there are three strategies available to my opponent, and that the payoff matrix is given by

His Strategy

		[1]	[2]	[3]
My Strategy	(1)	2	3	11
	(2)	7	5	2

The question is, what strategy should I play?

I might take a very optimistic point of view and say that I am after the largest possible gain. This is $11 shown in the upper right-hand corner in the matrix. Thus I say I am to play my strategy (1). However, as time goes on my opponent finds out that I play my strategy

(1) and he counteracts my strategy by playing his strategy [1]. In this case, then, my gain is only $2. Furthermore, suppose now that in some other game, there is a fourth strategy for the opponent, with payoff of $9 and $1. Under this condition, my opponent would never play his strategy [3], as in his strategy [3] he has to pay $11 or $2, whereas in this hypothetical fourth strategy he has to pay only $9 and $1. This means that his strategy [4] is always better than his strategy [3] (as he always loses less money by playing his strategy [4]). Therefore it would be vain for me to hope for the $11 gain, as he will never play his strategy [3]. It is seen, then, that my policy of going after the largest possible payoff is not necessarily a rational one.

According to the argument in Section 11 of Chapter 3, we suspect that I should play a combination of my two strategies, that is, I should alternate between my strategy (1) and my strategy (2). Perhaps I should play my strategy (1) half the time and my strategy (2) half the time. Suppose for the moment that the opponent always plays his strategy [1]. How much money am I going to get in the long run, if I play my strategy (1) 50% of the time my strategy (2) the other 50%? Clearly, the answer is halfway between the gain of $2 and $7, that is, my gain in the long run will be $4.50.

We now propose to extend this argument to a somewhat more complicated case. Let us assume again that my opponent still plays his strategy [1], but that I play a fraction x times my strategy (1) and the rest of the time, that is $(1 - x)$ times, my strategy (2). What is my gain under these conditions? I will get in the long run x times $2 and $(1 - x)$ times $7, which gives me

$$z = 2x + 7(1 - x) = 7 - 5x \qquad (1)$$

A graphical representation of this equation is shown in Fig. 1 by the line [1]. It can be verified that, if $x = 0.5$, that is, if I play my strategy (1) 0.5 times, then the gain is indeed $4.50. If I never play my strategy (1), x is zero and the gain is $7, as can again be seen in the figure. Furthermore, if I play my strategy (1) all the time, then x is 1 and the gain is $2. It is seen, then, that in Fig. 1 the straight line [1] shows any possible gain I can get, as long as my opponent plays his strategy [1].

Similarly, we can compute my possible gain if my opponent plays strategy [2]. This gain is given by

$$z = 3x + 5(1 - x) = 5 - 2x \qquad (2)$$

and is shown graphically in Fig. 1 by the straight line marked with [2].

Finally, if my opponent plays his strategy [3], then my gain is described by

$$z = 11x + 2(1 - x) = 2 + 9x \qquad (3)$$

which is again shown in Fig. 1 by the straight line [3].

Incidentally, if I play only my strategy (1) or only my (2), this is described in the theory as my playing a *pure* strategy. We observe that, in Fig. 1, my pure strategies are represented by either the value $x = 0$ or $x = 1$, and therefore the gains for pure strategies are given by

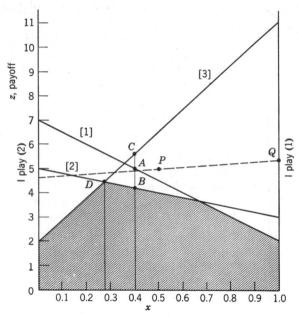

FIG. 1. Graphical representation of a two-person zero-sum game. The letter x denotes the fraction of times I play strategy (1). The gain is shown by the vertical axis z. (Each straight line refers to a pure strategy of the opponent.)

the left-hand or right-hand side verticals. We also note, that each of the straight lines in Fig. 1 refer to a pure strategy of the opponent.

We notice that being an optimist is not necessarily a rational way of playing the game. Another way to proceed is to use *the principle of insufficient reason*. I take the point of view that I have no idea what my opponent is going to play, and therefore I arbitrarily assume that one-third of the time he is going to play his strategy [1], one-third of the time his strategy [2], and one-third of the time his strategy [3]. Again, let us assume that I play my strategy (1) x fraction of the time. Now let us ask the question, "What is my gain under these conditions?" The way to compute this gain is to take the gain shown by equation (1) multiplied by one-third, take the gain shown by equation (2) multiplied by one-third, take the gain shown by equation (3) multiplied by one-third, and adding these three gains. On the basis of the principle of insufficient reason, then, we get the following gain:

$$z = \tfrac{1}{3}(7 - 5x) + \tfrac{1}{3}(5 - 2x) + \tfrac{1}{3}(2 + 9x) \tag{4}$$

This can be simplified to

$$z = \tfrac{14}{3} + \tfrac{2}{3}x \tag{5}$$

In Fig. 1 this line is shown by the dotted straight line. For instance, it can be seen that if I play my strategy (1) half the time and my strategy (2) half the time (and I assume that my opponent will play his three strategies in equal proportion) I can expect a gain of $5 (point P in Fig. 1). In order to make my gain the largest I should mix my strategies such that I reach the right-hand upper end of the dotted straight line. This means, that I should play my strategy (1) all the time, that is, I should have the pure strategy of (1). Then I can hope for a gain of $\tfrac{16}{3}$ or $5.33 (point Q in Fig. 1).

Let us now ask whether the principle of insufficient reason makes good sense. If I play my strategy (1) all the time, my opponent finds this out and counteracts by playing his strategy [1]. Therefore I collect only $2 instead of the $5.30 I hoped for. We can see, then, that the principle of insufficient reason is not necessarily a rational way to decide the strategy that I should use.

We propose now to examine another method of procedure, which could be described as the conservative method. If I play my pure strategy (1), I am certain to get at least $2. (I get exactly this amount if my opponent plays his strategy [1].) If he plays some other strategy, or a combination of his other strategies, I am going to get more than $2. However, the thing I am certain of is that, if I play my strategy (1), I am to get at least $2. Now suppose I play my pure strategy (2). It happens to turn out (this is just a coincidence) that in this case again I can be certain to get at least $2. Now I ask the question, "Suppose I mix my strategies (1) and (2) in some fashion, what is the number of dollars I can be certain of getting?" If I play my strategy (1) x number of times, then my respective gains, depending whether my opponent plays his strategy [1], [2], or [3], are given by one of the following three numbers:

$$(7 - 5x), \ (5 - 2x), \ (2 + 9x) \tag{6}$$

I can be certain that I am to get at least as much as the smallest of these three numbers. To illustrate, let us assume that $x = 0.4$, that is,

I play my strategy (1) 40% of the time. If he plays his strategy [1]. I am to get $5, as shown by the point A in Fig. 1. If he plays his strategy [2] I get $4.20 as shown by B, and if he plays his strategy [3] I get $5.60 as shown by the point C. However, I do not know which of these strategies he is going to play. All I know is that I can be certain of getting $4.20 which is the smallest of the three numbers. I can put this thought into mathematical form by saying that, whatever number of times I play my strategy (1), that is, for any value of x, I am certain to get the gain given by

$$z = \min \ (7 - 5x,\ 5 - 2x,\ 2 + 9x) \tag{7}$$

The word ahead of the parenthesis is an abbreviation for minimum, and it means that one is to take the minimum (that is, the smallest) of the three numbers. Now I ask the question, "What value of x should I use?" It will make good sense to select x so that this gain that I am certain to get becomes the largest possible. The three straight lines in Fig. 1 form a shape somewhat like a roof of a house, and our problem is to find the top of this roof, at which point my certain gain becomes the largest. In order to determine this point D on the diagram, we can either read the figures as shown, or we can compute the intersection by solving the equations for the two straight lines. The equations for these two lines are given by equations [2] and [3]. For the point of intersection D, the value of z must be the same in both equations or we must have

$$2 + 9x = 5 - 2x$$

From this we get the value $x = 3/11$. This gives the fraction of times I should play my strategy (1). The remaining time, that is, $8/11$ time, I should play my strategy (2). It is easy to compute that my expected gain is $49/11$ dollars, which is about $4.45. This gain is called the value of the game, and we denote it by V. It is seen, then, that mathematically speaking this gain is determined by selecting the value of x which maximizes the gain as given by equation (7). This means, then, that the value for this particular game we are discussing is given by the formula

$$V = \max_{0 \le x \le 1} \ [\min \ (7 - 5x,\ 5 - 2x,\ 2 + 9x)] \tag{8}$$

In summary, then, we see that, if I play my strategy (1) $3/11$ times and my strategy (2) $8/11$ times, then whatever my opponent does I am certain to get an average of $4.45 in the long run. The conservative point of view leads to a consistent method of solving our problem.

In order to prepare the groundwork for some more complicated mathematics, we will describe this same situation with a somewhat different mathematical notation. Let us denote by x_1 the number of times I am to play my strategy (1), and by x_2 the number of time I am to play my strategy (2). We must have

$$x_1 + x_2 = 1 \qquad\qquad (9)$$

With this notation we can say that my gain will be given by one of the three expressions

$$(2x_1 + 7x_2), (3x_1 + 5x_2), (11x_1 + 2x_2) \qquad (10)$$

depending on whether my opponent plays his strategy [1], [2], or [3]. For any value of x_1 and x_2 that satisfies equation (9), I am certain to get the smallest of these three numbers. My problem is to select the numbers x_1 and x_2 such that the smallest of these three numbers becomes a maximum. Therefore the value of the game is given by

$$V = \max_{x_1 + x_2 = 1} \ [\min (2x_1 + 7x_2), (3x_1 + 5x_2), (11x_1 + 2x_2)] \quad (11)$$

With this new notation, then, we can see that the problem is to select the numbers x_1 and x_2 that satisfy equation (9) and that give the maximum of the minimum as described by equation (11).

Let us look at the same problem again in a different way. Let v be a number such that

$$2x_1 + 7x_2 \geq v$$

$$3x_1 + 5x_2 \geq v \qquad\qquad (12)$$

$$11x_1 + 2x_2 \geq v$$

If v denotes number of dollars, then this number of dollars is smaller than or equal to any of the three numbers shown on the left-hand side of equation (12), and therefore the number v is smaller than or equal to the smallest of the three numbers. Consequently, if I mix my strategies (1) and (2) in proportions x_1 and x_2, I can be certain that I get at least v dollars, no matter what strategy my opponent plays. So with this notation I can formulate this problem in game theory by stating that the problem is to select the variables x_1, x_2, and v such that equations (9) and (12) hold, and that the unknown v takes the largest possible value.

This, of course, is just another way of formulating our problem. Incidentally, we know that, when we solve this problem, the value of the game is going to be equal to at least one of the three numbers shown on the left-hand side of Equation 12. Therefore, we can say that in the inequalities shown by equation (12) at *least* at one place the equality will hold.

We proceed now to develop a mathematical notation for expressing the gain of a rectangular game.

Let us again assume that I play my strategy (1) x_1 times, and my strategy (2) x_2 times, and that x_1 and x_2 add up to 1, as given by equation (9). Let us assume further that my opponent plays his strategy [1] y_1 times, his strategy [2] y_2 times, and his strategy [3] y_3 times. These, again, must add up to 1 or

$$y_1 + y_2 + y_3 = 1 \qquad (13)$$

How can we compute my expected gain? As an illustration, let us assume that $x_1 = 0.2$, $x_2 = 0.8$, $y_1 = 0.3$, $y_2 = 0.5$, $y_3 = 0.2$. What is my gain in this case? I will play my strategy (2) 80% of the time, and my opponent will play his strategy [3] 20% of the time, which means that I am going to play my strategy (2) and he is going to play his strategy [3] *simultaneously* 16% of the time. According to the payoff matrix, under this particular condition I get $2. Therefore, I can expect to have a gain of $2(0.8)(0.2) = 0.32$ dollars. In order to cover all possible combinations we prepare the percentage table shown here. (For instance the number in the lower right-hand corner shows the 0.16 figure.) In order to compute my expected gain, we have to take these percentage figures and multiply each of them with the respective gain. We can get the total expected gain by the formula

		$y_1 = 0.3$	$y_2 = 0.5$	$y_3 = 0.2$
		[1]	[2]	[3]
$x_1 = 0.2$	(1)	0.06	0.10	0.04
$x_2 = 0.8$	(2)	0.24	0.40	0.16

$$z = 0.06(2) + 0.10(3) + 0.04(11) + 0.24(7) + 0.40(5)$$
$$+ 0.16(2) = 4.86 \qquad (14)$$

It can be seen, then, that, for these particular values of x_1, x_2, y_1, y_2, and y_3, my expected gain is $4.86. Similarly, we find that, for any value of x_1, x_2, y_1, y_2, and y_3, my expected gain is given by

$$z = 2x_1y_1 + 3x_1y_2 + 11x_1y_3 + 7x_2y_1 + 5x_2y_2 + 2x_2y_3 \qquad (15)$$

The notation for the expected gain is given by $E(x_1, x_2; y_1, y_2, y_3)$. With this notation, the result of the numerical example we have just developed can be written as

$$E(0.2, 0.8; 0.3, 0.5, 0.2) = 4.86 \qquad (16)$$

With the same notation we can express the fact that, if I play my pure strategy (2) and my opponent plays his pure strategy [1], then my gain is $7:

$$E(0, 1; 1, 0, 0) = 7 \tag{17}$$

On the other hand, if my opponent counters my pure strategy (2) by playing his pure strategy [3], then my gain is given by

$$E(0, 1; 0, 0, 1) = 2 \tag{18}$$

With this notation we can say that

$$E(\tfrac{3}{11}, \tfrac{8}{11}; y_1, y_2, y_3) \geq \tfrac{49}{11} \tag{19}$$

In words this means that, if I play my strategy (1) 3/11 times and my strategy (2) 8/11 times, then, whatever strategy y_1, y_2, y_3 my opponent selects, my gain will certainly be 49/11 dollars, or more.

There is one further point here. When I inspect Fig. 1, it becomes clear that if I play any other combination of strategies I cannot be certain of getting this 49/11 dollars. For instance, if I play my strategy (1) half the time and my strategy (2) half the time, all I can be certain of is getting $4, because my opponent might select his strategy [2], which would then give me exactly the $4.

We can now ask the question whether this principle of visualizing the worst is really the proper way of determining the best strategy. Some work has been done in an attempt to answer this question, and discussion can be found in the literature. However, most results in the theory of games are based on the principle of visualizing the worst, and in our discussion we will restrict ourselves to this type of thinking.

2. THE STRATEGY OF THE OPPONENT

Let us now put ourselves into our opponent's shoes. What is the strategy that he should play? Again, we accept the concept of visualizing the worst, and so we will say that his problem is to prevent me from gaining too much money. In other words, he should try to keep my gain down. If he plays his pure strategy [1], all he can be certain of is that he will keep me below $7 (see Fig. 1). This is due to the fact that, if I play my pure strategy (2) and he plays his pure strategy [1], I get exactly $7. We suspect that he too should mix his strategies, and we propose to search for the best mixed strategy he can have.

Suppose he mixes his strategies [1] and [3], playing his strategy [1] half the time and his strategy [3] half the time. If it is assumed that I play my strategy (1) x number of times, then my gain will be given by the formula

$$z = \tfrac{1}{2}(7 - 5x) + \tfrac{1}{2}(2 + 9x) = 4.5 + 2x \qquad (20)$$

Figure 2 is a graphical representation of this mixture of his strategies [1] and [3]. For instance, it can be seen that, if I play my strategy (1) 80% of the time and he is mixing his strategies [1] and [3] in equal proportion, then my gain will be \$6.10 (point A). Furthermore, if he plays his strategies [1] and [3] half and half, all he can be certain of is that he is going to keep me down to \$6.50 as I can realize this gain by playing my pure strategy (1).

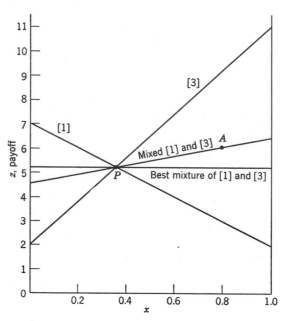

FIG. 2. Graphical representation of a two-person zero-sum game. The opponent's strategies [1] and [3] and their mixtures are shown.

Now we ask the question, "What mixture of his strategies [1] and [3] should he use in order to be certain to keep me down to the lowest gain?" The graphical representation of each of these mixed strategies is given by a straight line going through the point P in Fig. 2. We see that the best mixture of his strategies [1] and [3] will be represented by the horizontal line in Fig. 2. It is easy to verify the fact that this horizontal line is obtained by my opponent's playing his strategy [1] $y_1 = 9/14$ times and playing his strategy [2] $y_2 = 5/14$ times. In this case, my gain is given by the expression

$$z = \tfrac{9}{14}(7 - 5x) + \tfrac{5}{14}(2 + 9x) = \tfrac{73}{14} = 5.2 \qquad (21)$$

My gain (if he uses this particular mixed strategy) is \$5.20 independently of what strategy I play. (This means, then, that the line in Fig. 2 is really horizontal.) We can see that, if he plays this mixture of his strategies [1] and [3], then he can be certain to keep me down to a gain of \$5.20. However, by inspecting Fig. 1, we can see that he will be better off mixing his strategies [2] and [3] instead of [1] and [3]. More specifically, by playing his strategy [2] $y_2 = 9/11$ times and his strategy [3] $y_3 = 2/11$ times, he can keep me down to the gain of 49/11 dollars. This mixture of his strategies [2] and [3] would be represented by a horizontal line going through the point D in Fig. 1.

In summary, we can see that if he plays the strategy (0, 9/11, 2/11) he can be certain to keep me down to 49/11 dollars. If he plays this strategy, regardless of what I do my gain is not going to be over the 49/11 dollars. We can put this into mathematical form by writing

$$E(x_1, x_2; 0, \tfrac{9}{11}, \tfrac{2}{11}) \leq \tfrac{49}{11} \qquad (22)$$

This equation says that, whatever values of x_1 and x_2 as mixed strategies I select, my gain will always be less than or equal to 49/11 dollars. Furthermore, we also see that, if I play my best strategy of $x_1 = 3/11$ and $x_2 = 8/11$, then I get exactly this 49/11 gain. This can be written as

$$E(\tfrac{3}{11}, \tfrac{8}{11}; 0, \tfrac{9}{11}, \tfrac{2}{11}) = \tfrac{49}{11} \qquad (23)$$

We proceed now to take another look at the same problem. Let us assume that the opponent plays his strategies in proportions y_1, y_2, and y_3. If I play my pure strategy (1), my gain is given by:

$$z = 2y_1 + 3y_2 + 11y_3 \qquad (24)$$

If I play my pure strategy (2), my gain is given by

$$z = 7y_1 + 5y_2 + 2y_3 \qquad (25)$$

Assuming that he does not know which of these pure strategies I play (or in which way I mix them), all he can be certain of is that he can keep me down to the larger of these two numbers, or that he can keep me down to the gain of

$$z = \max_{y_1+y_2+y_3=1} (2y_1 + 3y_2 + 11y_3, 7y_1 + 5y_2 + 2y_3) \qquad (26)$$

Now of course he wants to keep me down to the lowest gain. This means, then, that his problem is to select the numbers y_1, y_2, and y_3 so that my gain, as shown by equation (26), becomes the smallest. His problem is to select y_1, y_2, and y_3 by the relationship

$$z = \min_{y_1+y_2+y_3=1} [\max (2y_1 + 3y_2 + 11y_3,\ 7y_1 + 5y_2 + 2y_3)] \quad (27)$$

To repeat, we see that equation (26) gives the gain to which he can be certain to keep me down, and equation (27) tells him how to select his mixed strategy so that this gain (to which he can be certain to keep me down) becomes the smallest. We know, of course, that in this particular case the answer to equation (27) is 49/11 dollars. If we compare equation (27) with equation (11), we see that the value of the game, that is, the 49/11 dollars, can be obtained either as maximizing a minimum or minimizing a maximum.

The celebrated theorem of the theory of games, the so-called minimax theorem, states that, whether we compute the value of the game as a minimax or as a maximin, we get the same answer for any rectangular two-person zero-sum game. Of course, this statement is obvious for the numerical illustration we are discussing here, but the theorem in the general case is one of the great achievements of modern mathematics.

Now, we propose to take again another point of view of this same specific problem. Let w be a number such that

$$2y_1 + 3y_2 + 11y_3 \leq w \quad (28)$$

$$7y_1 + 5y_2 + 2y_3 \leq w \quad (29)$$

If I play my strategy (1), I get as a gain the left-hand side of equation (28). If I play my strategy (2), I get the left-hand side of equation (29). My opponent can be certain, then, to keep me down to, or below, w number of dollars. My opponent's problem is then to select y_1, y_2, y_3, and w such that w becomes the smallest possible number. This strategy will assure him of keeping me down to the lowest possible gain.

We can now summarize the whole situation by the following single relationship:

$$E(\tfrac{3}{11},\ \tfrac{8}{11};\ y_1,\ y_2,\ y_3) \geq \tfrac{49}{11} \geq E(x_1,\ x_2;\ 0,\ \tfrac{9}{11},\ \tfrac{2}{11}) \quad (30)$$

The left-hand side of the relationship tells us that, if I play 3/11 and 8/11 as my mixed strategy, then I can be certain to get 49/11 dollars, irrespective of the strategy y_1, y_2, y_3 my opponent plays. On the other hand, the right-hand side tells us that, if my opponent plays 0, 9/11, and 2/11 as his strategy, he can be certain to keep me down to the 49/11 dollars. Whatever value x_1 and x_2 I select for my strategy, my gain will be no higher than this 49/11 dollars figure.

It is of interest to consolidate the seven relationships (9), (12), (13), (28), and (29) into a single system of equations. We can replace v and w by the value V of the game and write

$$x_1 + x_2 = 1 \tag{31}$$

$$2x_1 + 7x_2 \geq V \tag{32}$$

$$3x_1 + 5x_2 \geq V \tag{33}$$

$$11x_1 + 2x_2 \geq V \tag{34}$$

$$y_1 + y_2 + y_3 = 1 \tag{35}$$

$$2y_1 + 3y_2 + 11y_3 \leq V \tag{36}$$

$$7y_1 + 5y_2 + 2y_3 \leq V \tag{37}$$

We recognize that these seven equations with six unknowns have a single solution, and that the solution gives the value of the game and the respective optimum strategies. Is there any direct way to solve those seven equations with six unknowns?

Let us remember that in general for a system of linear equations, when there are the same number of unknowns as equations, we can obtain a single solution. This suggests that we could select six of these relations and use the equal sign instead of inequalities and solve these six equations for these six unknowns. Then we could take the seventh inequality and verify whether this seventh inequality holds. If we do not get into contradiction we could say that we have solved the problem. On the other hand, if we do get into a contradiction this means that we have selected the six equations the wrong way. If we substitute our actual numerical values into equation (32), we discover that the left-hand side has the value 62/11, whereas the right-hand side is 49/11. This means, then, that here the strict inequality sign holds. Therefore, if we omit this relationship and solve the remaining six equations, we get values for x_1, x_2, y_1, y_2, y_3, and V such that the inequality in equation (32) is automatically satisfied.

We see, then, that we could solve this problem by selecting seven different times six equations and solving seven times six simultaneous equations. This is, of course, a lot of work, and in a larger problem the procedure would lead to an impossible amount of work. The situation reminds us of linear programming, where in connection with the simplex method we showed that the solution could be obtained by solving, an enormous number of times, a large number of equations with a large number of unknowns. In order to be able to solve a problem in the theory of games we need some sort of a short-cut method. We will see later that the simplex method of linear programming is a method that can also solve problems in game theory.

Before we proceed to some more general discussion in connection with the theory of games, we want to make a few remarks. Suppose we deal with a rectangular game with the following payoff matrix:

| | | His Strategy | | | |
		[1]	[2]	[3]	[4]
My Strategy	(1)	6	4	5	7
	(2)	2	3	1	0

What amount of gain can I hope for, in this game? If I play my strategy (1), I can be certain of getting $4. If I play my strategy (2),

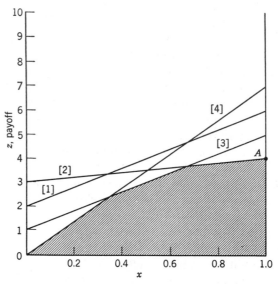

FIG. 3. Graphical representation of a two-person zero-sum game with a saddle point.

I can be certain of getting only nothing. This shows, then, that under no condition can I be certain of getting more than $4. On the other hand, as far as my opponent is concerned, if he plays his strategy [2], he can be certain of keeping me down to $4; whereas, if he plays any other strategy, he cannot be certain of keeping me down to this $4. This means, then, that the best strategy for me is to play my pure strategy (1), and the best strategy for him is to play his pure strategy [2].

A geometrical representation in Fig. 3 confirms this result. The top of the roof-like structure is point A, which shows that my best strategy is to play the pure strategy (1). On the other hand, my opponent will do best to play his pure strategy [2], as this strategy assures him of keeping me down to point A.

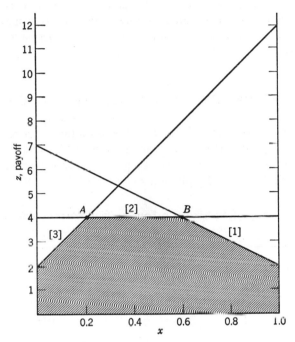

FIG. 4. Graphical representation of a two-person zero-sum game with infinitely many solutions.

In such a case, then, the solution is for both players to play pure strategies. A game with this sort of a payoff matrix is called a game with a saddle point. The solution of a game with a saddle point can be obtained by simple inspection of the payoff matrix.

Let us now consider a rectangular game with the following payoff matrix:

His Strategy

		[1]	[2]	[3]
My Strategy	(1)	2	4	11
	(2)	7	4	2

The geometrical representation of this game is shown in Fig. 4. The interesting point here is that my best strategy is to play my strategy (1) x_1 number of times, where x_1 must be between 0.2 and 0.6. I have a choice between infinitely many strategies, each of them being equally good. On the other hand, the opponent's best strategy is to play his pure strategy [2]. The value of the game in this case is $4. It is seen, then, that some rectangular games have infinitely many equally good solutions. We also see that sometimes a pure strategy is the best strategy.

3.   A FOUR BY FIVE TWO-PERSON RECTANGULAR GAME

Table 2 shows the payoff matrix of a rectangular game. Let us observe that my opponent is not going to play his strategy [3] as his strategy [5] is superior to his strategy [3]. In other words, regardless of the strategy I play, if he plays his strategy [5] he will keep me to a

TABLE 2.   Payoff Matrix for a Four by Five Rectangular Game

(Strategy [3] dominates [5])

	[1]	[2]	[3]	[4]	[5]
(1)	1,416	56	385	376	360
(2)	−444	596	432	916	420
(3)	1,392	52	413	351	317
(4)	396	636	317	156	300

lower gain than if he plays his strategy [3]. In the terminology of the theory of games, it is said that his strategy [5] dominates his strategy [3]. We proceed now to cross out his strategy [3], and we get the reduced payoff matrix in Table 3. Here I notice that I will never play my strategy (3) as my strategy (1) dominates my strategy (3), that is, whatever strategy the opponent plays, I have a higher gain by playing (1) than playing (3). Therefore, we will cross out strategy (3), and so we get to the reduced payoff matrix as shown in Table 4. From now on we will consider only the game as shown in Table 4, and we now show how a solution to this game can be obtained.

Suppose I play my strategies in proportions of x_1, x_2, and x_3, where

$$x_1 + x_2 + x_3 = 1 \tag{38}$$

Let us assume for the time being that my opponent plays his strategy [4], in which case my gain is given by

$$z_4 = 360x_1 + 420x_2 + 300x_3 \tag{39}$$

Now we will develop a geometrical representation of this problem.   In

TABLE 3.   Payoff Matrix for a Four by Four Rectangular Game

(Strategy (3) is dominated by (1))

	[1]	[2]	[3]	[4]
(1)	1,416	56	376	360
(2)	-444	596	916	420
(3)	1,392	52	351	317
(4)	396	636	156	300

TABLE 4.   Payoff Matrix for a Three by Four Rectangular Game

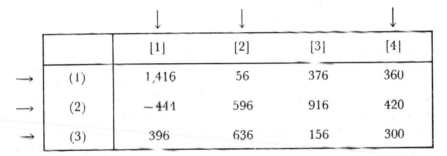

		[1]	[2]	[3]	[4]
→	(1)	1,416	56	376	360
→	(2)	-444	596	916	420
→	(3)	396	636	156	300

order to simplify matters, we introduce the notation

$$x_1 = x \tag{40}$$

$$x_2 = y \tag{41}$$

$$x_3 = 1 - x - y \tag{42}$$

The gain can be expressed as

$$z_4 = 360x + 420y + 300 (1 - x - y) \tag{43}$$

This can be written as

$$z_4 = 60x + 120y + 300 \tag{44}$$

In Fig. 5 a geometrical representation of this gain is given. Suppose, for instance, that I play the strategy 0.3, 0.3, 0.4. Then $x = 0.3$ and $y = 0.3$, and the point A represents the gain associated with this strategy. The payoff I receive can be computed with the aid of equation (44) as

$$z = 60(0.3) + 120(0.3) + 300 = 354 \qquad (45)$$

We see, then, that the triangle in Fig. 5 represents the case when my opponent plays his strategy [4]. Suppose now that my opponent plays his strategy [1]. How can we represent this geometrically? The quadrangle in Fig. 6 shows this strategy [1]. This figure was prepared by computing the gain when my opponent plays his strategy [1], which is given by

$$z_1 = 1416x_1 - 444x_2 + 396x_3 = 1020x - 840y + 396 \qquad (46)$$

Similarly, we can compute the payoff when he plays his strategy [2]:

$$z_2 = 56x_1 + 596x_2 + 636x_3 = -580x - 40y + 636 \qquad (47)$$

or when he plays his strategy [3]:

$$z_3 = 376x_1 + 916x_2 + 156x_3 = 220x + 760y + 156 \qquad (48)$$

In Fig. 7 all four strategies of the opponent are represented by planes, and all these planes form a structure similar to the roof of a house. This roof-like surface represents the payoffs I am certain to get, irrespective of what strategy my opponent follows. How can I determine my best strategy? I should select the strategy which makes this certain payoff the largest. This is given by the highest point on the roof, point P. This best strategy is characterized by $x = 0.4$ and $y = 0.5$. This, leads to the strategy of $x_1 = 0.4$, $x_2 = 0.5$, and $x_3 = 0.1$. The value of the game is given by the vertical coordinate of point P, or $384.

Let us remind ourselves again that if I play this strategy I am certain to get the $384. If my opponent does not play his best strategy, I might be able to get more money. On the other hand, if I play some other strategy, then I would be working at a lower level than the roof shown in Fig. 7, and my opponent might devise a strategy such that I would get less than the $384.

We proceed now to develop a mathematical notation, so we can deal with problems in game theory in a more general fashion. Let us denote the numbers in the payoff matrix by the letter p, and in particular let $p_{i,j}$ denote the number in the ith row and the jth column. For instance, the value of $p_{2,3}$ is 916 in Table 4. With this notation we can

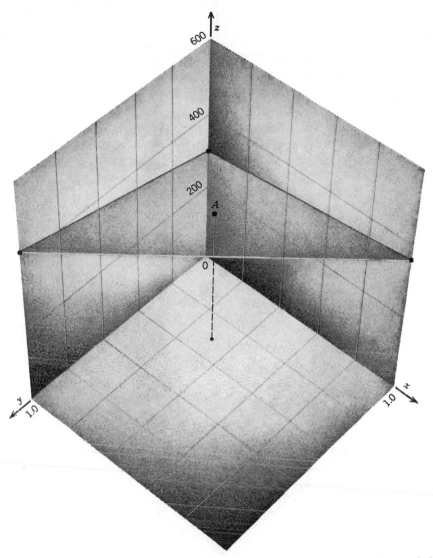

FIG. 5. Geometrical representation of a two-person zero-sum game. The shaded triangle represents the opponent's strategy [4].

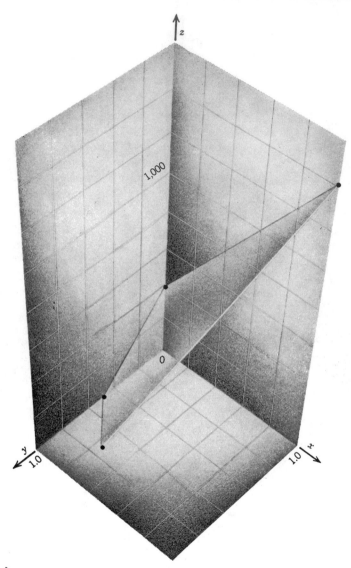

FIG. 6. Geometrical representation of a two-person zero-sum game.   The shaded quadrangle shows the opponent's strategy [1].

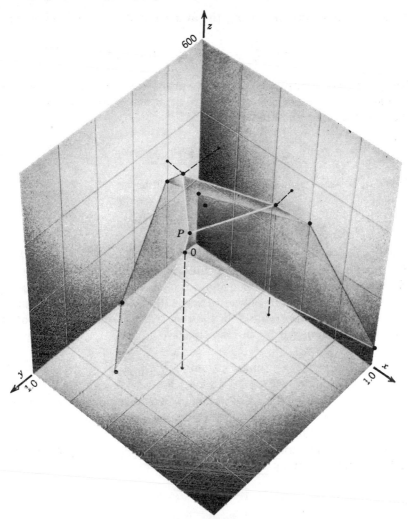

FIG. 7. Geometrical representation of a two-person zero-sum game. The roof-like structure represents the various strategies the opponent can play.

say that, if my opponent plays his strategy [2], then my gain is

$$z_2 = p_{1,2}x_1 + p_{2,2}x_2 + p_{3,2}x_3 \tag{49}$$

More generally, we can say that if my opponent plays his strategy j, then the payoff is given by

$$z_j = p_{1,j}x_1 + p_{2,j}x_2 + p_{3,j}x_3 \qquad j = 1, 2, 3, 4 \tag{50}$$

An abbreviated way of writing the above equation is the following:

$$z_j = \sum_{i=1}^{3} p_{i,j} x_i \qquad j = 1, 2, 3, 4 \tag{51}$$

Now, if I play strategy x_1, x_2, x_3, I can be certain to get at least the smallest of the gains z_1, z_2, z_3, and z_4. In other words, I can be certain that I get at least the amount

$$z = \min \left[\sum_{i=1}^{3} p_{i,1} x_i, \; \sum_{i=1}^{3} p_{i,2} x_i, \; \sum_{i=1}^{3} p_{i,3} x_i, \; \sum_{i=1}^{3} p_{i,4} x_i \right] \tag{52}$$

This can be written in an abbreviated fashion as

$$z = \min_{j} \left[\sum_{i=1}^{3} p_{i,j} x_i \right] \tag{53}$$

We recognize here that equations (52) and (53) describe the roof-like structure in Fig. 7. (Compare this relationship with equation (7), which describes the two-dimensional roof-like structure shown in Fig. 1.) Our problem in Fig. 7 was to select the strategies x_1, x_2, x_3 such that we obtain the top point P of the roof. Therefore, the value of the game can be expressed by the relationship

$$V = \max_{x_1 + x_2 + x_3 = 1} \left\{ \min_{j} \left[\sum_{i=1}^{3} p_{i,j} x_i \right] \right\} \tag{54}$$

We know that the value of V is 384. We recognize here that this method of expressing the value of the game is the same as the one we used in the two-dimensional case (see equation (11)).

Let us now have another look at our problem. Let v be a number such that for a strategy x_1, x_2, x_3 we have

$$p_{1,1} x_1 + p_{2,1} x_2 + p_{3,1} x_3 \geq v$$

$$p_{1,2} x_1 + p_{2,2} x_2 + p_{3,2} x_3 \geq v$$

$$p_{1,3} x_1 + p_{2,3} x_2 + p_{3,3} x_3 \geq v \tag{55}$$

$$p_{1,4} x_1 + p_{2,4} x_2 + p_{3,4} x_3 \geq v$$

As we have already demonstrated, I can be certain of getting at least v number of dollars. Therefore, the problem is to determine x_1, x_2, x_3, and v such that v takes the maximum possible value. (Again, compare equations (55) with equations (12), which refer to the two-dimensional case.)

We again introduce the notation $E(x_1, x_2, x_3; y_1, y_2, y_3, y_4)$ for the payoff function. Here,

$$y_1 + y_2 + y_3 + y_4 = 1 \qquad (56)$$

By using the same argument as we used in connection with equation (15), we deduce that the payoff function is given by

$$E = \sum_i \sum_j p_{i,j} x_i y_j \qquad (57)$$

With the aid of this notation we can express mathematically the fact that my strategy $x_1 = 0.4$, $x_2 = 0.5$, and $x_3 = 0.1$, is the best; that is, we can write

$$E(0.4, 0.5, 0.1; y_1, y_2, y_3, y_4) \geq 384 \qquad (58)$$

This says that, whatever strategy y_1, y_2, y_3, y_4 my opponent is using, I am certain to get at least \$384.

Let us proceed now to examine the best strategy of the opponent. He is to mix his strategies such that he keeps me down to this gain of \$384. By inspecting the roof in Fig. 7, we deduce that the top point is formed by his strategies [1], [2], and [4]; therefore, we conclude that he should use a mixture of these three strategies. (He should not use his strategy [3].) Moreover, we know that his mixed strategies [1], [2], and [4] can be represented by a plane going through point P. As he can only be certain to keep me down to the highest point of this plane (through the top of the roof), he should mix his strategies such that this particular plane becomes horizontal. (This is the same argument we used in connection with Fig. 1, when we decide that the opponent should mix his strategies [2] and [3] so that the line representing this mixture goes through D and is horizontal.) How should the opponent determine his strategies y_1, y_2, and y_4 such that the plane representing this mixture of strategies becomes horizontal? The payoff I am going to receive when he mixes his strategies in this proportion can be obtained by combining equations (44), (46), and (47). Therefore, my gain in this particular case is

$$z = y_1(1020x - 840y + 396) + y_2(-580x - 40y + 636) \\ + y_4(60x + 120y + 300) \quad (59)$$

which also can be written as

$$z = (1020y_1 - 580y_2 + 60y_4)x + (-840y_1 - 40y_2 + 120y_4)y \\ + 396y_1 + 636y_2 + 300y_4 \quad (60)$$

Now this plane becomes horizontal when the coefficient of x and y are zero. (In any other case, the gain would depend on a particular value of x or y and therefore the plane would not be horizontal.) We conclude, then, that the opponent should select his strategy y_1, y_2, and y_4

such that

$$1020y_1 - 580y_2 + 60y_4 = 0 \qquad (61)$$

$$-840y_1 - 40y_2 + 120y_4 = 0 \qquad (62)$$

Let us remember that the sum of y_1, y_2, y_3, and y_4 is 1, and that y_3 is zero.   Therefore,

$$y_1 + y_2 + y_4 = 1 \qquad (63)$$

We now have three equations for the three unknowns y_1, y_2, and y_4, and we can solve these equations and get

$$y_1 = 0.086$$

$$y_2 = 0.22$$

$$y_4 = 0.694$$

This is, then, the best strategy the opponent can employ.   This fact can be expressed mathematically by writing

$$E(x_1, x_2, x_3; 0.086, 0.22, 0, 0.694) \le 384 \qquad (64)$$

This says that, whatever strategy x_1, x_2, x_3 I select, the opponent can be certain to keep my gain at, or below, the \$384.   If he plays any other strategy, I will be able to develop a strategy such that I will get more than \$384.   On the other hand, if both of us play the best strategies, I get exactly \$384.   This can be expressed by the relationship

$$E(0.4, 0.5, 0.1; 0.086, 0.22, 0, 0.694) = 384 \qquad (65)$$

Let us develop now the minimax relationship.   Suppose that my opponent plays the strategy y_1, y_2, y_3, and y_4.   I might play my pure strategies (1) or (2) or (3), and he can be certain to keep my gain down to the largest of these three values.   In mathematical form, we say that he can be certain to keep me down to

$$z = \max_i [p_{i,1}y_1 + p_{i,2}y_2 + p_{i,3}y_3 + p_{i,4}y_4] \qquad (66)$$

This can also be written as

$$z = \max_i \left[\sum_{j=1}^{4} p_{i,j}y_j \right] \qquad (67)$$

As we said, he is certain to keep me down to this gain.   Now his problem is to mix his strategies such that this gain becomes the smallest. Therefore, his best strategy and the value of the game are given by

$$z = \min_{y_1+y_2+y_3+y_4=1} \left\{ \max_i \left[\sum_{j=1}^{4} p_{i,j}y_j \right] \right\} \qquad (68)$$

(Compare this with equation (27).)   We have here, then, the value of the game expressed as a minimax, and we recall that equation (54) expresses the value of the game as a maximim.   We recall that the value of the game is $384 whether computed from equation (64) or equation (68).

Finally, let us look again at the problem from a different point of view.   Let w denote a number such that

$$p_{1,1}y_1 + p_{1,2}y_2 + p_{1,3}y_3 + p_{1,4}y_4 \leq w \qquad (69)$$

$$p_{2,1}y_1 + p_{2,2}y_2 + p_{2,3}y_3 + p_{2,4}y_4 \leq w \qquad (70)$$

$$p_{3,1}y_1 + p_{3,2}y_2 + p_{3,3}y_3 + p_{3,4}y_4 \leq w \qquad (71)$$

We observe that w is larger than or equal to any of the numbers on the left-hand side, and, therefore, my opponent can be certain to keep me down at or below w.   My opponent's problem is, then, to select the values y_1, y_2, y_3, y_4, and w such that w becomes the smallest.   Compare this with the two-dimensional problem, where we used equations (28) and (29).

We can summarize, then, the state of affairs with the following mathematical statement:

$$E(0.4, 0.5, 0.1; y_1, y_2, y_3, y_4) \geq 384$$
$$\geq E(x_1, x_2, x_3; 0.086, 0.22, 0, 0.694) \qquad (72)$$

This corresponds to equation (30) of the two-dimensional case.   The left-hand side of equation (72) tells us that my best strategy is $x_1 = 0.4$, $x_2 = 0.5$, $x_3 = 0.1$, because, whatever strategy y_1, y_2, y_3, y_4 my opponent selects, I am certain to get at least $384.   The right-hand side of the equation tells us that the best strategy for my opponent is $y_1 = 0.086$, $y_2 = 0.22$, $y_3 = 0$, $y_4 = 0.694$; whatever strategy x_1, x_2, x_3 I use, he can be certain to keep me down to the $384.   We also know that, if I do not use my best strategy, he might counteract me with a strategy that would make me get less than the $384.   Furthermore, if he does not use his best strategy, I can develop a strategy that will give me more than the $384.

4.   THE m BY n RECTANGULAR GAME

We will now discuss the general two-person zero-sum rectangular game, with a payoff matrix of m rows and n columns.   We can assume that there are fewer (or at most equal number) rows than columns, because otherwise we can simply exchange the two players.   We denote by $p_{i,j}$ the elements of payoff matrix. The expected gain for the first person is given by

$$E(x_1, x_1, \cdots ; y_1, y_2, \cdots) = \sum_i \sum_j p_{i,j} x_i y_j \qquad (73)$$

In order to simplify matters, we will show the first person's gain as $E(x, y)$.

Suppose I play my mixed strategy $x_1, x_2, \cdots, x_m$, and my opponent plays his strategy [1]. Then I get the amount

$$z_1 = \sum_i p_{i,1} x_i \qquad (74)$$

On the other hand, if he plays his strategy [2] I get

$$z_2 = \sum_i p_{i,2} x_i \qquad (75)$$

We can similarly develop the formulas for other pure strategies my opponent may play. Now, I can be certain to get at least the smallest of these gains, or

$$z = \min_j \left(\sum_i p_{i,j} x_i \right) \qquad (76)$$

My problem is to mix my strategy $x_1, x_2, \cdots, x_m$ such that the gain I can be certain to get becomes the largest. This gain, which is the value of the game, is given by

$$V = \max_{\Sigma x_i = 1} \left[\min_j \left(\sum_i p_{i,j} x_i \right) \right] \qquad (77)$$

Now, let us consider my opponent's point of view, and assume that he plays the strategy $y_1, y_2, \cdots, y_n$. If I play my pure strategy (1), he keeps me down to the gain of

$$z_1 = \sum_j p_{1,j} y_j \qquad (78)$$

On the other hand, if I play my pure strategy (2), he can keep me down to

$$z_2 = \sum_j p_{2,j} y_j \qquad (79)$$

Naturally if he plays this strategy I will select the largest of these possible gains. Therefore, he can only be certain to keep me down to the gain of

$$z = \max_i \left(\sum_j p_{i,j} y_j \right) \qquad (80)$$

Now, my opponent's job is to select a strategy such that he will keep me down to the lowest possible figure. Consequently, his problem is to select y_1, y_2, $\cdots$, y_n such that this payoff becomes a minimum. Therefore, the value of the game is given by the relationship

$$z = \min_{\Sigma y_j = 1} \left[\max_i \left(\sum_j p_{i,j} y_j \right) \right] \tag{81}$$

We can see again that there are two ways to compute the value of the game, namely, by equation (77) or equation (81). According to the minimax theorem of the theory of games, these two ways always yield the same answer.

Let us denote my best strategy by $x_1{}^*$, $x_2{}^*$, $\cdots$, $x_m{}^*$ and my opponent's best strategy by $y_1{}^*$, $y_2{}^*$, $\cdots$, $y_m{}^*$. With this notation, we can put the fundamental theorem of the theory of games into the form

$$E(x^*; y) \geq V \geq E(x; y^*) \tag{82}$$

(This last equation is to be compared with equations (30) and (72)). The left-hand side of the equation says that, if I select my best strategy, then, whatever my opponent does, I am certain to get at least the amount V. The right-hand side of the equation says that, if my opponent selects his best strategy, then, whatever counter strategy I use, he can be certain to keep me down at least to the amount V.

We also know that, if I do not select my best strategy, then my opponent can develop a counterstrategy so that I am not going to get V dollars. Furthermore, if my opponent does not select his best strategy, I can choose a strategy so that I am going to get more than V dollars. Finally, if both of us use our best strategies, then my gain is exactly V dollars.

The problem arises now of how to compute these best strategies, and how to compute the value of the game for the m by n rectangular case.

5. COMPUTATION OF OPTIMUM STRATEGIES

Suppose I play the strategy x_1, x_2, $\cdots$, x_m. Let us consider the system of inequalities

$$
\begin{aligned}
p_{1,1}x_1 + p_{2,1}x_2 + \cdots + p_{m,1}x_m &\geq v \\
p_{1,2}x_1 + p_{2,2}x_2 + \cdots + p_{m,2}x_m &\geq v \\
\cdot \qquad\qquad \cdot \qquad\qquad\quad\; \cdot & \\
\cdot \qquad\qquad \cdot \qquad\qquad\quad\; \cdot & \\
\cdot \qquad\qquad \cdot \qquad\qquad\quad\; \cdot & \\
p_{1,n}x_1 + p_{2,n}x_2 + \cdots + p_{m,n}x_m &\geq v
\end{aligned}
\tag{83}
$$

and the equation

$$x_1 + x_2 + \cdots + x_m = 1 \tag{84}$$

The left-hand sides express my gain if my opponent plays his pure strategies [1], [2], and so on. Whichever of these strategies he selects, I am certain to get at least v number of dollars. Consequently, my problem is to select the $x_1, x_2, \cdots, x_m$ and v so that v becomes the largest possible number. Let us rewrite these equations with the aid of the notation

$$v = x_{m+1} \tag{85}$$

We get:

$$p_{1,1}x_1 + p_{2,1}x_2 + \cdots + p_{m,1}x_m - x_{m+1} \geq 0$$

$$p_{1,2}x_1 + p_{2,2}x_2 + \cdots + p_{m,2}x_m - x_{m+1} \geq 0$$

$$\tag{86}$$

$$p_{1,n}x_1 + p_{2,n}x_2 + \cdots + p_{m,n}x_n - x_{m+1} \geq 0$$

Let us consider now the linear programming problem with the restrictions given by equation (84) and (86), with the payoff function

$$z = c_1x_1 + c_2x_2 + \cdots + c_mx_m + c_{m+1}x_{m+1} \tag{87}$$

where the coefficients in the last equation are given numbers. Suppose our problem is to maximize the payoff function as given by equation (87). With the aid of the simplex method, we can solve this problem for any given values of the coefficient. Suppose, now, that we select these coefficients such that the first m of them are all zero, and the final one is exactly 1. This payoff function is exactly v. Therefore, if we solve this problem in linear programming with this particular payoff function, we automatically solve the game problem too. It can be seen, then, that the problem in the theory of games can be reduced to a problem in linear programming, and therefore can be solved by linear programming.

Let us now find the best strategy for the opponent. Let us assume that he plays the mixed strategy $y_1, y_2, \cdots, y_n$ and that w satisfies the following set of inequalities:

$$p_{1,1}y_1 + p_{1,2}y_2 + \cdots + p_{1,n}y_n \leq w$$

$$p_{2,1}y_1 + p_{2,2}y_2 + \cdots + p_{2,n}y_n \leq w$$

$$\tag{88}$$

$$p_{m,1}y_1 + p_{m,2}y_2 + \cdots + p_{m,n}y_n \leq w$$

The left-hand sides of these relations give the gains I would receive if I play my pure strategies (1), (2), and so on, and therefore my opponent can be certain to keep me down to the largest of these numbers, which is still smaller than or equal to w. Therefore, he can be certain to keep me down to w number of dollars. My opponent's problem is, then, to select the quantities $y_1, y_2, \cdots, y_n$ and w such that w takes the smallest value. We must not forget that

$$y_1 + y_2 + \cdots + y_n = 1 \qquad (89)$$

We can see, then, that my opponent's problem is to select the y's so that the above relations are satisfied and w becomes a minimum. Just the same way we did before, we introduce y_{n+1} instead of w and express the problem as a linear programming problem with a special payoff function. This linear programming problem, like any linear programming problem, can again be solved with the simplex method. Consequently, we see that the opponent's strategy can be determined again with the aid of linear programming.

Suppose we carry through these two computations as indicated. Are we going to obtain two numbers for the value of the game? The minimax theorem of the theory of games, states that this will not be the case. In the special cases we dealt with before, a geometrical argument showed that the minimax theorem holds. However, in the general case the minimax theorem is not self-evident at all. We are now able to show that the minimax theorem holds in the general case too.

6. "PROOF" OF THE MINIMAX THEOREM

Let us write equations (84) and (86) in the following form:

$$-p_{1,1}x_1 - p_{2,1}x_2 - p_{2,1}x_3 - \cdots - p_{m,1}x_m + x_{m+1} \leq 0$$
$$-p_{1,2}x_1 - p_{2,2}x_2 - p_{3,2}x_3 - \cdots - p_{m,2}x_m + x_{m+1} \leq 0$$

$$\qquad\qquad\qquad\qquad\qquad\qquad\qquad\qquad\qquad (90)$$

$$-p_{1,n}x_1 \quad p_{2,n}x_2 - p_{3,n}x_3 - \cdots - p_{m,n}x_m + x_{m+1} \leq 0$$
$$x_1 + \quad x_2 + \quad x_3 + \cdots \qquad\qquad + x_m \leq 1$$

As we know, the problem is to maximize z (which happens to be x_{m+1}). Notice that the last relationship, that is, the last row in (90), is a little bit different from equation (84) as we have here the inequality sign, instead of equality.   It is easy to show that this makes no difference, as the optimum solution to this new problem will automatically lead to such values of the x's that they will add up to one.

Similarly, we can write the relations (88) and (89) in the following form:

$$-p_{1,1}y_1 - p_{1,2}y_2 - \cdots - p_{1,n}y_n + y_{n+1} \geq 0$$

$$-p_{2,1}y_1 - p_{2,2}y_2 - \cdots - p_{2,n}y_n + y_{n+1} \geq 0$$

$$\tag{91}$$

$$-p_{m,1}y_1 - p_{m,2}y_2 - \cdots - p_{m,n}y_n + y_{n+1} \geq 0$$

$$y_1 + y_2 + \cdots + y_n \geq 0$$

The problem here is to minimize the payoff function y_{n+1}.   (Again the sum of the y's is assumed to be more than, or equal to, 1.   We can easily show again that the optimum solution automatically yields y's that add up to 1.)   The minimax theorem claims that the solution to these two problems are the same.   However, we recognize that the two problems we have stated here are each other's duals.   We have already proven in Chapter 5 that the dual problems lead to the same answer; therefore, we can see that the minimax theorem follows from the dual theorem.   We can therefore be certain that, whether we look at the problem from the first player's point of view or from the second player's point of view, we always get the same answer as the value of the game.   This fact forms the basis of the theory of games, and without it the theory could not exist.

PART III

PROGRAMMING
IN
PRODUCTION
AND
INVENTORY CONTROL

CHAPTER 10

Statistical
INVENTORY CONTROL

1. PROTECTION AGAINST UNCERTAINTY

In the business problems so far considered, we have assumed that all the facts of the problems are known in advance. For instance, we assumed that we are to produce to meet a known shipping schedule, or that the capacity of the warehouses is known in advance. We recognize that in all business situations there is a degree of uncertainty. Even when we produce to meet a firm shipping schedule, the customer may advance or delay delivery dates, or a warehouse may burn down or collapse. So far, we have ignored the possibility of such events and built our theory on the assumption that the future is known. Now we propose to study problems where it is essential to consider the future as uncertain. For instance, the inventory problem of a department store is such that future sales are not known in advance; in this problem uncertainty dominates. The scientific method of dealing with uncertainty involves the use of statistical theory; consequently, in this chapter we shall use the tools of statistics. However, we shall not assume a knowledge of statistics on the part of the reader, and shall develop our conceptual framework as the discussion proceeds.

To demonstrate, let us visualize a problem that might be faced by the buyer of a supermarket. He has to decide how many loaves of bread he should purchase every day. We assume that he orders in the evening and gets delivery (once a day) the next morning. If he orders too much bread, he is going to have stale bread left over; this repre-

sents a loss of money.   On the other hand, if he orders too little, there
is going to be an insufficient quantity of bread on hand.   This not
only represents a loss of sales but might also antagonize customers.
We are to set up a policy which determines how much bread is to be
ordered.   (We emphasize that we are presenting the case of this supermarket only as an example.)

Let us assume that the buyer keeps records of past demand; Fig.
1 shows the sales of bread for the past 100 days.   It is observed that
more than 9 loaves of bread were sold every day.   In one particular
day 31 loaves were sold.   We will assume that in the past there was an
ample supply of bread and that some stale bread was returned every

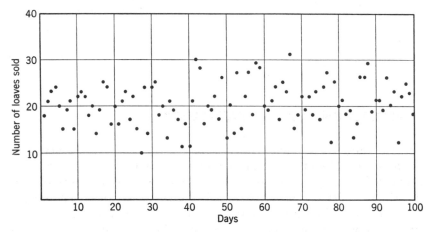

FIG. 1.   Record of sales of loaves of bread.

evening.   This is tantamount to saying that the demand (sales) was
less than supply.   (For instance, if the supermarket opens every
morning with a supply of 35 loaves of bread, then some stale bread
would have been returned every day.)   On the basis of the past
record, we will try to find out how much bread we should order for
tomorrow.

If we order 40 loaves, then probably we will never be short.   If we
order 35 loaves, again probably we will never be short; however, we do
not feel so secure in our belief that we will never be short.   Suppose
now that we had adopted a policy of ordering only 30 loaves of bread
for the past 100 days.   Then we observe from the diagram that we
would have been short just once, because it happened just once that
the demand was 31 loaves of bread, and the demand was never more
than that.   From our past experience, we can determine a frequency
distribution diagram as shown in Fig. 2.   This diagram shows that

during the past 100 days on four days 26 loaves of bread were sold;
and on eight days 22 loaves of bread were sold, that is, it shows the
frequency of sales for each particular number of loaves sold. Had we
ordered 29 loaves of bread a day during the past 100 days, we would
have been short twice, as once the demand was 30 and once 31. On the
other hand, had we ordered 26 loaves of bread each day during the last
100 days, we would have been short nine times. This can be determined from the diagram by adding up the number of times the demand
was 27, 28, 29, 30, and 31.

Let us now put this analysis into a mathematical form. Instead of
saying that the sales were 26 loaves four times, we say that 4% of the

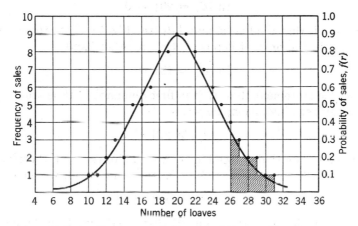

FIG. 2.   Frequency of demand of loaves of bread.

times the sales were 26 loaves of bread. This is a better way of putting
things, because we do not wish to distinguish, say, whether there were
eight times 26 loaves of bread sold in 200 days, or four times 26 loaves
of bread in 100 days To use the language of statistics, we say that
the probability of a demand being 26 is 0.04. We write this in
equation form as

$$\Pr\{D = 26\} = 0.04$$

The probability of a demand being equal to, or more than 26 is
0.09, and we write this in the form

$$\Pr\{D \geq 26\} = 0.09$$

On the other hand, the probability that the demand is less than, or
equal to, 26 is 0.91, and this can be written as

$$\Pr\{D \leq 26\} = 0.91$$

At this point, we introduce a new type of function that we will call an *indicator* function.   Let us consider a *true statement;* we say that the indicator function is 1, and we write

$$\text{In } \{\text{true statement}\} = 1$$

On the other hand, we say that the indicator function of a false statement is 0, and we write

$$\text{In } \{\text{false statement}\} = 0$$

We will give an illustration: Let us denote the past demand by d_1, $d_2, \cdots, d_{100}$.   We can write

$$\text{In } \{d_1 = 20\} = 0$$

The reason is that the first demand d_1 (see Fig. 1), is 18; therefore, the statement in the bracket is false.   On the other hand,

$$\text{In } \{d_1 = 18\} = 1$$

because the statement that d_1 (the first demand) is 18 is true.

As a further illustration, we write

$$\text{In } \{d_{10} \geq 22\} = 1$$

as sales on the tenth day (see Fig. 1) were 22 loaves, and, therefore, the statement in the bracket is true.   On the other hand, we have

$$\text{In } \{d_{10} < 18\} = 0$$

We observe in Fig. 1 (or in Fig. 2) that the demand was 26 loaves of bread four times.   We can put this into a mathematical equation

$$\sum_{1}^{100} \text{In } \{d_k = 26\} = 4 \tag{1}$$

To explain this in words: We have a series of 100 numbers, and these numbers are either zeros or ones, depending on whether the statement in the bracket is true or false.   As the statement is 96 times false, we have 96 zeros, and as the statement is only four times true, we have four times 1.   Consequently, the sum shown on the left-hand side of the equation is 4.   On the other hand, we can write that

$$\sum_{1}^{100} \text{In } \{d_k > 26\} = 9 \tag{2}$$

This equation holds because there are only nine terms for which the statement in the bracket is true.

What is the probability that the demand is more than 26?   In order to answer this question we survey the past demand in Fig. 1, add the number of cases where the demand is more than 26, and then divide this sum by 100.   With our mathematics we can write

$$\Pr \{D > 26\} = \tfrac{1}{100} \sum_{1}^{100} \text{In } \{d_k > 26\} \tag{3}$$

What is the probability that the demand equals a given value r? We can write

$$\Pr \{D = r\} = \tfrac{1}{100} \sum_{1}^{100} \text{In } \{d_k = r\} \tag{4}$$

To each value of the demand r there is a number which gives the probability that the demand is r number of loaves.   These probabilities form the frequency function shown in Fig. 2.   As such frequency distribution functions appear throughout our theory, we will denote them by $f(r)$.   So we write

$$\Pr \{D = r\} - f(r) \tag{5}$$

For instance, the value of $f(26)$ is 0.04, as shown in Fig. 2.

In addition to this probability, we are also interested in knowing the probability that the demand is below, or equal to, a certain level.   We denote this function, which is usually referred to as the cumulative distribution function, by $F(r)$.   So we write

$$\Pr \{D \le r\} = F(r) \tag{6}$$

For instance, $F(26)$ is 0.91, as the probability that the demand is equal to, or less than, 26 equals 0.91.

Finally, we are also interested in the probability of a shortage, that is, the probability that the demand is more than a given number r. We denote this probability distribution function by $G(r)$; then

$$\Pr \{D > r\} = G(r) \tag{7}$$

Of course, the demand is either more than r, or less than r, or equal to r.   Therefore,

$$F(r) + G(r) = 1 \tag{8a}$$

or

$$F(r) = 1 - G(r) \tag{8b}$$

The function $G(r)$ is shown in Fig. 3.   For instance, it can be seen that $G(26)$ is 0.09.

With this notation we can write the equation

$$F(r) = \sum_{i=1}^{r} f(i) \tag{9}$$

The left-hand side represents the probability that the demand is less than or equal to r.   On the right-hand side we have the sum of all the probabilities, that the demand equals 1, or 2, or 3, etc., up to r.

These are, then, the statistical distribution functions that summarize our knowledge of past sales.   A further important quantity is the average demand during the past 100 days.   This we get by adding all the loaves of bread sold and dividing by 100.   So we compute that the average demand is 20 loaves of bread.   Now if we order 26 loaves of bread, for instance, then we order 6 more than the average demand. We can say that these 6 loaves of bread represent a sort of protection (or insurance) against the uncertainty of demand.   If the demand were exactly 20 all the way through, we would order 20 loaves of bread.

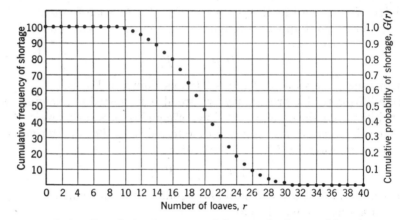

FIG. 3.   Cumulative frequency of shortage for loaves of bread.

However, owing to the fact that there is an uncertainty, we order more and expect to have a certain amount of stale bread.

Incidentally, the probability of the shortage can be computed from the frequency distribution with the aid of the formula

$$G(r) = \sum_{r+1}^{\infty} f(i) \tag{10}$$

The right-hand side of this equation can be represented by the shaded area in Fig. 2.   Each term corresponds to a rectangle which has the height of the distribution curve.   This area is often referred to as the area of the *tail* of the distribution curve.

So far, we have represented the distribution of demand as a series of dots in Fig. 2.   It is often easier to work with a smooth function, and more convenient to replace the dots shown in Fig. 2 by the smooth curve. With this type of representation, the area under the tail of the distribution curve can be computed with the aid of integral calculus. If we denote the continuous distribution function by $f(x)$, we get the relationship

$$\int_{r+1}^{\infty} f(x)\, dx = G(r) = 1 - F(r) \tag{11}$$

This gives us the cumulative distribution function as an integral. (All we have here is a new form of (10) with the aid of integral calculus.) We can also write

$$\int_{0}^{r} f(x)\, dx = F(r) \tag{12}$$

It will be seen in later examples that it is often easier to compute these integrals than the sums for the discrete distribution functions. The probability that the demand is less than infinite is, of course, 1. We can write this in a mathematical form as

$$F(\infty) = \int_{0}^{\infty} f(x)\, dx = 1 \tag{13}$$

Finally, there is one more distribution function that we will find useful. This is the so-called first moment of the distribution function, and can be defined as

$$\int_{0}^{r} x\, f(x)\, dx = F^{*}(r) \tag{14}$$

As an illustration of these various distribution functions, we will show a formal way of computing the mean demand (which in this particular case is 20 loaves of bread). We agreed that the way to get the mean is to add up all the various demands and divide by 100. We will make the problem a little more general, and assume that we are dealing with N number of days. Then we can write

$$\bar{d} = \frac{1}{N} \sum_{i=1}^{N} d_i \tag{15}$$

where $\bar{d}$ is the mean demand. How do we compute the mean if we know the probability distribution function? Let us replace the last equation by

$$\bar{d} = \frac{1}{N} \sum_{i=1}^{N} \left[\sum_{r=1}^{\infty} r \, \text{In} \, \{d_i = r\} \right] \tag{16a}$$

However,

$$f(r) = \frac{1}{N} \sum_{i=1}^{N} \text{In} \, \{d_i = r\} \tag{16b}$$

From this follows

$$\bar{d} = \sum_{i=1}^{\infty} r\,f(r) \qquad (17)$$

This is the method of computing the mean demand. If we deal with continuous distribution functions, we can write

$$\bar{d} = \int_0^{\infty} x\,f(x)\,dx \qquad (18)$$

We recognize here that the integral on the right-hand side is the same as the integral on the left-hand side of (14), except that we have to integrate from zero to infinity. Consequently, we have the result that the mean demand is given by evaluating the moment function at infinity or

$$F^*(\infty) = \bar{d} \qquad (19)$$

We see, then, that with the aid of these distribution functions we can answer questions relating to ordering policies that yield a given level of protection or probability of shortage. We realize that in our particular illustration of purchasing bread in a supermarket we can answer such questions directly with the aid of Figs. 1 and 2, and that the mathematics just summarizes matters in a convenient way. As our theory develops further, we will see that the mathematical analysis will yield answers in problems where a verbal or graphical analysis would be inadequate.

Before we proceed with our discussion, we wish to mentioned a relation that will be useful later. We obviously have

$$\int_r^{\infty} x\,f(x)\,dx = \int_0^{\infty} x\,f(x)\,dx - \int_0^r x\,f(x)\,dx \qquad (20)$$

and, consequently, with the aid of (14) and (19) we get

$$\int_r^{\infty} x\,f(x)\,dx = \bar{d} - F^*(r) \qquad (21)$$

2. THE NORMAL DISTRIBUTION

We have shown in the previous section that the illustrative example of an inventory control problem in a supermarket (how much bread to purchase) can be treated with the aid of statistical distribution functions. The particular shape of the distribution function (Fig. 2) will depend on the particular problem under consideration. Statisticians have studied a great variety of distribution functions, and we proceed now to acquaint the reader with some of the most important ones.

Perhaps the most important distribution function in statistics is the normal distribution function. For instance, the continuous line shown in Fig. 2 represents a normal distribution. The general formula* for the normal distribution is given by

$$f(r) = \frac{1}{\sigma \sqrt{2\pi}} \exp - \frac{1}{2}\left(\frac{r - \bar{d}}{\sigma}\right)^2 \tag{22}$$

where $\bar{d}$ represents the mean value of the variable, and σ denotes the standard deviation. For instance, the equation of the continuous line shown in Fig. 2 is given by

$$f(r) = \frac{1}{4.46 \sqrt{2\pi}} \exp - \frac{1}{2}\left(\frac{r - 20}{4.46}\right)^2 \tag{23}$$

Tables of values for the normal distribution function can be found in any book on statistics. For convenience, we reproduce in Table 1 the normal distribution function as expressed by the formula

$$\phi(\xi) = \frac{1}{\sqrt{2\pi}} e^{-\xi^2/2} \tag{24}$$

Let us illustrate the use of this table. The normal frequency distribution can be computed with the aid of formula

$$f(r) = \frac{1}{\sigma} \phi(\xi) \tag{25}$$

For instance, let us compute in Fig. 2 the value of the distribution at $r = 26$. We have here $\bar{d} = 20$, and $\sigma = 4.46$. Consequently,

$$\xi = \frac{r - \bar{d}}{\sigma} = \frac{26 - 20}{4.46} = 1.34 \tag{26}$$

We read the value of ϕ from Table 1 at 1.34, and get

$$\phi(1.34) = 0.163 \tag{27}$$

So we get for the distribution function

$$f(1.34) = \frac{\phi(1.34)}{4.46} = 0.037 \tag{28}$$

We can now compare this value with the value of 0.04 in Fig. 2 and see that the computed value is, indeed, close enough.

---

* When superiors to e are difficult to set in type, the expression exp is often used instead of e. Thus exp x would mean e^x. However, in simple formulas, there is no need for this notation.

TABLE 1. The Normal Distribution

ζ	$\phi(\zeta)$	$\Phi(\zeta)$	ζ	$\phi(\zeta)$	$\Phi(\zeta)$	ζ	$\phi(\zeta)$	$\Phi(\zeta)$
0.0	.398 942	.500 000	1.5	.129 518	.933 193	3.0	.004 432	.998 650
0.1	.396 952	.539 828	1.6	.110 921	.945 201	3.1	.003 267	.999 032
0.2	.391 043	.579 260	1.7	.094 049	.955 435	3.2	.002 384	.999 313
0.3	.381 388	.617 911	1.8	.078 950	.964 070	3.3	.001 723	.999 517
0.4	.368 270	.655 422	1.9	.065 616	.971 283	3.4	.001 232	.999 663
0.5	.352 065	.691 462	2.0	.053 991	.977 250	3.5	.000 873	.999 767
0.6	.333 225	.725 747	2.1	.043 984	.982 136	3.6	.000 612	.999 841
0.7	.312 254	.758 036	2.2	.035 475	.986 097	3.7	.000 425	.999 892
0.8	.289 692	.788 145	2.3	.028 327	.989 276	3.8	.000 292	.999 928
0.9	.266 085	.815 940	2.4	.022 395	.991 802	3.9	.000 199	.999 952
1.0	.241 971	.841 345	2.5	.017 528	.993 790	4.0	.000 134	.999 968
1.1	.217 852	.864 334	2.6	.013 583	.995 339	4.1	.000 089	.999 979
1.2	.194 186	.884 930	2.7	.010 421	.996 533	4.2	.000 059	.999 987
1.3	.171 369	.903 200	2.8	.007 915	.997 445	4.3	.000 039	.999 991
1.4	.149 727	.919 243	2.9	.005 953	.998 134	4.4	.000 025	.999 995
						4.5	.000 016	.999 997

In Fig. 4, we show graphically the ϕ function which is tabulated in Table 1.   The curve in Fig. 4 has the same shape as the one in Fig. 2. The only difference is that the horizontal and vertical scales are changed.

We return now to our problem of ordering bread in the supermarket and describe the solution in a somewhat different way.   Suppose the order quantity is 26, which is 6 above the mean of 20.   Let us compare this protective level of 6 with the standard deviation 4.46.   We note that the protective level is 1.34 times the standard deviation.   The normal curve as tabulated in Table 1 gives directly the answer to the

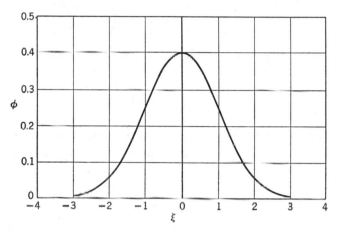

FIG. 4.   The normal distribution, $\phi(\xi)$.

question, "What is the probability that the demand is 1.34 times the standard deviation?"

We can put this into mathematical form in the following way: we say that the order quantity is $\bar{d} + \xi\sigma$, which means that we are ordering above the mean by an amount expressed as a multiple of the standard deviation.   The probability distribution for this demand is then given by

$$f(\bar{d} + \xi\sigma) = \frac{1}{\sigma\sqrt{2\pi}} e^{-\xi^2/2} = \frac{\phi(\xi)}{\sigma} \tag{29}$$

As a further illustration, suppose that we order 24 units.   This is 4 above the mean of 20, and this 4 is 0.9 times the standard deviation of 4.46.   Consequently, we need to look up in the normal distribution table the ϕ value for 0.9, and we get

$$\phi(0.9) = 0.266$$

and

$$f(24) = 0.06$$

We can compare this with Fig. 2 and observe that the normal distribution line in Fig. 2, at 24, has the value of 0.055. This is quite close to the number given by the formula.

We have seen in Section 1 of this chapter that in order to compute probabilities of shortages it is necessary to have the cumulative distribution function or the area "under the tail." It follows from equations (12) and (22) that the cumulative normal distribution is given by

$$F(r) = \frac{1}{\sigma \sqrt{2\pi}} \int_{-\infty}^{r} \exp\left[-\frac{1}{2}\left(\frac{x - \bar{d}}{\sigma}\right)^2 \right] dx \qquad (30)$$

In Table 1, third column, we have tabulated the cumulative normal distribution function

$$\Phi(\xi) = \frac{1}{\sqrt{2\pi}} \int_{-\infty}^{\xi} \exp\left(-\frac{1}{2}t^2 \right) dt \qquad (31)$$

and we plot this function in Fig. 5. This Φ function is related to the

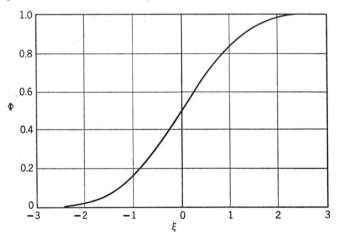

FIG. 5.   The cumulative normal distribution, $\Phi(\xi)$.

cumulative normal distribution function through

$$F(r) = \Phi(\xi) \qquad (32)$$

and

$$G(r) = 1 - F(r) = 1 - \Phi(\xi) \qquad (33)$$

where again

$$\xi = \frac{r - \bar{d}}{\sigma} \qquad (34)$$

As an illustration, let us assume that the ordering quantity is 26. We have already discovered that the ξ value for this case is 1.34. In Table 1 we can read the value of the cumulative normal distribution function as

$$\Phi(\xi) = 0.910$$

from which it follows

$$G(26) = 0.090$$

This means that the probability of a shortage is 0.090. Compare this with Fig. 3. It so happens that the number in Fig. 3 is exactly 0.09. However, this agreement is only a coincidence; the important thing is that the formula gives a good approximation.

The probability of a shortage can also be written with the aid of equation (33) as

$$\Pr \{D > \bar{d} + \xi\sigma\} = 1 - \Phi(\xi) \tag{35}$$

This relationship gives the probability of a shortage directly, provided that the order quantity is expressed above the mean as a multiple of the standard deviation. As an example, suppose that we want to order so that the probability of a shortage is 0.01. This implies a Φ value of 0.99, which implies from Table 1 a ξ value of 2.32. The quantity that we have to order above the mean of 20 is given by

$$w = 2.32(4.46) = 10.4$$

which means that the order quantity is $20 + 10.4 = 30.4$. (From a practical point of view, this means that we order either 30 or 31.)

In summary, we can say that with the aid of Table 1 we can determine any ordering level which corresponds to a prescribed level of protection, or, in other words, for any given ordering quantity we can compute the level of protection.

In these computations one begins by determining the mean value and standard deviation from a given set of past data. The mean value is easy to get as all we have to do is add all the past demand and divide by the number of cases, or

$$\bar{d} = \frac{1}{N} \sum_{1}^{N} d_i \tag{36}$$

The formula for standard deviation is more complicated, so we just mention here without proof that

$$\sigma = \sqrt{\frac{\Sigma(d_i - \bar{d})^2}{N}} \tag{37}$$

Before we leave our discussion of the normal distribution, we will give for later use the formulae for the moment functions. These are given by

$$F^*(r) = \frac{1}{\sigma \sqrt{2\pi}} \int_{-\infty}^{r} x \exp\left[-\frac{1}{2}\left(\frac{x - \bar{d}}{\sigma}\right)^2\right] dx \qquad (38)$$

and

$$F^*(r) = \bar{d}\, F(r) - \sigma^2 f(r) \qquad (39)$$

3. THE POISSON DISTRIBUTION

Another important type of distribution is given in Fig. 6. This might represent a case where the average demand is 3. In such a case the picture cannot be symmetrical (as in Fig. 2), as the only possible demand below 3 is 0, 1, or 2, whereas there are many possible demands

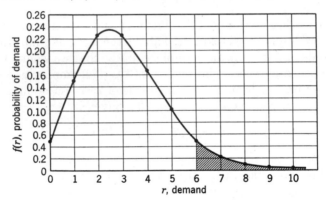

FIG. 6. Probability distribution of demand given by Poisson distribution. (Average demand is 3.)

above 3. Nonsymmetrical distribution functions of this type often follow the Poisson rule. The formula for this distribution is given by

$$f(r) = \Pr\{D = r\} = \frac{e^{-\bar{d}}\bar{d}^r}{r!} \qquad (40)$$

We can illustrate this formula by writing it out for different values of r. For instance, when r is 1 we get the probability that the demand is 1:

$$f(1) = e^{-\bar{d}}\bar{d} \qquad (41)$$

When r is 2, we get

$$f(2) = \tfrac{1}{2}\, e^{-\bar{d}}\bar{d}^2 \qquad (42)$$

When r is 5, we get

$$f(5) = \frac{1}{5(4)(3)(2)} e^{-\bar{d}}(\bar{d})^5 \tag{43}$$

The expression r factorial in the denominator of equation (40) represents the product of the first r numbers; for instance, 10 factorial is given by

$$10! = (10)(9)(8)(7)(6)(5)(4)(3)(2) \tag{44}$$

$$= 3,628,800$$

Just like a normal distribution, the Poisson distribution has been tabulated by statisticians.*

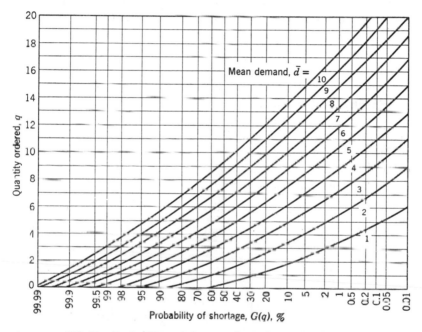

FIG. 7. Probability of shortage for Poisson distribution.

We know from our previous work that it is not enough to have the probability distribution function; we also need to know the cumulative distribution function so we can compute the probability of a shortage. With the aid of equations (11) and (12), these cumulative distribution functions can be computed, and the Molina tables gives these values too.   For convenience, in Fig. 7 we present a graphical picture of the

* E. C. Molina, *Poisson's Exponential Binomial Limit*, D. Van Nostrand, Princeton, N. J., 1942.

probability of a shortage for the Poisson distribution. Suppose, for
instance, that we deal with a case where the mean value $\bar{d}$ is 3 and the
quantity ordered $q = 6$.   In Fig. 7 we select the curve $\bar{d} = 3$ and find
that the probability of a shortage, that is, the value of $G(q)$, is 0.034.
(We can, of course, also get this value from our Fig. 6, which shows the
Poisson distribution when the mean is 3.)

When the value of the mean becomes larger and larger, the Poisson
distribution becomes more and more symmetrical, and more and more
like a normal distribution.   The fact of the matter is that for our work
it is adequate to use the normal distribution when the mean is more
than 10.   However, in order to be able to use the normal distribution,
it is not enough to have the mean; we also need to know the standard
deviation.   We state here, without proof, that the standard deviation σ for the Poisson distribution is given by the square root of the
mean, or

$$\sigma = \sqrt{\bar{d}}$$

4. THE RECTANGULAR DISTRIBUTION

Before we return to our work in inventory control, there is one more
distribution function we want to discuss.   Let us assume that the
demand is equally distributed between 11 and 30, or that the probability is 0.05 that the demand is 11 units, 12 units, etc., all the way up

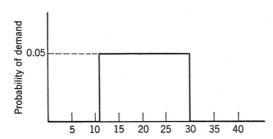

FIG. 8.   Rectangular probability distribution function.

to 30 units.   Such a distribution function is given in Fig. 8.   Mathematically speaking, we say that the distribution is given by

$$f(r) = 0 \qquad \text{for} \quad r \leq 10 \tag{45a}$$

$$f(r) = 0.05 \quad \text{for} \quad 10 < r \leq 30 \tag{45b}$$

$$f(r) = 0 \qquad \text{for} \quad r > 30 \tag{45c}$$

We can express this relationship with the aid of our indicator function as

$$f(r) = 0.05 \text{ In } \{10 < r \leq 30\} \qquad (45d)$$

The probability of having no shortage, that is, the cumulative distribution function, is given by

$$F(r) = 0 \qquad \qquad \text{for} \quad r \leq 10 \qquad (46a)$$

$$F(r) = 0.05(r - 10) \quad \text{for} \quad 10 < r \leq 30 \qquad (46b)$$

$$F(r) = 1 \qquad \qquad \text{for} \quad r > 30 \qquad (46c)$$

This cumulative function is shown in Fig. 9. For instance, if we order 25 units, then the cumulative distribution function has a value of 0.75, which means that the probability of not having a shortage is 0.75 and the probability of having a shortage is 0.25.

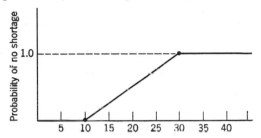

FIG. 9. Cumulative probability distribution function for rectangular distribution.

How do we compute the quantity q to be ordered that gives a given level of protection? Let us say that we want to have a probability of a shortage of 0.1, or $G(q) = 0.1$. This means that

$$F(q) = 0.9 \qquad (47)$$

From equation (46b) it follows that

$$0.05(q - 10) = 0.90 \qquad (48)$$

and therefore

$$q = 28 \qquad (49)$$

We see, then, that in order to have a 10% probability of a shortage, we have to order 28 units.

Let us now develop the equations for the general case of a rectangular distribution. Let us assume that the demand is between M and $\bar{M}$. Then, the distribution function is given by

$$f(r) = \frac{1}{\bar{M} - M} \qquad \text{when } M < r \leq \bar{M}, \text{ otherwise zero} \qquad (50)$$

and the cumulative distribution is given by

$$F(r) = \int_M^r \frac{dx}{\bar{M} - M} = \frac{r - M}{\bar{M} - M} \tag{51}$$

The probability of a shortage, if we order a quantity q, is given by

$$G(q) = 1 - F(q) = \frac{\bar{M} - q}{\bar{M} - M} \tag{52}$$

which can also be written as

$$\Pr\{D > q\} = \frac{\bar{M} - q}{\bar{M} - M} \tag{53}$$

As an illustration, let us consider the case when $M = 100$, $\bar{M} = 300$, which means that the demand is between 100 and 300. Let us assume that we want a protection against a shortage of 1%, that is, a probability of a shortage of 0.01. Equation (53) indicates that we have to order 298 units to get this level of protection.

Finally, we mention here for later use that the moment distribution function for rectangular distribution is given by

$$F^*(r) = \int_M^r \frac{x\,dx}{\bar{M} - M} = \frac{r^2 - M^2}{2(\bar{M} - M)} \tag{54a}$$

The mean is given by

$$\bar{d} = \frac{M + \bar{M}}{2} \tag{54b}$$

5. PROTECTION AGAINST LOSS OF BUSINESS

Let us again put ourselves (as an exercise) in the place of the manager of the hypothetical supermarket. So far, we assumed that he can take a chance of being out of bread once or twice in every hundred days. It is conceivable, however, that we should look at the matter in a different fashion. The manager might feel that his problem is the number of dissatisfied customers. Not the profit made on bread but the good will of the customers is important. When a customer finds that there is no bread, he will be dissatisfied, and if this happens too many times he is not going to shop in this particular supermarket. Therefore, the manager might argue that he can tolerate one customer out of a hundred (or one out of a thousand) to be dissatisfied. The problem is to balance dissatisfied customers against the quantity of stale bread.

Suppose that he decides to order 26 loaves of bread every morning. How many dissatisfied customers is he going to have? We can observe from Fig. 2 that he sold 27 loaves three times, 28 loaves twice, 29 loaves twice, 30 loaves once, and 31 loaves once. Had he ordered only 26 loaves of bread, he would have been short z times, where

$$z = 3(1) + 2(2) + 2(3) + 1(4) + 1(5) = 22 \qquad (55)$$

The total number of sales is approximately 2,000, as we have records for a hundred days, and the average sale is 20 loaves of bread. Twenty-two dissatisfied customers out of 2,000 means a dissatisfaction level of 1.1%. In terms of probability, we can say that had he ordered 26 loaves of bread, the probability of having a dissatisfied customer would have been 0.011.

We want to put this method of calculation into mathematical form so that we can handle this problem in general. With the aid of our indicator function, we can say that the number of dissatisfied customers is given by

$$z - \text{In } \{d = 27\} + 2 \text{ In } \{d = 28\} + 3 \text{ In } \{d = 29\} + \cdots \qquad (56)$$

which can be written as

$$z = 100[f(27) + 2\,f(28) + 3\,f(29) + \cdots] \qquad (57)$$

where, for instance, $f(27) = 0.03$, $f(28) = 0.02$, and so on. We can write this in a more concise form as

$$z = N \sum_{r=q+1}^{\infty} (r - q) f(r) \qquad (58)$$

where q is the order quantity and N is the number of days for which we have a record. We denote by $\bar{d}$ the mean demand (in this case, 20); then the total number of sales is given by N times $\bar{d}$. Consequently, the fraction of dissatisfied customers is obtained by taking the right-hand side of equation (58) and dividing it by $N\bar{d}$

$$z^* = \frac{1}{\bar{d}} \sum_{r=q+1}^{\infty} (r - q) f(r) \qquad (59)$$

This can be written with the aid of the continuous distribution function as

$$z^* = \frac{1}{\bar{d}} \int_{q+1}^{\infty} (x - q) f(x)\, dx \qquad (60)$$

The fraction of dissatisfied customers can be evaluated with the aid of equations (12), (14), and (21). We get

$$z^* = \frac{1}{\bar{d}} [q\, F(q) - F^*(q) - (q - \bar{d})] \tag{61}$$

We see, now, that in this problem the moment distribution function appears, and this is precisely the reason we have computed these moment functions in advance for the normal distribution and for the rectangular distribution. For instance, if the distribution is normal, we can use equation (39) and get for the fraction of dissatisfied customers the formula

$$z^* = \frac{1}{\bar{d}} [\sigma^2 f(q) + (q - \bar{d})\, F(q) - (q - \bar{d})] \tag{62}$$

Let us express again the order quantity with the aid of a deviation w above the mean, and let ξ denote the ratio of w to the standard deviation σ of the normal distribution. In other words, let us write again

$$q = \bar{d} + w = \bar{d} + \xi\sigma \tag{63}$$

With this notation, the fraction of dissatisfied customers can be expressed as

$$z^* = \frac{\sigma}{\bar{d}} [\phi(\xi) + \xi\Phi(\xi) - \xi] \tag{64}$$

As a verification of this last formula, let us take the case where the order quantity q is 26. We know that the mean $\bar{d}$ is 20, and that therefore w (the quantity above the mean) is 6. In our particular case, the standard deviation was 4.46 and consequently the value for ξ is 1.34. Therefore, we get for the fraction of dissatisfied customers

$$z^* = \frac{4.46}{20} [\phi(1.34) + 1.34\Phi(1.34) - 1.34]$$

$$= \frac{4.46}{20} [0.163 + 1.34(0.91) - 1.34]$$

If this computation is carried out, we get 0.009 for the fraction of dissatisfied customers, which means that 0.9% of the customers will be dissatisfied. This compares with the 1.1% which was obtained directly from Fig. 2. It can be seen that the agreement is very good.

As a further illustration of equation (61), let us assume now that the demand is rectangular. With the aid of equations (51) and (54) we can compute the fraction of dissatisfied customers as

$$z^* = \frac{(\bar{M} - q)^2}{\bar{M}^2 - M^2} \tag{65}$$

Suppose we are dealing with a case where the demand is rectangular and between 200 and 300, and let us assume that we allow 1% of dissatisfied customers. With the aid of equation (65) we can immediately compute that the order quantity must be 278.

We have seen here an illustration of how statistical distribution functions help to solve problems in inventory control. We will now re-examine the underlying reasoning used so far and, specifically, examine the problem of how we should specify the probability of a shortage, or the probability of having a dissatisfied customer.

6. THE IMPUTED COST OF A SHORTAGE; LOSS FUNCTIONS

Suppose the manager of this hypothetical supermarket tolerates a 5% probability that a shortage occurs; we propose to make a cost analysis of this policy. Let us assume that each loaf of bread costs 8 cents and that there is a refund of 2 cents on stale bread. This means that there is a loss of 6 cents on each loaf of bread not sold. A detailed computation shows that the policy of allowing a 5% level of shortage leads to an ordering quantity of 27.34 loaves of bread. (The decimal digits do not mean anything from a practical point of view; we carry them only for our calculations.) What is the loss on stale bread during the 100-day period?

We will purchase 2,734 loaves of bread and sell 2000 − 22 = 1,978 loaves. (According to equation (55) there will be 22 dissatisfied customers, and so there will be 22 lost sales.) There will be 756 loaves of stale bread, and, as there is a 6-cent loss on each loaf, there will be a total loss of $45.36. This is, then the loss that the supermarket is willing to risk to get an insurance of not being out of bread more than 5% of the time. Let us now compute this cost for some other policy. Suppose we permit a shortage to be tolerated only 4% of the time. With the aid of the formulae we have developed so far, it is easy to compute that this policy leads to the somewhat higher ordering quantity of 27.81 loaves of bread. The dollar loss associated with this ordering policy can be computed easily as $48.18. It can be seen that there is a difference of $2.82 between the two policies, and this is the penalty the supermarket has to pay for the policy of allowing fewer shortages. The policy of 5% shortages implies that it is not worth paying $2.82 for the advantage of having one shortage less per 100 days. If we assume, now, that there is a cost to be associated with each shortage, we can say that the imputed cost of a shortage per 100 days is certainly not more than $2.82. Otherwise, the manager would decide to pay this difference of $2.82 and decrease the probability of a shortage.

Let us look at the problem from the other end now, and assume that the policy is one of allowing six shortages per hundred, that is, of allowing a probability shortage of 0.06. This level of protection leads to ordering a quantity of 26.94 loaves of bread, and the loss due to stale bread is $42.96. We can see, then, that we could save $2.40 if only we allowed one more shortage. The policy, however, dictates that the supermarket is not willing to take this additional shortage. Therefore, we must assume that the imputed cost of a shortage is more than $2.40. We see, then, that the policy of allowing a 5% shortage implies that the cost of a shortage is between $2.40 and $2.82.

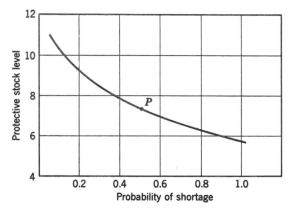

FIG. 10.   Protective stock level versus probability of shortage.

In order to refine this argument, we have plotted in Fig. 10 the protective stock level required for each probability of shortage. For instance, point P shows that the probability of 0.05 requires an ordering level of 7.4 above the average of 20. Instead of showing the protective stock level, we could plot the cost associated with each level of protection. By taking the slope of the curve at point P, we can determine more accurately that the imputed cost of a shortage is $2.69. We must remember that this imputed cost is a consequence of the policy of a 5% shortage. If the policy were at some other level of protection, we would get a different value of the imputed cost. Mathematically, the cost of shortage z is given by

$$z = 2.69 \ln \{d > q\} \qquad (66)$$

This equation means that the cost of each shortage is $2.69, as the right-hand side of the equation is 1 only when the demand d is more than the order quantity q. (It might not be unnecessary to remark that, although we reached this result on the basis of an analysis of 100 days of operations, we would get the same result had we analyzed a longer historical record.)

More generally, we say that in each inventory control problem there is a cost of shortage, depending on the order quantity and the demand. We will call this function the *loss function* and we will denote it by $W(q, d)$. In the present case, therefore, we can say that the loss function is given by

$$W(q, d) = 2.69 \text{ In } \{d > q\} \tag{67}$$

At this point, let us question the ordering policy in this hypothetical supermarket. Is it really proper to assign a loss of $2.69 to each shortage? In order to answer this question, we have to analyze what happens in case of a shortage. Perhaps bread has to be reordered on a rush basis and a truck has to be sent over to get the extra bread, involving a cost of $2.69. If an analysis is made of what happens in the case of a shortage, we may be able to determine the true cost involved and then, with the aid of the curve shown in Fig. 10, we can determine the proper level of protection. For instance, we might say that each customer, when he does not get what he wants, is antagonized and that there is a loss of good will, and this loss of good will is proportional to the number of dissatisfied customers. If we say that a cost of 5 cents is assigned to each of these dissatisfied customers, then the cost of shortage would be 0.05 times the number of loaves of bread we are short. This can be put into mathematical form by writing

$$W(q, d) = 0.05(d - q)_+ \tag{68}$$

Let us remember that the little plus sign on the right-hand corner of the parenthesis denotes the fact that, when d is larger than q, then the factor on the right hand side is $d - q$ and that, when d is less than q (that is, the quantity is negative in the parenthesis), then it is 0. This is the proper symbolism to use because, if the demand is less than the quantity ordered, then of course there should be no loss. (This is the same notation we used in Chapter 8, Section 4.) Incidentally, with the aid of an indicator function, we can write

$$(x)_+ = x \text{ In } \{x \geq 0\} \tag{69}$$

Now suppose that we have a record of past sales $d_1, d_2, \cdots, d_N$, and we want to compute the average loss suffered as a consequence of a policy of ordering q loaves of bread. Every day the loss is given by $W(w, d)$. Therefore the total loss is given by adding all these losses together, and the average loss is obtained by dividing by the number of days N. Consequently, we get for the average loss

$$\bar{W}(q) = \frac{1}{N} \sum_{i=1}^{N} W(q, d_i) \qquad (70)$$

So far, we have not considered the sale price of bread. Suppose that the sale price is 20 cents, whereas the cost is 8 cents again, and suppose that there is a refund of 2 cents on each loaf of stale bread. Suppose that on a particular day the demand is d, but that this demand d is less than the quantity q ordered. What would the profit be this day? We get 20 cents for each loaf of bread sold, we get 2 cents for each stale loaf returned, and we have to pay 8 cents for each loaf of bread purchased. Consequently, we can say

$$\text{Profit} = 0.20d + 0.02(q - d) - 0.08q$$

Many publications in inventory control deal with the concept of a loss or cost. In this terminology profit appears as negative cost (or negative loss), and therefore the loss function in this particular problem would be written as

$$W(q, d) = 0.08q - 0.20d - 0.02(q - d) \qquad \text{when } d \leq q \quad (71a)$$

(We remind ourselves on the right-hand side that this equation holds only when the demand d is less than the order quantity q.) When the demand d is more than q, we sell q loaves of bread and there is a 12-cent profit on each loaf; this appears as a negative loss. Consequently, the loss function in case of a shortage can be written as

$$W(q, d) = -0.12q + 2.69 \qquad \text{when } d > q \qquad (71b)$$

The \$2.69 refers to the penalty suffered when a shortage occurs.

Another possibility is that we cannot reorder when there is a shortage. In this case, we can still write that the loss when we meet the demand is given by

$$W(q, d) = 0.08q - 0.20d - 0.02(q - d) \qquad \text{when } d \leq q \quad (72a)$$

However, when there is a shortage, there is a profit of 12 cents for each loaf of bread sold, or

$$W(q, d) = -0.12q \qquad \text{when } d > q \qquad (72b)$$

Incidentally, these two equations can be written as one by using the following symbolisms

$$W(q, d) = -0.12q + 0.18(q - d)_+ \qquad (72c)$$

We might argue that the above loss function is not a very realistic one as we ignore the loss of customer good will. Suppose that there is a 5-cent penalty when there is loss of sale. We can still write our loss function when there is no shortage as

$$W(q, d) = 0.08q - 0.20d - 0.02(q - d) \qquad d \leq q \qquad (73a)$$

However, the loss function when there is a shortage becomes

$$W(q, d) = -0.12q + 0.05(d - q) \qquad d > q \qquad (73b)$$

These two equations again can be summarized into a single equation by writing

$$W(q, d) = -0.12q + 0.18(q - d)_+ - 0.05(d - q)_+ \qquad (73c)$$

We obtain another type of a loss function if, each time we face a shortage, we purchase another loaf of bread at a premium price. If we assume that there is a 6-cent premium on each additional loaf of bread that has to be purchased, we can write the loss function in the following form

$$W(q, d) = 0.08q - 0.20d - 0.02(q - d)_+ + 0.14(d - q)_+ \qquad (74)$$

We have listed here a number of possible loss functions that can occur in connection with this hypothetical problem. How do we determine the proper loss function?   A study must be made of actual operations in the business; we have to evaluate the various costs involved and reach a rational estimate of the loss.

There are many business problems where it is very difficult or even impossible to arrive at a cost of a shortage. We will see later, as we develop our theory further, that there are some alternative ways of making decisions even when loss functions are not available.   However, for the time being we assume that a loss function can be established, and we will predicate our theory on this assumption.   The great advantage of having a loss function is that the profit of the business enterprise can be written down and then mathematical techniques can be developed for maximizing the profit.   However, before we develop this optimizing technique, we want to elaborate further on the concept of a loss function.   Therefore, we proceed now to describe some other inventory problems where loss functions play an important role.

When the United States Navy makes an aircraft carrier or a battleship, it is customary to make certain large spare parts for each individual ship.   These spare parts might be very expensive, but, if they are not made initially, it is practically impossible to make them at a later date.   For instance, making one spare part might cost \$90,000 at the time when the aircraft carrier is made, but, if the aircraft carrier is damaged and no spare is available, then the whole carrier has to be reworked involving a loss of, say, \$10,000,000.   Let us denote by A the cost of a spare and by B the cost of the aircraft carrier.   Let q spares be made at the time of construction of the aircraft carrier, and let d denote the total demand for spares.   Then the loss function can be written as

$$W(q, d) = Aq + B \text{ In } \{d > q\} \tag{75}$$

This formula says that, if the demand d is less than q, then the cost is A times q.   On the other hand, if the demand d exceeds the quantity of spares, the cost will be the cost of the spares plus the cost of rework on the aircraft carrier.

Another possible situation is the following: an airline is purchasing a fleet of airplanes and wants to determine how many spare engines should be ordered.   After the first batch of engines are made, the tools are scrapped and no further engines can be made.   The loss function in this case is the number of spare engines multiplied by the price of each engine plus the cost involved in scrapping airplanes which lack engines. Mathematically speaking, we can write this in equation form as

$$W(q, d) = Aq + B(d - q)_+ \tag{76}$$

where A is the cost of each engine and B is the loss suffered when an airplane is scrapped.

A further different situation is the following: the airline has a fleet of airplanes and some spare engines.   The airline is still in a position to order some more engines, but this is the last chance—if they do not order now, they will not be able to get more engines.   In this case the loss function will depend on the quantity u they already have, the quantity q that they reorder, and on the demand d.   We write such a loss function in the form $W(u, q, d)$.   In this particular case, the form of the loss function is the following:

$$W(u, q, d) = Aq + B(d - q - u)_+ + C \text{ In } \{q > 0\} \tag{77}$$

where A is the cost of each engine, B is the cost of losing a plane, and C is the cost of reordering engines.   It is conceivable that the best policy is not to reorder, in which case this last term is 0.   On the other hand, if they do reorder, there is the cost of reordering.

For a further illustration of loss functions, let us return again to our problem in the hypothetical supermarket.   Let us consider the possibility that we can reorder bread at noontime.   This is a two-stage problem, the first stage being the morning and the second stage the afternoon. In order to describe this business situation, we need two loss functions, one for the morning and one for the afternoon. Let us denote by q_1 the quantity ordered for morning and by d_1 the demand in the morning. Under the assumption that the morning demand is less than the quantity ordered in the morning, the loss is given by

$$W_1(q_1, d_1) = 0.08q_1 - 0.20d_1 \qquad \text{if } d_1 \leq q_1 \qquad (78a)$$

On the other hand, if the demand in the morning is more than the quantity at hand, then the loss function is given by

$$W_1(q_1, d_1) = -012q_1 \qquad \text{if } d_1 > q_1 \qquad (78b)$$

Let us turn our attention now to the afternoon situation. If the demand in the morning was less than the quantity ordered, we start at noon with an inventory of $q_1 - d_1$ loaves of bread. On the other hand, if the morning demand is equal to or higher than the quantity at hand, we have no inventory at noontime. Let us denote by v the inventory of bread at noontime; then

$$v = (q_1 - d_1)_+ \qquad (79)$$

Let us denote by q_2 the quantity ordered at noontime. (q_2 might be zero.) The cost of ordering say is given by

$$z = 2.69 \text{ In } \{q_2 > 0\} \qquad (80)$$

Let us denote by d_2 the demand in the afternoon Then the loss during the afternoon is given by

$$W_2(v, q_2, d_2) = 2.69 \text{ In } \{q_2 > 0\} + 0.08q_2 - 0.20d_2$$
$$- 0.02(v + q_2 - d_2) \qquad \text{when } d_2 \leq v + q_2 \quad (81)$$

where it is assumed that the demand in the afternoon is less than the noon inventory plus the quantity reordered. On the other hand, if the demand in the afternoon is higher than the inventory plus the quantity reordered (if a shortage occurs), then

$$W_2(v, q_2, d_2) = 2.69 \text{ In } \{q_2 > 0\} + 0.08q_2$$
$$- 0.20(v + q_2) \qquad \text{when } d_2 > v + q_2 \quad (82)$$

The total loss function for the two-stage problem is obtained by adding the loss for the morning and the afternoon, or

$$W(q_1, d_1, q_2, d_2) = W_1 + W_2 \qquad (83)$$

As a final illustration of the use of loss functions, let us consider an inventory problem in a manufacturing firm that faces a combined production and purchasing problem. Let us take a particular production period (which might be a week or a month), and let u denote the quantity on hand and q the quantity ordered. Let A denote the cost of producing one of these parts and B the sale price of the part. Let us assume that inventory carrying costs are C dollars per part for this production period, and that there is a penalty of D dollars for each shortage. We also assume that, if there is a surplus of parts, those parts must be sold at a discount of B' dollars. In order to determine the loss function, let us begin by computing the inventory carrying costs. If we denote by v the inventory at the end of the period, then

$$v = (u + q - d)_+ \tag{84}$$

where d denotes the demand in this production period. We assume that the average inventory level is halfway between the initial inventory u and final inventory v. Consequently, we get for the inventory carrying cost

$$z = \frac{C}{2}(u + v) \tag{85}$$

Now we can write the loss for the production period as

$$W(u, q, d) = Aq - B(u + q - v) + \frac{C}{2}(u + v)$$
$$+ D \text{ In } \{d > u + q\} - B'v \tag{86}$$

The first term on the right-hand side refers to the production cost of the part, the second term to the revenue, the third term is the inventory carrying cost, the fourth term is the penalty if there is a shortage, and the fifth term is the discount value of the surplus parts.

Another type of a loss function must be considered if each shortage is avoided by providing parts at a premium cost of A' dollars. Under this condition, the loss is given by

$$W(u, q, d) = Aq + A'(d - u - q)_+ - Bd + \frac{C}{2}(u + v) - B'v \tag{87}$$

The first term refers to the cost of the part, the second to the premium cost of the extra parts that have to be made (or purchased), the third term is the revenue, the fourth term is the inventory carrying cost, and the fifth term is the discount value of the surplus.

So far, we have developed a series of different types of loss functions to illustrate in what problems and in what way these loss functions can be used. Now we will use loss functions to develop ordering policies, which lead to maximum profit for the business enterprise.

7. OPTIMUM INVENTORY RULE FOR A NAVAL PROBLEM

As a first illustration of the use of loss functions, we will discuss the case of the aircraft carriers, where the loss function is given by equation (75). We assume that there is a record of spare requirements for 1,000 ships of this type. The record shows that out of these 1,000 cases, 40 times there was a need for 1 spare, 10 times for 2 spares, and once for 3 spares. (More than 3 spares were never required.) In order to put this into a mathematical form, let us denote by d_1 the number of spares required for the first ship, by d_2 the demand for the second ship, etc., and so by $d_{1,000}$ the spares required for the 1,000th ship. The fact that there were 40 cases where 1 spare was required can be expressed with the aid of the indicator function as

$$\sum_k \text{In} \{d_k = 1\} = 40 \tag{88}$$

The fact that there were 10 cases where 2 spares were required can be written as

$$\sum_k \text{In} \{d_k = 2\} = 10 \tag{89}$$

There was a single case where three spares were required

$$\sum_k \text{In} \{d_k = 3\} = 1 \tag{90}$$

For any higher value of the demand, the indicator function is zero as there is no case on record where more than 3 spares were required. We can say that the probability that the demand equals 1 is 0.04, and we can write

$$f(1) = \text{Pr} \{D = 1\} = 0.04 \tag{91}$$

The probability of the demand being 2 is 0.01 or

$$f(2) = \text{Pr} \{D = 2\} = 0.01 \tag{92}$$

and finally the probability of the demand being 3 is 0.001 or

$$f(3) = \text{Pr} \{D = 3\} = 0.001 \tag{93}$$

The probability that the demand is more than 3 is zero. A graphical representation of the probability distribution of spare requirements is given in Fig. 11.

In order to determine the probability of a shortage, we need the cumulative probability distribution function. We have a total of 51

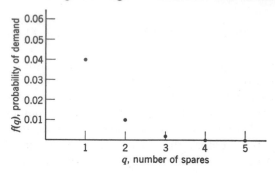

FIG. 11.   Frequency of spare requirement in naval problem.

cases where there was a need for spares; therefore, we can write

$$\sum_k \mathrm{In}\ \{d_k > 0\} = 51 \qquad (94)$$

We had 11 cases where the demand was more than 1 spare and so

$$\sum_k \mathrm{In}\ \{d_k > 1\} = 11 \qquad (95)$$

There was only one case where the demand was more than 2 spares and, therefore

$$\sum_k \mathrm{In}\ \{d_k > 2\} = 1 \qquad (96)$$

Finally, the demand never being more than 3, we write

$$\sum_k \mathrm{In}\ \{d_k > 3\} = 0 \qquad (97)$$

From these we determine the cumulative distribution function, that is, the probability of a shortage:

$$G(0) = \mathrm{Pr}\ \{D > 0\} = 0.051 \qquad (98)$$

$$G(1) = \mathrm{Pr}\ \{D > 1\} = 0.011 \qquad (99)$$

$$G(2) = \mathrm{Pr}\ \{D > 2\} = 0.001 \qquad (100)$$

$$G(3) = \mathrm{Pr}\ \{D > 3\} = 0 \qquad (101)$$

A graphical representation of the probability of a shortage is given in Fig. 12.

From these data we can easily determine how many spares we should order to get a given level of protection.   However, a more fundamental problem is the determination of how many spares to order so that the total expected cost becomes the smallest.   Let q denote the number of

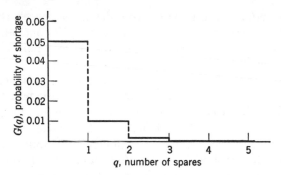

FIG. 12.   Cumulative frequency of spare requirements in naval problem.

spares ordered and N the number of ships considered (in this case, 1,000).   The average (or expected) loss is

$$\bar{W}(q) = Aq + \frac{B}{N} \sum_{1}^{N} \text{In } \{d_k > q\} \qquad (102)$$

or

$$\bar{W}(q) = Aq + B\,G(q) \qquad (103)$$

Here A is \$90,000, the cost of the spare, and B is \$10,000,000, the cost of rework on the ship.

In Fig. 13 we show graphically the expected cost as a function of q, the number of spares ordered.   For instance, if the policy is to purchase (or manufacture) 1 spare per ship, then the expected cost of spares is \$90,000 per ship.   The probability of reworking each ship is 0.011, the loss involved in reworking each ship is \$10,000,000, and the expected loss per ship is \$110,000. Therefore the total expected loss is \$200,000, as shown in Fig. 13, where $q = 1$.

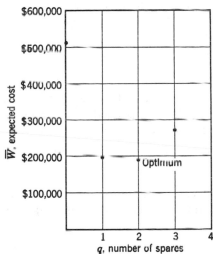

FIG. 13.   Cost versus number of spares provided in naval problem.

Similarly, with the aid of equation (103), we see that, if the policy is to order 2 spares per ship, then the expected cost is \$190,000.   If the policy is not to order any spares, the expected cost is 0.051 times \$10,000,000, that is, \$510,000.

On the other hand, if the policy is to order three spares, then the cost of spares is $270,000, and there is no rework.   We conclude, then, that the cheapest policy is to order two spares, as this policy leads to an expected cost of $190,000.

It is obvious that, if information about spare requirements is available, and if the cost of a shortage is known, then it is possible to determine the policy that leads to the least cost.   The number of spares to be ordered (or inventory to be kept) is not a matter of "judgment." The order quantity follows from the policy of minimizing costs.

As a further illustration of the use of probability distribution and loss functions, we will re-examine a similar problem under somewhat different conditions.   Let us assume that the demand for spares forms a normal distribution with a mean of 20 and a standard deviation of 4.46.   (This is the distribution we used for the demand of bread in the hypothetical supermarket.)   A further simplification we can make is to approximate the distribution function with a continuous normal distribution.   (We assume that we can handle the distribution function with the aid of calculus.)   We know from calculus that the way to obtain the minimum of a function is to take the derivative and make the derivative equal to zero (this makes the slope of the curve zero). Our expected cost is given by equation (103), and we need to determine the lowest point on the curve.   The derivative (with respect to q) of the first term on the right-hand side of equation (103) equals A and, therefore,

$$\frac{d\bar{W}}{dq} = A + B\frac{dG}{dq} \tag{104}$$

However, it follows from equation (11) that the derivative of the cumulative distribution function is given by the ordinary distribution function, or

$$\frac{dG}{dq} = -\frac{dF}{dq} = -f(q) \tag{105}$$

Therefore, the ordering quantity which makes the expected cost minimum is given by the following relation

$$f(q) = \frac{A}{B} \tag{106}$$

(This will make the right-hand side of equation (104) zero.)   This is a very simple result; the ratio of the two costs, gives the value of the distribution function directly.   In our particular case, A is $90,000 and B is $10,000,000; therefore, the ratio is 0.009.

In order to be able to use the ϕ function (tabulated in Table 1) we use equation (25). The value of the standard deviation is 4.46, therefore

$$\frac{1}{4.46} \phi(\xi) = 0.009 \tag{107}$$

from which we get, with the aid of Table 1, $\xi = 2.15$. In order to get the quantity of spares to be ordered, we write

$$q = \bar{d} + 2.15\sigma = 29.6 \tag{108}$$

We see that the best quantity of spares to be ordered is approximately 30.

As a further exercise, let us consider the problem when the average demand for spares is 3 and the distribution of demand is Poisson. With the aid of Fig. 7, we can get the values of the cumulative distribution function $G(0)$, $G(1)$, and so on; then with the aid of equation (103), we can compute the expected cost for each ordering policy.

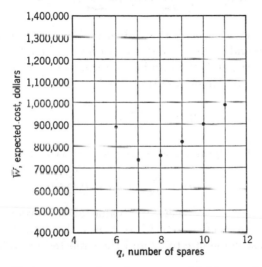

FIG. 14. Cost versus number of spares provided in naval problem.

The result of this computation is shown graphically in Fig. 14, and it can be deduced that the cheapest policy is to order seven spares, which results in an expected cost of $750,000.

As an alternative approach, we can assume that the Poisson distribution can be approximated by a continuous curve and use equation (106). The right-hand side in equation (106) has the value of 0.009, and we conclude from Fig. 6 that the best policy is to have eight spares ordered.   This leads to a cost of \$760,000, which is only \$10,000 off from the minimum cost which we have determined by the previous detailed computation.   We can see that using the continuous approximation gives a close answer to the problem.

8.   OPTIMUM INVENTORY RULES FOR SINGLE-STAGE PROBLEMS

We propose now to develop a more general mathematical treatment of single-stage inventory problems.   We will assume no inventory at the beginning, and wish to determine what is the best order quantity q.   We assume, again, that if the order quantity is q and the demand is d, then the loss function is $W(q, d)$.   According to equation (70) the expected loss is

$$\bar{W}(q) = \frac{1}{N} \sum_{r=0}^{\infty} W(q, r) \sum_{i} \text{In } \{d_i = r\} \tag{109}$$

For each given value of r, the indicator function takes the value 0 when the demand is not r and the value 1 when the demand is r; consequently, we get $N f(r)$ number of terms for each specific value of r on the right-hand side of equation (109).   Therefore,

$$\bar{W}(q) = \sum_{r=0}^{\infty} W(q,r) f(r) \tag{110}$$

With the aid of integral calculus this can be written as

$$\bar{W}(q) = \int_{0}^{\infty} W(q, x) f(x) \, dx \tag{111}$$

Our problem now is to select the value of the ordering quantity q such that this expected loss $\bar{W}$ becomes the lowest possible.   We denote the best value of q by Q and the expected minimum loss by V. Consequently,

$$\bar{W}(Q) = V \tag{112}$$

We have already seen in the case of the aircraft carriers, how to get the smallest expected loss V and best q, and now we proceed to apply the same method to a more general case.   We assume a particular type of loss function

$$W(q, d) = \alpha_1 q + \beta_1 d + \gamma_1 \qquad \text{when } d \leq q \tag{113a}$$

where α_1, β_1, and γ_1 are given constants.   Such a function is called a linear function in the quantities q and d. When the demand is more than the quantity ordered, we assume that the loss is given by another linear function

$$W(q, d) = \alpha_2 q + \beta_2 d + \gamma_2 \quad \text{when } d > q \quad (113b)$$

It can be seen that the loss function is composed of two linear functions; such a function is often referred to as a quasilinear or as a piecewise, linear function. As an illustration let us assign the following values to the coefficients in these equations

$$\alpha_1 = 0.06, \quad \beta_1 = -0.18, \gamma_1 = 0$$

$$\alpha_2 = -0.12, \beta_2 = 0, \quad \gamma_2 = 0$$

These numerical values lead to the loss function given by equation (72a–72c), which is the loss function associated with the inventory problem in the supermarket. We also recognize that, by giving appropriate numerical values to these coefficients, we can reproduce the loss function as expressed by Equations (73), (74), (76), or (77). We see that, if we find a method of computing the best ordering quantity for the loss function of equation (113), then we can get answers to a number of different problems we discussed previously.

The expected value of the loss as a function of the order quantity q can be expressed with the aid of equation (111). We get

$$\bar{W}(q) = \int_0^q (\alpha_1 q + \beta_1 x + \gamma_1) f(x) \, dx$$
$$+ \int_q^\infty (\alpha_2 q + \beta_2 x + \gamma_2) f(x) \, dx \quad (114)$$

This can also be written as

$$\bar{W}(q) = (\alpha_1 q + \gamma_1) \int_0^q f(x) \, dx + \beta_1 \int_0^q x f(x) \, dx$$
$$+ (\alpha_2 q + \gamma_2) \int_q^\infty f(x) \, dx + \beta_2 \int_q^\infty x f(x) \, dx \quad (115)$$

With the aid of equations (11), (12), (14), and (21) the integration indicated in this last equation can be carried through

$$\bar{W}(q) = [(\alpha_1 - \alpha_2)q + (\gamma_1 - \gamma_2)] F(q) + (\beta_1 - \beta_2) F^*(q)$$
$$+ (\alpha_2 q + \gamma_2 + \beta_2 \bar{d}) \quad (116)$$

We are to take the value of q which minimizes this expression. Consequently, we must seek the value of q, which makes the derivative zero. It follows from equations (12) and (14) that the derivative of the function $F(q)$ is $f(q)$ and the derivative of $F^*(q)$ is $q f(q)$. Therefore, the derivative of the expected loss $\bar{W}(q)$ is given by

$$\frac{d\bar{W}(q)}{dq} = (\alpha_1 - \alpha_2) F(q) + [(\alpha_1 + \beta_1 - \alpha_2 - \beta_2)q$$
$$+ (\gamma_1 - \gamma_2)] f(q) + \alpha_2 \quad (117)$$

The best value of q is obtained by making this expression zero. Consequently, we get for q the following equation:

$$(\alpha_1 - \alpha_2) F(q) + [(\alpha_1 + \beta_1 - \alpha_2 - \beta_2)q + (\gamma_1 - \gamma_2)] f(q) + \alpha_2 = 0 \quad (118)$$

We realize that on the left-hand side we have a known function of q which must be made equal to zero. (We are, of course, assuming that the coefficients α, β, and γ are known.) There are many mathematical methods to solve problems of this type; the problem is to determine the *root* of a given equation. A simple method of solution is the preparation of a graph and the selection of the point where the function takes the value zero. There are also many numerical methods available, but discussion of these is beyond the scope of this book.

As a specific illustration of this analysis, let us consider the problem of ordering bread in the supermarket using the loss functions of equation (73). Let us denote by A the cost of purchasing bread, by B the sale price of the bread, by B' the refund on stale bread, and finally by D the penalty that is suffered when there is a dissatisfied customer. With this notation, the loss is given by

$$W(q, d) = (A - B')q + (B' - B)d \qquad \text{when } d \leq q \quad (119)$$

When the demand is higher than the quantity ordered, the loss function is given by

$$W(q, d) = (A - B - D)q + Dd \qquad \text{when } d > q \quad (120)$$

On the right-hand side, the first term refers to the cost of bread and the second term expresses the penalty. By comparing equations (119) and (120) with equation (113), we get the following values for the coefficients:

$$\alpha_1 = A - B', \qquad \beta_1 = -(B - B'), \gamma_1 = 0$$
$$\alpha_2 = -(B - A + D), \beta_2 = D \qquad \gamma_2 = 0 \quad (121)$$

Substituting these values into equation (118), we get

$$F(q) = \frac{B + D - A}{B + D - B'} \quad (122)$$

This is, then, the equation which must be solved in order to obtain the optimum quantity of bread to be ordered. It is indeed a very simple formula, because the right-hand side can be computed directly from cost information and the left-hand side is nothing but the cumulative distribution function.

Suppose, for instance, that the demand follows the rectangular distribution function between M and $\bar{M}$. Equation (51) gives the cumulative distribution function, and, therefore, equation (122) becomes

$$\frac{q - M}{\bar{M} - M} = \frac{B + D - A}{B + D - B'} \tag{123}$$

Let us return, for instance, to our loss function as given by equation (73), where A, the cost of bread, is 8 cents; B, the sale price of bread, is 20 cents; B', the refund on stale bread, is 2 cents; and D, the penalty of not being able to satisfy a customer is 5 cents. Let us assume that the demand is rectangular between 1,000 and 2,000, which means that M is 1,000 and $\bar{M}$ is 2,000. From our equation (123) we find that the best order quantity q is 1,740 loaves of bread. This is, then, the policy that the manager must adopt if he wants to minimize his loss (or maximize his profit).

What happens if he imputes 20 cents of loss to each dissatisfied customer? The formula for the best ordering quantity yields 1,842 loaves of bread, which is 102 loaves above the previous ordering quantity. We should expect a higher ordering quantity when the manager imputes a higher value of the loss to dissatisfied customers. If he imputes a $1 penalty for each dissatisfied customer, the formula gives 1,950 loaves of bread. Of course, under no condition should we order more than 2,000 loaves of bread, because we assumed that the probability distribution function is rectangular between 1,000 and 2,000; this means that the demand is never above 2,000 loaves of bread. Incidentally, if we assume that D is zero (no penalty for unsatisfied demand), then the optimum ordering quantity is 1,667 loaves of bread.

Suppose the sales price of bread is increased to 40 cents. What happens now? The formula tells us that the best policy is to order 1,842 loaves of bread. It is obvious that, if all conditions remain the same but the sales price increases, then it is better to order more bread and to take a higher chance on returning stale bread.

So far, we have only determined the best ordering policy, but we have not computed the loss (or profit) connected with this best policy. In order to get an answer, we must evaluate the expected cost as expressed by equation (116). This can be done with the aid of equations (51) and (54). Omitting details of the computation, we get

$$(\bar{M} - M)\,\bar{W}(q) = \left(\alpha_1 + \frac{\beta_1}{2} - \frac{\beta_2}{2} - \alpha_2\right)q^2$$
$$- (\alpha_1 M - \alpha_2 \bar{M} - \gamma_1 + \gamma_2)q$$
$$+ \left(-\gamma_1 M + \gamma_2 \bar{M} - \frac{\beta_1}{2}M^2 + \frac{\beta_2}{2}\bar{M}^2\right) \quad (124)$$

Let us apply this last formula to the problem where the loss function is given by equation (72). We get for the values of the coefficients

$$\alpha_1 = 0.06, \quad \beta_1 = -0.12, \; \gamma_1 = 0$$
$$\alpha_2 = -0.12, \; \beta_2 = 0, \quad \gamma_2 = 0$$

Putting these numbers into equation (124), we get the expression for the expected loss

$$\bar{W}(q) = 0.00009q^2 - 0.3q + 90 \quad\quad\quad (125)$$

As an illustration of this formula, let us assume that we order 1,000 loaves of bread every day. The expected loss, according to equation (125), is $-\$120$, which means that the expected profit is $\$120$. This is, however, obvious, as the demand for bread is between 1,000 and 2,000 loaves; therefore, if we order 1,000 loaves of bread all this bread is sold. The profit on each loaf is 12 cents; the total profit is $\$120$. In Fig. 15 we show a graphical representation of this profit function. It can be seen that the maximum profit (that is, the minimum loss) is at 1,666 loaves of bread, and the profit in this case is $\$160$. If we buy more than 1,666 loaves of bread, then we have too much stale bread, and the expected profit decreases. For instance, if we order 2,000 loaves of bread, then the profit is only $\$150$. This can be deduced directly in the following way. The demand is between 1,000 and 2,000, and is always satisfied. We need to determine how much stale bread is left, on the average. The demand is rectangular between 1,000 and 2,000 and so, on the average, 1,500 loaves of bread will be sold and 500 loaves will be left. As each loaf of bread is sold for 20 cents, the expected revenue from selling bread will be $\$300$. The revenue from each loaf of stale bread is 0.02 cents, or $\$10$ total for the 500 loaves of stale bread. Consequently, the total expected revenue is $\$310$. On the other hand, the cost for 2,000 loaves of bread is $\$160$. This results, then, in an expected profit of $\$150$ in agreement with our previous figure.

Incidentally, we note that the optimum of 1,666 loaves of bread can be obtained directly by taking the derivative of equation (125) and equating this derivative with zero.

We now propose to extend our method of solution to a somewhat more complicated problem.   Let us assume that we may also order bread at noontime, and focus attention on the problem of determining the optimum policy for noon ordering.   (We are dealing with a two-stage problem but are concentrating only on solving the problem of the second stage, that is, what to order for the afternoon).   Let us assume that the demand in the afternoon is rectangular between 1,000 and

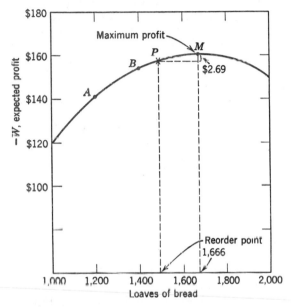

FIG. 15.   Profit associated with order quantity.

2,000 loaves of bread.   We also assume that at noontime some bread may be left over from the morning, and that there is a cost of $2.69 associated when ordering bread at noontime.

If there is no bread left at noontime, we know from our previous analysis that the best policy is to order 1,666 loaves of bread.   However, if the supermarket has, say, 1,665 loaves of bread left, then it is not worth while to order another loaf of bread at noon because of the cost of $2.69.   However, if there are 1,000 loaves of bread left at noontime, it is better to order more.   If we do not order bread, the profit is $200.   (As a convention, we charge the price of purchasing bread in the morning to the morning transactions.)   If we do order bread and order 666 loaves, then it can be shown, on the basis of our previous calculations, that the gross profit increases by $40. From this, we subtract the ordering cost of $2.69 and obtain a net increase in profit of $37.31. We conclude that if, we have only 1,000 loaves of bread left at noon (or less than 1,000 loaves of bread left), then it is a good policy to order up to 1,666 at noon. The question is where is the reorder point? Above the reorder point we should not order at noon; below the reorder point we should order up to 1,666 loaves of bread.

Let us consider Fig. 15 again. Suppose we have 1,200 loaves of bread left at noon as represented by point A, and let us order, say, 200 loaves at noon. This brings us up to 1,400 loaves (point B). The increase in gross profit can be read by taking the difference between $153.60 and $140.40; this amounts to $13.20. By subtracting the ordering cost of $2.69 we obtain a net increase of $10.51. The maximum increase of profit is obtained if we replenish up to 1,666 loaves, as represented by point M on the diagram. Let P represent the point on the diagram which is $2.69 below the maximum M. If the noon inventory is below P, we should reorder; if it is above P, we should not. The profit at point P is $157.31; therefore, in order to determine the reorder point, P, we need to determine the ordering quantity in Fig. 15 which gives a profit of $157.31. With the aid of equation (125), we get

$$0.00009s^2 - 0.3s + 90 = -157.31 \qquad (126)$$

where s is the reorder point. By solving this equation, we get the value of 1,493. This is, then, our noon reorder quantity (point P). If we have less than 1,493 loaves of bread at noon, we should order up to 1,666 loaves; if we have more than 1,493 loaves, then there is no profit in reordering, because the ordering cost of $2.69 overbalances the expected profit that may be made on the additional loaves of bread.

In the literature, such an ordering rule is sometimes referred to as an S-s policy. Let us denote by u the initial inventory; then, in our particular case, the quantity to be ordered is given by:

$$Q(u) = (1,660 - u) \text{ In } \{u < 1,493\} \qquad (127)$$

The quantity to be ordered for the more general S-s policy is given by:

$$Q(u) = (S - u) \text{ In } \{u < s\} \qquad (128)$$

This means that, as long as the initial inventory u is below the reorder point s, the policy specifies to order up to S; when u is above the reorder point s, then the policy is not to order.

Let us turn our attention now to a more general mathematical formulation of single-stage inventory control problems. Let u denote the initial inventory on hand at the time of ordering; and let us assume that the loss function is not only a function of the quantity ordered q and the demand d but that it is also a function of the initial inventory level u. Mathematically, this means that the loss function has the form $W(q, u, d)$. If we denote by $f(d)$ the distribution function of the demand, we get for the expected value of the loss:

$$\bar{W}(u, q) = \int_0^\infty W(q, u, x) f(x) \, dx \qquad (129)$$

We compare this with equation (111) and note that the expected loss (or profit) depends not only on the value of the ordering quantity q but also on the initial inventory u. Our problem now is to determine the best value of the ordering quantity q such that the loss, as expressed by equation (129), becomes the smallest. We expect that, for different values of the initial inventory u, the quantity to be ordered will vary, that is, the order quantity will be a function of u. Mathematically speaking, our problem is to determine the best ordering quantity $Q(u)$. (Incidentally, the optimum ordering policy is not necessarily of an S-s type, as will be shown later.) Let us denote by $V(u)$, the minimum loss. Then,

$$V(u) = \min_q \bar{W}(u, q) \qquad (130)$$

With the aid of our expression for the expected loss, equation (129), this last equation can be written as

$$V(u) = \min_q \int_0^\infty W(q, u, x) f(x) \, dx \qquad (131)$$

We also see that the optimum ordering function, $Q(u)$, can be defined by the equation

$$\bar{W}(u, Q) = V(u) \qquad (132)$$

This is, of course, just a mathematical way of saying that the best ordering quantity is associated with the minimum loss. Another way of putting this fact into mathematics is to say that

$$\bar{W}(u, Q) \leq \bar{W}(u, q) \qquad (133)$$

This says that, for any value of the ordering quantity q, the loss is larger than or equal to that loss which is associated with the optimum ordering quantity Q.

How do we determine this optimum Q? If the loss, as expressed by equation (129), is a function of the type that has a derivative with respect to q, then we take the derivative and equate it to zero. The derivative of the loss function is obtained from equation (129)

$$\frac{d\bar{W}}{dq} = \int_0^\infty \frac{dW\,(q,\,u,\,x)}{dq} f(x)\,dx \qquad (134)$$

This is, then, the type of integral we have to evaluate in order to get the optimum ordering policy. We mention here that in many cases the loss function is not a "smooth" function (i.e., it may be a quasi-linear function), and then we have to be careful when taking the derivative under the integral sign in equation (134).

9. OPTIMUM INVENTORY RULES FOR MANY-STAGE PROBLEMS

Let us return again to our hypothetical problem of purchasing bread in the supermarket, and let us consider simultaneously the policy of ordering in the morning and at noon. We know from our previous study that, if at noontime we have less than 1,493 loaves of bread, we should order up to 1,666; whereas, if we have more than 1,493 loaves of bread, we should not order. Let us assume now that the demand in the morning is rectangular too, and that it is also between 1,000 and 2,000 loaves of bread. How much bread should we order in the morning? We are certain to have a sale of 1,000 loaves of bread in the morning, so we certainly should order at least 1,000 loaves. More-over, we know that, if at noontime we end up with less than 1,493 loaves of bread, than we should reorder; therefore, we conclude that we should order in the morning at least 2,493 loaves of bread. How-ever, there is no reason to assume that this is the optimum ordering quantity, as it is more likely that we should order more than 2,493. In fact, what we should do is to order so much that in many cases we avoid reordering, and so save the $2.69 that is the cost of reordering. On the other hand, we do not wish to order too much in the morning, as this can lead to too much stale bread in the evening. What is the best ordering policy for the morning? This is a two-stage inventory prob-lem as we have both morning and noon orders. We will now set up the mathematics of this two-stage inventory problem.

We propose to consider the problem under somewhat more general conditions. Let us denote by u the starting morning inventory, and by v the noontime inventory. (In the problem in the supermarket, we have assumed that the morning inventory u equals zero.) Now we do not know v, the inventory level at noontime, but if we did know v we could determine the optimum policy for purchasing at noontime from our previous method of solving single-stage problems. Mathematically speaking, we know how to determine the best ordering quantity q_2 for any given noon inventory v. We denote this ordering quantity by $q_2(v)$ and the associated minimum afternoon loss (or maximum profit) by $V^*(v)$.

Suppose, now, that in the morning we purchase q_1 quantity of bread and that the demand in the morning is d_1. What is the combined loss for the whole day? We denote by $W(u, q_1, d_1)$ the loss function for the morning; this is the loss in the first stage of the problem. We have an inventory of v at noontime, and therefore, if we follow an optimum ordering rule for the afternoon, we experience a loss of $V^*(v)$ for the afternoon. Consequently, the combined loss for the two stages is given by

$$z = W(u, q_1, d_1) + V^*(v) \qquad (135)$$

The inventory at the beginning of the second stage (that is, at noontime) is given by

$$v = (u + q_1 - d_1)_+ \qquad (136)$$

Our first step in the solution is to compute the average (or expected) loss for arbitrary u and q_1. This can be done with the aid of a formula similar to equation (111)

$$z(u, q_1) = \int_0^\infty [W(u, q_1, x) + V^*(v)] f(x) \, dx \qquad (137a)$$

where

$$v = (u + q_1 - x)_+ \qquad (137b)$$

There is one important point to mention here. We assume that the quantity of bread sold in the afternoon is independent of the quantity of bread sold in the morning. Conceivably, this might not be true; for instance, it might turn out that when we sell more in the morning we sell less in the afternoon, or vice versa. Using the language of the statistician we assume that the statistics of the demand is given both in the morning and in the afternoon, and that the demands are statistically independent.

The expected loss as given by equation (137) can be rewritten in the following form

$$z(u, q_1) = \int_0^{u+q_1} [W(u, q_1, x) + V^*(u + q_1 - x)] f(x) \, dx$$
$$+ \int_{u+q_1}^\infty [W(u, q_1, x) + V^*(0)] f(x) \, dx \qquad (138)$$

How do we get the combined minimum loss for this two-stage problem? Let us denote by $V(u)$ the minimum loss for an arbitrary initial morning inventory u. If we compute the expected loss as given by equation (138) for each value of the first ordering quantity q_1, then the lowest value of this function gives this minimum loss. Consequently,

$$V(u) = \min_{q_1} z(u, q_1) \tag{139}$$

We can see, then, that our problem is to compute the function as given by the integral in equation (138), and then to determine the minimum of this function. The optimum morning ordering quantity Q_1 has the property that

$$z(u, Q_1) = V(u) \tag{140}$$

This simply means that the best ordering policy results in the minimum loss (or maximum profit).

We recognize that the approach of solving this two-stage problem is similar to the one used in dynamic programming. First, we determine the best ordering policy for the second stage of the problem for an arbitrary inventory level v; then we proceed to solve the two-stage problem by reducing it to a single-stage problem. This same method can be applied when we have three, four, or any number of stages. First, we determine the optimum ordering policy for the last stage; then we determine the optimum policy for the last two stages. Then we solve the problem for the last three stages, and continue this method until the complete problem is solved. This means that integrals of the type of equation (138) must be evaluated several times, and the minimum value of these integrals must be computed. As we have more and more stages in the problem, these integrals get more and more complicated, and it becomes very cumbersome to evaluate them. Therefore, we see that conceptually we know how to solve such problems, but from the practical point of view the computations might get so complicated that it becomes too difficult to carry them through. We will see later that there is an alternate approach which avoids this difficulty.

10. THE TWO-BIN SYSTEM OF INVENTORY CONTROL

One of the most common inventory systems used by business firms is the *two-bin system* of inventory control. In this system, parts are considered to be kept in two bins. One bin contains parts for immediate supply; the second bin contains parts that are to be used during the replenishment period. (The parts do not have to be contained physically in these two separate bins; inventory records are to be kept in accordance with this scheme.)   Parts are disbursed from the first bin to begin with; when the supply in the first bin is exhausted the part is reordered, and disbursement is continued from the second bin. When new parts arrive, the second bin is filled up, the rest of the parts are put in the first bin, and the cycle starts over again.

In order to implement such an inventory policy, two quantities must be determined.   We need to know the reorder level which protects against a shortage during the replenishment period; this is the quantity of parts in the second bin.   Also, we need to know the quantity that must be ordered when the first bin's supply is exhausted.

To be specific, let us assume that the yearly demand is 1,300 units, or

$$Y = 1,300 \text{ units/year}$$

and that the cost of each part is $6.50, or

$$C = \$6.50/\text{unit}$$

We assume, furthermore, that the cost of ordering is $5, or

$$A = \$5/\text{order}$$

and, finally, that the inventory carrying cost is 20%, or

$$p = 0.20/\text{year}$$

Let us denote the order quantity by q, then the combined yearly carrying and ordering cost is given by

$$z_1 = A\frac{Y}{q} + \tfrac{1}{2}Cpq \tag{141}$$

We can determine the optimum ordering quantity by the conventional economic lot size formula used in Chapter 8, Section 3, which minimizes the above cost.   Using the formula we get for the order quantity

$$q = \sqrt{2YA/pC} \tag{142}$$

In our particular case, this is 100 units.   We conclude that we should order every four weeks, that is, on the average, 13 times a year, and order 100 parts each time.   The next problem is to determine the reorder level, that is, the quantity that will be ideally in the second bin.

The second bin is an insurance against a shortage; therefore, the problem is a statistical one.   Suppose that our past record of demand shows that the average elapsed time from ordering to receiving is one week.   Let us denote by $f(d)$ the probability distribution function of the weekly demand.   Let s denote the reorder point.   Then the probability of a shortage during a reorder period (of one week) is given by

$$\Pr\{D \geq s\} = 1 - F(s) \tag{143}$$

where $F(s)$ is the cumulative distribution function. Suppose, now, that the plant has a policy of tolerating one shortage in every five years. We order 13 times a year, and, therefore, in five years we order 65 times; the policy of tolerating one shortage in five years is tantamount to tolerating one shortage in 65 replenishment periods. Therefore, we must have

$$1 - F(s) = \tfrac{1}{65} = 0.0154 \tag{144}$$

In order to get a numerical illustration, we need to know something about the distribution of demand. What is the average demand during the replenishment period of one week? The yearly demand is 1,300 units, and consequently the average weekly demand is 25 units. We will assume now, in the absence of actual records, that the demand is distributed normally, that the standard deviation is the square root of 25 (as suggested by the Poisson distribution), or that σ equals 5. From equations (144) and (32) we get for the Φ function

$$\Phi(\xi) = 0.9846 \tag{145}$$

From Table 1 we get

$$\xi = 2.16 \tag{146}$$

Denoting again by $\bar{d}$ the average demand per week (25 here), we get for the reorder point

$$s = \bar{d} + \xi\sigma = 35.8 \tag{147}$$

We see that w (or $\xi\sigma$), the level of the protective stock, is 10.8 units. By rounding off the figure we can say that we need 11 parts as insurance against a shortage. We remind ourselves that this protective stock level of 11 is a direct consequence of our policy that we tolerate one shortage in every five years.

We can now visualize an inventory record as shown in Fig. 16. At the beginning of the study (left-hand side), there is an inventory of 36 units. This is at reorder level, as we need, on the average 25 units for disbursement, and an additional 11 units for protection. Therefore, at this point, we reorder 100 units. After one week these 100 units arrive; at this time our inventory is down to 11 units, and therefore after replenishment we are up to 111 units. If the demand is exactly 25 units every week, after four weeks we get down to 36 units again, reorder 100 units, and at the fifth week, when we are down again to 11 units, we receive 100 units again. According to the diagram, the demand in each of the sixth, seventh, and eighth periods is higher than 25 units, and, therefore, the reorder quantity is reached in the eighth week. We now order 100 parts, but, as the demand is higher than 25 during the ninth period, we experience a shortage. During the ninth week the parts ordered in the eighth week arrive, and, as we have no parts in stock at this time, our replenishment brings us up to 100 units. Now the demand is such that we reorder in the eleventh week, when we reach the reorder level. We get new parts in the twelfth week, but, as the demand is less than expected, we still have 20 units on hand when the new order arrives. Therefore, after replenishment we are up to 120 units.

Let us compute the average or the expected cost. We recognize that there are three types of costs: (1) the cost of carrying the "active"

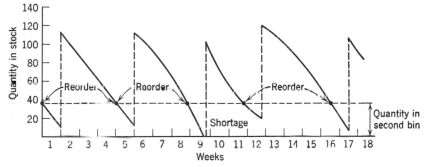

FIG. 16. Two-bin system of inventory control.

inventory; (2) reordering costs; (3) the cost of carrying the protective inventory. The first two of these is given by equation (141), whereas the third one is given by

$$z_2 = Cpw \tag{148}$$

The total cost is given by

$$z_3 = A\frac{Y}{q} + (\tfrac{1}{2}q + w)Cp \tag{149}$$

where w is the quantity of protective inventory required. By using the numerical values of our illustration, we get for this total cost $144.30.

However, there is the question here whether this $144.30 represents the minimum total cost. Let us review our method of computation. First, let us remember that we accepted the policy of tolerating one shortage in five years, and then (on the basis of this policy) determined q and w such that the cost as expressed by equation (141) becomes a minimum. This cost, however, does not include the cost of carrying the protective inventory.   What we should have done is to minimize the cost as given by equation (149).

In order to solve this more complicated problem, we first formulate the mathematics under somewhat more general conditions.   Let us denote by z_4 the tolerable probability of shortage per year.   The probability of a shortage in a single replenishment period is given by

$$\Pr \{D \geq \bar{d} + w\}$$

The number of orders per year is $\dfrac{Y}{q}$, and consequently the tolerable probability of a shortage per year can be approximated by

$$z_4 = \frac{Y}{q} \Pr \{D \geq \bar{d} + w\} \tag{150}$$

In our particular case, z_4 is 0.2, as we allow one shortage for each five years, or 0.2 shortage per year.   Our problem, then, is the following: assuming a policy which allows a shortage probability z_4 as expressed by equation (150), determine the ordering quantity, q, and protective stock level, w, such that the cost as expressed by equation (149) becomes a minimum.

One way to solve this problem is to assume a series of different q values and determine w from equation (150); this, then, gives a tolerable probability of shortage.   With these values of q and w, we compute the cost z_3 as given by equation (149).   Then we prepare a plot of costs for the different values of the ordering quantity q, and select from the graph the lowest possible cost (this gives the optimum ordering quantity q) and the best protective stock level w.   If this computation is carried through in our illustrative example, we find that the best policy is to have 12 orders per year, with an ordering quantity of 108 units and a protective level of 10.6 units.   The minimum cost, if this inventory policy is followed, can be computed as $144.60.   This essentially agrees with the result of our first computation, and therefore the first solution is just as satisfactory as the second one.*   However, we want to make a point here: there is an interaction between the best ordering quantity and the protective stock level, and it is conceivable that for some cases the simple solution does not gives an accurate enough answer.†

We now replace the policy of tolerating a certain probability of

---

* The fact that the new figure is $0.30 *higher* than the original one is not significant, as this difference is less than the accuracy of the computations.

† Cf. T. M. Whitin, *The Theory of Inventory Management*, Princeton University Press, Princeton, N. J., 1953.

shortage with a minimum cost analysis. As an illustration, let us assume that in case of a shortage there is a cost of $E = \$20$ associated with expediting. What should be the level of the protective stock? The expected yearly cost of expediting has three factors: the number of replenishment periods $\dfrac{Y}{q}$, the cost of a shortage E, and the probability of a shortage. Or

$$z = (Y/q)E \Pr \{D \geq \bar{d} + w\} \tag{151}$$

In order to get the combined cost z_5, we need to add the cost of carrying the protective stock, or

$$z_5 = Cpw + \frac{EY}{q}[1 - F(\bar{d} + w)] \tag{152}$$

To keep matters simple, we assume that the ordering quantity q follows the economic lot size formula (which minimizes the cost given by equation (141)). Neglecting the interaction between these two different types of cost, we can determine the protective stock level w by minimizing the cost as given by equation (152). We assume that the probability distribution of the demand (in each period) is normal. By replacing w with $\xi\sigma$, we get for the combined cost

$$z_5 = Cp\sigma\xi + \frac{EY}{q}[1 - \Phi(\xi)] \tag{153}$$

We determine w by selecting the value ξ, which minimizes the cost z_5 as given by equation (153). This ξ can be determined by computing the derivative with respect to ξ

$$\frac{dz_5}{d\xi} = Cp\sigma + \frac{EY}{q}\frac{d\Phi}{d\xi} \tag{154}$$

Now it follows from equation (31) that

$$\frac{d\Phi}{d\xi} = -\frac{1}{\sqrt{2\pi}}e^{-\xi^2/2} \tag{155}$$

and from equation (24) that

$$\frac{d\Phi}{d\xi} = -\phi(\xi) \tag{156}$$

Consequently, when equating the derivative to zero, we get from equation (154)

$$\phi(\xi) = \frac{Cp\sigma q}{EY} \tag{157}$$

For instance, in our numerical example the right-hand side is 0.025, and so from Table 1 we get for ξ the value 2.35. From this it follows that w is 11.8, and so the reorder quantity (which is computed by adding the protective level of 11.8 to the mean demand of 25) is $s = 36.8$. What is the probability of a shortage? From Table 1 we get $\phi(\xi) = 0.9906$, which means that the probability of a shortage is 0.0094, or roughly speaking, one shortage out of 100. As we have 13 orders per year, this means that we allow one shortage in every 7.7 years.

Let us compare now this with our previous policy which allows one shortage in each five years. In this case, the probability of a shortage is 0.0154, which gives a value of 2.16 for ξ. We can interpret equation (157) as an equation which gives an imputed value to the cost of a shortage E,

$$E = \frac{Cp\sigma q}{Y\phi(\xi)} \tag{158}$$

We can show that permitting one shortage in each five years is equivalent to imputing the cost of $14.40 to each shortage. We can see, then, that if we know the cost of a shortage we can determine the protective level required. On the other hand, if there is a policy of specifying how many shortages we permit, we can compute the imputed cost of a shortage.

So far, we have assumed that the optimum order quantity is determined from the ordinary economic lot size formula which minimizes the cost as expressed by equation (141). Let us, however, recognize that it would be more accurate to add both costs as given by equations (141) and (152) and determine the economic order quantity q and the protective stock level w such that this combined cost becomes a minimum. This total cost is given by

$$z_6 = A\frac{Y}{q} + \tfrac{1}{2}Cpq + Cpw + \frac{EY}{q}[1 - F(\bar{d} + w)] \tag{159}$$

and our problem is to determine q and w such that this cost becomes the minimum.

Let us again assume that the distribution of the demand is normal, and let us again replace w with $\xi\sigma$. We get for the total cost

$$z_6 = \frac{AY}{q} + \tfrac{1}{2}Cpq + Cp\sigma\xi + \frac{EY}{q}[1 - \Phi(\xi)] \tag{160}$$

We proceed now to determine the partial derivatives of this expression with respect to the unknowns q and ξ. When we make the derivative with respect to ξ equal to zero, we get back our equation (157), and therefore we see that this equation still holds. Equating the derivative with respect to q to zero, leads to

$$q = \sqrt{\frac{2Y}{pC} \{A + E[1 - \Phi(\xi)]\}} \qquad (161)$$

This replaces, then, equation (142). The problem is to solve simultaneously equations (161) and (157) for the two unknowns q and ξ.

There are many ways to do this. One of them is to use a method of successive approximations. First we determine q from equation (142), and then ξ from equation (157). These values form the first pair of approximations. Then we proceed to determine the second approximation for q from equation (161) by using the first value of ξ. We obtain the second approximation for ξ from equation (157) by using the new value of q. We proceed, then, step by step, alternating between the two equations, until we get values for q and ξ that do not change. In our particular case, we get for the first approximation of q the value 102. When we compute the value of ξ we discover that in equation (161) the correction term $[1 - \Phi(\xi)]$ has the value of 0.0094, which is too small to alter the value of q. We see, then, that in our particular case the interaction between the two costs is insignificant, and that our assumption that these costs can be separated is valid. It is conceivable, however, that under some other conditions the interaction is important, and then this new method of computation gives a more accurate answer.*

Before we leave the two-bin system of inventory control, we want to point out that our method of minimizing costs is only an approximate one. For instance, if the penalty for a shortage is small, and if we allow a fair number of shortages, then we do not meet the entire yearly demand Y. Consequently, we do not order Y/q number of times, as we assumed in the analysis. Furthermore, we assumed in the analysis that the inventory disbursement follows a straight line. If this is not the case, then our computation is in error. A further assumption is that we disburse in small lots, and, therefore, when we reach a reorder level we immediately reorder. However, if we disburse the parts in large lots, then by the time we notice that we have reached the reorder point we are below the reorder point. This results in more frequent shortages than assumed. We worked with the average replenishment period of one week, although the statistical distribution of the replenishment periods might be a significant factor. A more complete analysis should also include a statistical distribution of next year's

* See T. M. Whitin, footnote on p. 334.

forecast, as there is uncertainty involved there too. This more complete analysis of the problem is too involved to examine here; therefore we will take it up in later sections.

11. CYCLIC INVENTORY CONTROL SYSTEMS

The two-bin inventory control discussed so far is one of the most commonly used inventory systems. Another common inventory control system is the cyclic system where it is specified that inventory levels are inspected at periodic intervals, say, every week, every month, or whatever the cycle is. In order to simplify matters we assume that delivery is immediate.

We will begin our discussion of the cyclic inventory control system by re-examining the example considered in the previous section, but under the assumption that delivery is immediate.

Suppose that the inventory is inspected in every four weeks. What should the reorder quantity be? We need a supply for four weeks, that is, four times 25 or 100 units, to meet the demand of four weeks. In addition, we need some inventory to form an insurance against a shortage. Let us assume again that we tolerate one shortage in five years, or 0.0154 shortage per order. Let us assume a Poisson distribution of the demand with the mean of 100 units for each four-week period. Then the standard deviation of the demand is $\sqrt{100}$ or 10.0. Approximating with a normal distribution, we get from Table 1

$$\Phi(\xi) = 0.9808 \qquad \xi = 2.07$$

This results in a protective stock level of $10 \times 2.07 \sim 21$ units. We can see, then, that our total order should be up to $100 + 21$ or up to 121 units every four-week period. The level of protective stock in this cyclic inventory system is 21 units. If we used the two-bin system of inventory control, we would need no protective stock as we have assumed immediate delivery. Generally speaking, the two-bin inventory control system leads to more ordering and to a smaller inventory level than the cyclic inventory control system.

One disadvantage of the cyclic inventory control system is that we have to order up to the replenishment level even if this means ordering only a very few units. If, for example, we have 120 units at the ordering time, we still have to order 1 unit. However, if ordering is expensive, it would be better not to order but to save the ordering cost and take a chance on a shortage. We could modify the cyclic inventory control system by specifying that we will order only if our stock is below a certain level. This is, however, very close to the two-bin system of inventory control, and, in fact, the two-bin system can be considered as a cyclic inventory control system if the inventory records are examined every day.

We will now study in more detail cyclic inventory control systems, and apply the theory we have developed in Sections 7, 8, and 9 of this chapter.

We will assume that, at the time we inspect our inventory, we also order, and that we order up to a replenishing quantity of S. The problem we want to solve is to determine the optimum value of this unknown replenishing level S.

This ordering quantity is given mathematically by

$$q_i = S - u_i \qquad i = 1, 2, \cdots, N \qquad (162)$$

where u_i is the inventory level at the beginning of the ith inventory period and q_i is the quantity ordered. To simplify our discussion, we assume that the initial inventory level u_1 is 0 or

$$u_1 = 0 \qquad (163)$$

The first ordering quantity is given by

$$q_1 = S \qquad (164)$$

Let us denote by $d_1, d_2, \cdots, d_N$ the demand for parts. If v_i denotes the inventory at the end of each period, then

$$v_i = (S - d_i)_+ \qquad i = 1, 2, \cdots, N \qquad (165)$$

We note that

$$u_i = v_{i-1} - (S - d_{i-1})_+ \qquad i = 2, 3, \cdots, N \qquad (166)$$

We also recognize that the ordering quantity can be expressed as

$$q_i = S - (S - d_{i-1})_+ \qquad i = 2, 3, \cdots, N \qquad (167)$$

Our optimum quantity S is determined by minimizing the cost, and so we need to know the loss function associated with this problem. For our computations we use the loss function given by equation (86). For the time being, we will assume that there is no penalty for a shortage, or $D = 0$. We also assume that, if there is inventory left at the end of any period, then this inventory is carried over to the next period. With this notation, the loss in the ith period is given by

$$W_i = Aq_i - B(S - v_i) + \frac{C}{2}(u_i + v_i) \qquad i = 1, 2, \cdots, N - 1 \qquad (168)$$

As a particular case, the loss for the first period is given by

$$W_1 = Aq_1 - B[S - (S - d_1)_+] + \frac{C}{2}(S - d_1)_+ \qquad (169)$$

The loss for any of the other periods (except the Nth) can be expressed as

$$W_i = A[S - (S - d_{i-1})_+] - B[S - (S - d_i)_+]$$
$$+ \frac{C}{2}[(S - d_{i-1})_+ + (S - d_i)] \quad (170)$$

Finally, the loss for the Nth period is given by

$$W_N = A[S - (S - d_{N-1})_+] - B[S - (S - d_N)_+]$$
$$+ \frac{C}{2}[(S - d_{N-1})_+ + (S - d_N)] - B'(S - d_N)_+ \quad (171)$$

Parts left at the end of the Nth period will be sold at a discount of B dollars.

We want to determine S such that the average (or expected) value of the sum of all these costs becomes the smallest possible. The expected cost can be evaluated with the aid of equation (111). We apply this formula term by term to each of the costs in equations (169), (170), and (171). For instance, we need the formula for the expected value of $(S - d_i)_+$

$$\text{Exp}\,[(S - d_i)_+] = \int_0^\infty (S - x)_+ f(x)\, dx \qquad i = 1, 2, \cdots, N \quad (172)$$

The integral on the right-hand side of this equation can be evaluated by the following formula

$$\int_0^\infty (S - x)_+ f(x) = \int_0^S (S - x) f(x)\, dx = S \int_0^S f(x)\, dx$$
$$- \int_0^S x f(x)\, dx \quad (173)$$

Let us remember here that $f(x)$ is the probability distribution function of the demand for each inventory period. The integrals on the right-hand side of the equation can be expressed with the aid of the F and the F^* function introduced in equations (12) and (14), and, consequently,

$$\text{Exp}\,[(S - d_i)_+] = SF(S) - F^*(S) \qquad (174)$$

The expression on the right-hand side will appear in many places in our further studies, and therefore we will denote this function by $H(S)$

and assume that it will be tabulated the same way as we have tabulated the normal distribution. From here on, then, we work with

$$SF(S) - F^*(S) = H(S) \tag{175}$$

as a function given by our data.

Let us proceed now to apply equation (174) to each term in equation (170). The expected value of the loss in each production period is given by

$$\text{Exp}\,[W_i] = A[S - H(S)] - B[S - H(S)] + CH(S)$$
$$i = 2, 3, \cdots, N - 1 \tag{176}$$

This can also be written as

$$\text{Exp}\,[W_i] = (A - B)S - (A - B - C)\,H(S)$$
$$i = 2, 3, \cdots, N - 1 \tag{177}$$

For the loss in the first production period we get

$$\text{Exp}\,[W_1] = (A - B)S - \left(-B - \frac{C}{2}\right) H(S) \tag{178}$$

The expected loss in the last period is given by

$$\text{Exp}\,[W_N] = (A - B)S - (A - B - C)\,H(S) - B'\,H(S) \tag{179}$$

(Surplus parts are sold at a discount of B' dollars.)

In order to get the expected value of the loss for all the inventory periods, we have to add these terms and divide by N. Thus we get

$$\bar{W}(S) = \left[B - A\left(1 - \frac{1}{N}\right) + C\left(1 - \frac{1}{2N}\right) - \frac{B'}{N}\right] H(S) - (B - A)S \tag{180}$$

How do we select the best value of S? We want the expected loss to be a minimum; so we need the minimum of equation (180). Let us take the derivative of equation (180) with respect to S and make it equal to 0. Before we carry out this computation, let us recognize that, with the aid of equation (14), we can get

$$\frac{dH}{dS} = S f(S) + F(S) - S f(S) = F(S) \tag{181}$$

With equation (181), we get for the derivative of the expected loss

$$\frac{d\bar{W}}{dS} = \left[B - A\left(1 - \frac{1}{N}\right) + C\left(1 - \frac{1}{2N}\right) - \frac{B'}{N}\right] F(S) - (B - A) \tag{182}$$

For the best value of S the derivative must be zero; consequently, we equate the right-hand side to zero and solve for the $F(S)$ function

$$F(S) = \frac{B - A}{B - A\left(1 - \dfrac{1}{N}\right) + C\left(1 - \dfrac{1}{2N}\right) - \dfrac{B'}{N}} \qquad (183)$$

The right-hand side of this formula can easily be computed as it depends only on the various costs of the problem. On the left-hand side we have the cumulative distribution function; this is supposed to be known from the past history of demand. Consequently, the first thing to do is to compute the right-hand side, which gives the value of the cumulative distribution function. Then we can determine the optimum value of S. If the demand distribution is normal, then the cumulative distribution function is given in Table 1 by $\Phi(\xi)$.

So far, we have assumed that there is no penalty for a shortage, or $D = 0$. If there is a penalty, then the additional cost to be included is given by

$$z = D \ln \{d > S\} \qquad (184)$$

The average or expected value of this shortage is

$$\text{Exp}\,[z] = D[1 - F(S)] \qquad (185)$$

In order to get the expected loss in this new case, we have to add this last term to the loss in equation (180). We get

$$\bar{W}(S) = \left[B - A\left(1 - \frac{1}{N}\right) + C\left(1 - \frac{1}{2N}\right) - \frac{B'}{N}\right] H(S)$$
$$- (B - A)S + D - D\,F(S) \qquad (186)$$

This loss becomes a minimum when the derivative with respect to S is 0. Consequently, we must have

$$\left[B - A\left(1 - \frac{1}{N}\right) + C\left(1 - \frac{1}{2N}\right) - \frac{B'}{N}\right] F(S) - D\,f(S)$$
$$- (B - A) = 0 \qquad (187)$$

The optimum value of S is obtained by solving this equation for S. Note that both the ordinary distribution function $f(S)$ and the cumulative distribution function $F(S)$ occur on the left-hand side.

As an illustration, let us solve a problem in which the distribution function is rectangular. We substitute equations (50) and (51) into equations (175) and (186), and get the following expression for the expected loss

$$\bar{W}(S) = \frac{1}{2}\left[B - A\left(1 - \frac{1}{N}\right) + C\left(1 - \frac{1}{2N}\right) - \frac{B'}{N}\right]\frac{(S - M)^2}{\bar{M} - M}$$

$$- (B - A)S + D\frac{M - S}{\bar{M} - M} \quad (188)$$

The best value of S is obtained by solving equation (187), which for rectangular distribution becomes

$$\left[B - A\left(1 - \frac{1}{N}\right) + C\left(1 - \frac{1}{2N}\right) - \frac{B'}{N}\right]\frac{S - M}{\bar{M} - M}$$

$$- \frac{D}{\bar{M} - M} - (B - A) = 0 \quad (189)$$

This last equation can be written in the form

$$F(S) = \frac{S - M}{\bar{M} - M} = \frac{B - A + D\dfrac{1}{\bar{M} - M}}{B - A\left(1 - \dfrac{1}{N}\right) + C\left(1 - \dfrac{1}{2N}\right) - \dfrac{B'}{N}} \quad (190)$$

This gives then a direct method of computing the optimum value of S. As a numerical illustration, let us assume that M is 1,000 and $\bar{M}$ is 2,000, which means that the demand is between 1,000 and 2,000 and let us also assume: (1) that A, the cost of each part, is \$100; (2) that B, the sales price of each part, is \$200; (3) that B', the discount price of surplus parts, is \$20; (4) that C, the inventory carrying cost for each production period, is \$20. We still leave the value of D, that is, the penalty, open, and so equation (190) becomes

$$\frac{S - M}{\bar{M} - M} = \frac{100 + D/1,000}{120 + 70/N} \quad (191)$$

For instance, if we assume that D is zero and that we are dealing with a single-stage inventory problem ($N = 1$), we get for S the value 1,526. On the other hand, if N is 10, then the optimum ordering quantity becomes 1,788. If we deal with an indefinitely long problem (N is infinite), we get for S the value 1,833. Does it make good sense that as we have more and more inventory periods the replenishing level S gets higher and higher? If we have only one inventory period, then we take quite a chance if we order too much as we may have to sell the parts at a discount. However, if we have ten inventory periods, then we can carry over our inventory and therefore the chance of obsolescence is lower. If we deal with infinitely many periods, there is no chance of obsolescence and therefore we replenish to higher levels.

Let us assume that there is a penalty of \$10,000 connected with a shortage ($D = 10,000$). The replenishment level must be higher now, as we do not want to take the risk of being short. Let us assume that we have an indefinitely long problem (N is infinite). With the aid of equation (191), we get for our replenishing level 1,917 units; when there was no penalty, the level was 1,833 units. We can see, then, that we will replenish to a level which is 84 units higher than before. We order these extra parts, paying extra inventory costs because we want insurance against the shortage cost of \$10,000.

Incidentally, where N is very large equation (190) can be simplified as all terms which are divided by N become 0. We get

$$\frac{S - M}{\bar{M} - M} = \frac{B - A + D/\bar{M} - M}{B - A + C} \tag{192}$$

It is interesting to note that the inventory carrying cost C enters only into the denominator in the expression. This shows that, when inventory costs go up, the replenishing level S goes down.

With the aid of equation (188) we can compute the loss (or cost) for any value of S. Assuming again that there is no penalty, we get for the expected loss

$$\bar{W}(S) = \frac{1}{2}\left(120 + \frac{70}{N}\right)\frac{(S - M)^2}{\bar{M} - M} - 100S \tag{193}$$

If this function is plotted for different values of S, we get a parabola and the bottom point on the parabola represents the minimum loss (or maximum profit). As a check on the formula let us assume that the demand is between 1,000 and 2,000 and that we are ordering up to 1,000 units. According to our formula the loss is $-\$100,000$ or the profit is \$100,000. This is correct because, the demand being between 1,000 and 2,000 we will not have any inventory and will make exactly \$100 on each unit.

By taking the derivative of equation (193) with respect to S and equating it with zero, we can verify that the best value of the replenishment level S is given by equation (191).

As a further illustration, let us consider the loss function, given by equation (87), which covers the case where a shortage is always liquidated by providing parts at a premium of A' dollars. As we are interested only in the variable part of the loss we may omit the fixed revenue. (We always meet the demand.) The loss is given now by

$$W_i = Aq_i + A'(d_i - S)_+ + \frac{C}{2}(u_i + v_i) \qquad i = 1, 2, \cdots, N - 1)$$

$$\tag{194a}$$

and

$$W_N = AG_N + A'(d_N - S)_+ + \frac{C}{2}(u_N + v_N) - B'v_N \quad (194b)$$

This can also be written as

$$W_i = Aq_i - A'(S - d_i) + A'(S - d_i)_+ + \frac{C}{2}(u_i + v_i)$$
$$- B'v_i \qquad i = 1, 2, \cdots, N - 1 \quad (195a)$$

and

$$W_N = Aq_N - A'(s - d_N) + A'(S - d_N)_+ + \frac{C}{2}(u_N + v_N) - B'v_N$$
$$(195b)$$

In order to get the expected loss, we have to take the expected value of each term on the right-hand side. We can use equations (162), (165), (166), and (174) and obtain this expected value. Here is the result that we get:

$$F(S) - \frac{A' - A}{A' - A\left(1 - \dfrac{1}{N}\right) + C\left(1 - \dfrac{1}{2N}\right) - \dfrac{B'}{N}} \quad (196)$$

We recognize that this equation is similar to equation (183) but A' (the premium cost of a part) takes the place of B (the revenue for each part).

When we have a problem with very many stages (N is infinite), equation (196) simplifies to

$$F(S) = \frac{A' - A}{A' - A + C} \quad (197)$$

As a numerical illustration let us assume that the cost of each part A is \$100, the premium cost of each part A' is \$200, the inventory carrying cost C is \$20, and the discount value of each part B' is \$20. Then the right-hand side of equation (196) takes the value of 0.833. If we assume a rectangular distribution between 1,000 and 2,000, we get the replenishment level of 1,833. This is, then, the value of S that leads to the minimum cost.

12. INVENTORY ORDERING FUNCTIONS; PREDICTORS; RETROSPECTIVE SIMULATION

The inventory theories so far described have two basic concepts in common: the first concept is the distribution function summarizing the past demand; the second concept is the loss (or profit) function.   The theory yields optimum ordering rules provided these distribution and loss functions are available.   There are several limitations to this approach.   First of all, it is possible that the past demand is too irregular and as a result a significant distribution function cannot be deduced. Second (and we have already discussed this before), the loss function might not be available.   Furthermore, the mathematics for many-stage problems (and many problems are of this type) becomes complex and even unmanageable.   We will now extend our theory by introducing some new concepts which will make it possible to overcome these difficulties.

Let us return to our original illustrative example of the purchase of bread in the hypothetical supermarket.   Let us recall that we analyzed the past demand and concluded that the daily average was 20 loaves of bread.   The reason we relied on this number of 20 was that we suspected that the future demand will be, on the average, 20 loaves of bread.   We can say, then, that we used our past record to forecast the future demand.   Now it is conceivable that the forecast of daily requirements should be deduced from a more complicated rule.   For instance, it is conceivable that there is a daily variation in each week. Suppose that the demand is larger on Fridays than on Mondays.   Let us denote by R the forecast for tomorrow's demand.   This R is the significant factor that should enter into our decision of how much bread to order.   We have found in our previous analysis (when using normal distribution) that it is appropriate to measure the protective stock level as the square root of the demand.   Consequently, we introduce here the quantity

$$\sigma = \sqrt{R} \tag{198}$$

and postulate that the order quantity q is given by a formula of the type

$$q = R + \xi \sqrt{R} \tag{199}$$

Here, the quantity ξ (which is the measure of the level of protective stock) is yet to be determined.   Suppose, now, that we do have some rule to determine the forecast R; let us ask what value we should assign to ξ.   We can examine our past record say for the past 100 days, assume a numerical value of ξ, and compute what would have happened had we used the ordering function of equation (199).   For any value of ξ, we could compute the number of shortages that would have occurred and also the quantity of stale bread.   We can prepare a diagram showing the expected number of shortages and the expected quantity of stale bread for each value of ξ. We assume that there is a way to select the best ordering quantity if the number of shortages and the quantity of stale bread can be predicted. Therefore, by inspecting our diagram we should be able to determine the best value of ξ, which then gives the best ordering quantity. In this method of analysis we have not specified how the forecast R is to be prepared. If R is simply the average of the past demand (20 loaves of bread), then the method outlined here results in the same answer as the one presented previously. However, if there are variations in demand (say from day to day within each week), then with the aid of a more complicated forecasting rule we can get a better answer to our problem.

In a certain sense, this new method of analysis is a "simulation" of the past under the assumption that some fixed ordering rule was accepted in the past. We call such a method *retrospective simulation*. The Monte Carlo method described in Chapter 1, Section 12, is also a simulation technique, but there it is assumed that statistical distribution functions are available and that the operations of the business can be simulated with the aid of random numbers.

Let us recognize that retrospective simulation of an inventory control system can also be performed when a loss function is given. All we have to do is to assume a certain type of ordering rule, compute the past performance on the basis of this ordering rule, and then compute the loss (or profit). Then, by changing the parameter ξ in the ordering rule of equation (199), we can compute alternate past histories and select the value of ξ which results in a minimum loss.

Let us apply this technique to a cyclic inventory control system with immediate delivery. Let us denote by R the forecast of demand for the next inventory period, and by u the inventory at hand at the beginning of the inventory period. Let us assume that the quantity q to be ordered is given by

$$q = R + \xi \sqrt{R} - u \qquad (200)$$

More precisely, we should say that

$$q = (R + \xi \sqrt{R} - u)_+ \qquad (201)$$

because it is conceivable that the quantity forecasted is small and therefore the right-hand side of equation (200) might become negative. Equation (201) avoids this difficulty because it specifies that when the right-hand side is negative no part should be ordered.

The ordering quantity of equation (201) still has the disadvantage that we might order small quantities of parts. Let us assume that we do not wish to order parts unless we are below a certain reordering level, and let us assume that this level is proportional to the square root of the demand. Such an ordering rule can be expressed mathematically as

$$q = (R + \xi \sqrt{R} - u)_+ \cdot \text{In } \{u \leq \eta \sqrt{R}\} \qquad (202)$$

where both ξ and η are unknown parameters. These parameters can be determined by assuming numerical values of ξ and η, and by making a retrospective analysis under the hypothesis that this ordering rule was used. We must count the number of shortages and determine the inventory level and other factors which might influence the effectiveness of the inventory control scheme. Then we need to repeat this computation for various values of the parameters ξ, η and to select ξ, η such that we get the best ordering rule.

As an illustration let us apply this analysis to a two-bin system of inventory control. We will treat this system as a cyclic inventory control system, where inventory records are examined every day. Let ω be a parameter which takes the value of 1 when there is no back order on the books, and the value of 0 when there is a back order. Let us assume that our ordering quantity can be expressed the following way

$$q = \left(\sqrt{\frac{2yA}{pC}} - u\right)_+ \cdot \text{In } \{u \leq \eta \sqrt{R}\} \cdot \text{In } \{\omega = 0\} \qquad (203)$$

The right-hand side of equation (203) is zero when there is a back order on the books. (The value of ω is 1, the statement in the bracket is false, and the indicator function takes the value zero.) The last factor on the right-hand side takes the value 1 when there is no back order, and therefore the only time we do order is when there are no back orders. The second factor on the right-hand side indicates that we order only when the inventory level is below the reorder level $\eta \sqrt{R}$. Finally, the first factor specifies that we replenish up to a quantity given by a square root formula; this is the same formula which we used in our economic lot size relation equation (142). We can see, then, that equation (203) embodies a generalization of our former economic lot size formula equation (142), and also of our concept of the proper level of reordering. We can get the best values of ξ and η by making a retrospective analysis for various numerical values of ξ and η. The number of shortages, the inventory levels, the number of orders, and some other factors that are important for the problem must all be computed to complete such an analysis.

Let us now consider an alternate ordering quantity which can be expressed with the aid of a piecewise linear function:

$$q_i = (aR_i + bY_i - cu_i)_+ \qquad (204)$$

Here R_i is the forecast of demand for the next period, Y_i is the forecast of demand for the next year, and u_i is the inventory at the time of ordering.

The quantity in the parenthesis on the right-hand side of equation (204) gives the quantity to be ordered when we have a positive number in the parenthesis. When the number is zero or negative, then we do not order. Such a rule makes good sense because when the forecast for the next period R_i is high we order more, and when the forecast for the next year Y_i is high then again we order more, but, on the contrary, when inventory is large, we order less.

In the ordering rule of equation (204), we rely on the forecast for the next period and for the next year. A more elaborate ordering rule can be obtained by assuming that before each order a new forecast is made for each future production period. Let $r_{i,i}$ denote the forecast of demand made before the ith period for the $(i + 1)$st period; let $r_{i+1,i}$ denote the forecast for the $(i + 2)$nd period; let $r_{i+2,i}$ denote the forecast for the $(i + 3)$rd period, and so on. We are using a double index here: the second index i indicates that the forecast is made before the ith period, and the first index refers to the period for which the forecast is made. We anticipate that a long-range forecast will be less accurate than a short-range forecast. The order quantity will depend on the forecasts and on the inventory at hand:

$$q_i = \alpha_0 r_{i,i} + \alpha_1 r_{i+1,i} + \alpha_2 r_{i+2,i} + \cdots + \alpha_j r_{i+j,i}$$
$$+ \cdots - Cu_i \qquad (205)$$

This can also be written as

$$q_i = \left(\sum_{j=0}^{\infty} \alpha_i r_{i+j,i} \right) - Cu_i \qquad (206)$$

We recognize that this type of ordering rule does make sense; if the forecast for any of the future inventory periods goes up the ordering quantity goes up too, but, on the contrary, if inventory on hand, goes up, then the quantity ordered decreases. Incidentally, we note here that

$$r_{i,i} = R_i \qquad (207)$$

as the forecast made before the ith inventory period for the next period was previously denoted by R_i (equation (204)).

So far, we have not specified the forecasting rule to be employed. As the order quantity depends on the forecast, these equations cannot be used unless the method of forecasting is specified. We could, for instance, assume that the forecast of demand for the next inventory period equals the demand for the past period, or

$$R_i = d_{i-1} \tag{208}$$

A somewhat more elaborate rule forecasts the demand for the next inventory period from the average of the past three periods or

$$R_i = \tfrac{1}{3} (d_{i-1} + d_{i-2} + d_{i-3}) \tag{209}$$

Or perhaps a stronger weighting factor should be assigned to the more recent past, resulting in a forecasting rule of

$$R_i = 0.5d_{i-1} + 0.3d_{i-2} + 0.2d_{i-3} \tag{210}$$

In order to use equation (204), we also need to specify the forecast for the next year's demand. We could, for instance, assume that the demand for next year will equal the demand for the past year. This can be written as

$$Y_i = \sum_{k=1}^{12} d_{i-k} \tag{211}$$

There are many different ways of forecasting the demand, since such matters as monthly or yearly trends, seasonal variations, and other factors must be taken into account. One of the important concepts in the mathematical theory of forecasting is the concept of linear predictors. The linear predictor expresses the demand for any future period as a linear combination of the past demand. For instance, the forecast for the $(i + 1)$st period is given by

$$r_{i,i} = \beta_{0,1}d_{i-1} + \beta_{0,2}d_{i-2} + \beta_{0,3}d_{i-3} + \cdots \tag{212}$$

where the β's are fixed coefficients. The forecast for the $(i + 2)$nd period is given by

$$r_{i+1,i} = \beta_{i,1}d_{i-1} + \beta_{1,2}d_{i-2} + \beta_{1,3}d_{i-3} + \cdots \tag{213}$$

and, in general, the forecast for the $(i + j - 1)$th period is given by

$$r_{i+j,i} = \beta_{j,1}d_{i-1} + \beta_{j,2}d_{i-2} + \beta_{j,3}d_{i-3} + \cdots \tag{214}$$

Forecasting with the aid of linear predictors can be summarized with the aid of the following equation

$$r_{i+j,i} = \sum_{k=1}^{\infty} \beta_{j,k}d_{i-k} \tag{215}$$

Assuming this method of forecasting, we can get the ordering quantity from equation (206)

$$q_i = \left(\sum_{k=1}^{\infty} \sum_{j=0}^{\infty} \alpha_j \beta_{j,k} d_{i-k} \right) - C u_i \qquad (216)$$

The ordering quantity here depends only on the past demand and on the inventory at the time of ordering. The question is how to determine the coefficients α, β, and C in order to obtain an optimum ordering rule? We can assume a fixed forecasting method and a given set of β's; then we still have to determine the unknown α's and C. This can be done by retrospective analysis, that is, we can assume various numerical values for the α's and C, make a study of the past, and repeat this process for various combinations of the α's and C until the optimum ordering policy is reached.

Let us now turn our attention to the problem of determining the coefficients in the predictor formulas. One way to do this would be to assume various numerical combinations of α's, β's, and C in equation (216), make a retrospective analysis for each combination, and then select the combination which gives the best answer. This approach involves an enormous amount of numerical work and may become impractical. What we need is some sort of a simplified approach. Such an approach can be worked out by least square analysis.

In order to illustrate this approach, let us assume that we are to determine a linear predictor for the next inventory period which uses only the demand of the last three periods

$$R_i = \beta_1 d_{i-1} + \beta_2 d_{i-2} + \beta_3 d_{i-3} \qquad (217)$$

How do we determine the best values for β_1, β_2, and β_3? We could make a retrospective analysis and see how far off we would have been in the past had we used this forecasting formula. Let us agree that we can measure the "goodness" of a forecasting formula by computing the sum of the squares of the deviations from actuals. This means, then, that the measure of goodness of our predictor is given by

$$z = \sum_{i=4}^{N} (\beta_1 d_{i-1} + \beta_2 d_{i-2} + \beta_3 d_{i-3} - d_i)^2 \qquad (218)$$

In this formula the d's, the demand, are given, and the problem is to get the values of β_1, β_2, and β_3 such that the sum of the squares of the deviations, or z, becomes a minimum. We know from calculus that z will be a minimum when the partial derivatives with respect to β_1, β_2, and β_3 become zero. For instance, the partial derivative with respect to β_1 is given by

$$\frac{\partial z}{\partial \beta_1} = \sum_{i=4}^{N} 2(\beta_1 d_{i-1} + \beta_2 d_{i-2} + \beta_3 d_{i-3} - d_i)d_{i-1} \qquad (219)$$

and the right-hand side of this equation must equal zero. Consequently, we get

$$\beta_1 \left(\sum_{i=4}^{N} d_{i-1}^2 \right) + \beta_2 \left(\sum_{i=4}^{N} d_{i-2}d_{i-1} \right) + \beta_3 \left(\sum_{i=4}^{N} d_{i-3}d_{i-1} \right)$$

$$= \sum_{i=4}^{N} d_i d_{i-1} \qquad (220)$$

At this point, it is convenient to introduce the correlation coefficients which are given by

$$\rho_1 = \frac{\Sigma d_i d_{i-1}}{\Sigma d_i{}^2} \qquad (221)$$

$$\rho_2 = \frac{\Sigma d_i d_{i-2}}{\Sigma d_i{}^2} \qquad (222)$$

$$\rho_3 = \frac{\Sigma d_i d_{i-3}}{\Sigma d_i{}^2} \qquad (223)$$

With this notation equation (220) becomes

$$\beta_1 + \rho_1 \beta_2 + \rho_2 \beta_3 = \rho_1 \qquad (224)$$

Similarly, the partial derivatives with respect to β_2 and β_3 must be zero and, therefore, we have

$$\rho_1 \beta_1 + \beta_2 + \rho_1 \beta_3 = \rho_2 \qquad (225)$$

$$\rho_2 \beta_1 + \rho_1 \beta_2 + \beta_3 = \rho_3 \qquad (226)$$

We see, then, that we have three linear equations for the three unknowns β_1, β_2, and β_3. By solving these three equations we get the unknowns β_1, β_2, and β_3.

The method described here of getting optimum coefficients for linear predictors is widely used in filter theory and in the theory of time series. For more details we refer to the work of Norbert Wiener.*

Let us suppose now that with this method (or some other method), we determine the predictor to be used in the problem. Then we can proceed to determine the coefficients β and C in equation (216) with

---

* The *Extrapolation, Interpolation, and Smoothing of Stationary Time Series with Engineering Applications*, John Wiley & Sons, 1949. See in particular Appendix B by Norman Levinson.

the aid of retrospective analysis. In particular, we assume various numerical combinations of β's and C and make an analysis of the past under the assumption that equation (216) has been used as the ordering rule. The performance of various ordering rules is compared for each set of values of β's and C, and then a choice is made on the basis of the best performance.

13. THE S-s RULE OF INVENTORY CONTROL

In the previous section we introduced some concepts with the purpose of developing inventory control systems when the past demand does not follow a simple statistical pattern, when no complete cost analysis is available, and when the profit or loss function is unknown. In order to apply these concepts, let us consider a hypothetical manufacturing firm (or department store) which is confronted with the problem of manufacturing (or purchasing) parts, and let us assume that the cyclic inventory control system is used. Parts are delivered immediately, and we propose to study an ordering rule which can be expressed by

$$q = (S - u)_+ \cdot \text{In } \{u \leq s\} \tag{227}$$

The second factor on the right-hand side is 1 only when the inventory level u is less than the reorder quantity s. Consequently, the only time we place an order is when the inventory is below the reorder level s. The first factor on the right-hand side specifies that the order quantity is $S - u$ as long as u is less than S. This means, then, that when we do order we replenish up to the level S. This inventory control system is the S-s inventory control system, discussed on p. 326. This is a combination of the cyclic and the two-bin inventory control systems. We order, say, every week or every month, depending upon the order cycle. However, we order only in case we are below the ordering point, and then we order up to a fixed level of inventory. The problem we propose now to solve is how to determine S and s such that the inventory control system becomes an optimum one.

Let us use the method of retrospective simulation. Let d_1, d_2, $\cdots$, d_N denote the past demand, and let u_1 denote the inventory at the very beginning. If we use the inventory rule of equation (227), we can compute the quantity that would have been ordered at each period in the past. This ordering quantity is given for the ith period by

$$q_i = (S - u_i)_+ \cdot \text{In } \{u_i \leq s\} \tag{228}$$

where u_i denotes the inventory level at the beginning of the ith period. We recognize here that

$$u_{i+1} = (u_i + q_i - d_i)_+ \qquad (229)$$

We can now assume a pair of numerical values for s and S, and with the aid of equations (228) and (229) we can compute for each inventory period the quantity that would have been ordered and the inventory level that would have been realized.   We can repeat this calculation for a number of combinations of s and S, and then we can ask which of these S-s values is the best?   If we had all the costs available, including the cost of a shortage, we could compute from this retrospective simulation the cost associated with each pair of s and S, and we could select the values which give the lowest cost.   Suppose, however, that we do not have all the costs available.   What can we do in such a case?

The thing to do is to compute the various pertinent factors or measures that describe the effectiveness of the inventory control system. One of the important factors or measures is the average level of inventory, given by

$$z_1 = \frac{1}{N} \sum_1^N u_i \qquad (230)$$

We desire to keep inventory levels low, but also we would like to keep the number of purchase (or production) orders low, as there is a cost associated with each order.   The average number of orders is given by the formula

$$z_2 = \frac{1}{N} \sum_1^N \text{In } \{u_i \le s\} \qquad (231)$$

A third measure of effectiveness of an inventory control system is the probability that a shortage occurs during an inventory period.   This probability can be computed with the aid of the following relationship

$$\text{Pr} = z_3 = \frac{1}{N} \sum_1^N \text{In } \{u_i + q_i \le d_i\} \qquad (232)$$

Suppose, now, that we compute these three measures of effectiveness $z_1, z_2,$ and z_3 for various numerical combinations of s and S, and that we put the results into graphical form as shown in Fig. 17.   Along each of the lines shown in this diagram, the probability of a shortage is fixed.   For instance, on the lowest curve the probability of a shortage is 4% or 0.04.   The horizontal axis shows the expected inventory level, and the vertical axis shows the expected production orders per period.

Imagine now that the manager of the production department takes this chart, examines it, and applies his judgment to the proper selection of the parameters s and S. Supposedly, he balances in his mind an increase in the probability of a shortage against an increase in inventory and an increase in the expected number of purchase (or production) orders. For instance, he will consider whether he should operate at point A or B in Fig. 17. Both these operating points represent the same inventory levels but the probability of a shortage is 0.03 at point A and 0.02 at point B. He recognizes, though, that point B involves more purchase (or production) orders than point A. The manager's problem is to balance an increase in purchasing (or production) orders

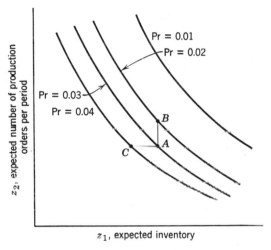

FIG. 17. Chart showing relationship between inventory level, z_1, probability of shortage, Pr, and number of production orders, z_2.

against the probability of decreasing the occurrence of a shortage. On the other hand, he might compare point A with point C. If he operates at C, he still has the same number of purchase (or production) orders per period but he needs a smaller inventory level. He gets this lower inventory at the expense of increasing the probability of a shortage from 0.03 to 0.04. The manager will have to balance these facts and use his judgment to determine which of these operating points is the best.

There is one further important remark. Suppose someone proposes an inventory control system which has the same inventory level as point A but a higher than 0.03 probability of shortage, and, simultaneously, a higher expected number of purchasing (or production) orders than point A. This proposed new inventory system is certainly inferior to the one represented by point A. Consequently, the manager will reject this new inventory control system. He has to do this in spite of the fact that no detailed cost analysis is available. This is, then, an illustration of the situation when a decision can be made though detailed cost figures are missing.*

We have assumed here that the occurrence of a shortage is one of the significant measures of the effectiveness of the inventory control system. However, a situation might arise where not so much the occurrence of a shortage but the unfilled demand is the significant measure. In such a case we need to determine the expected value of the unfilled demand

$$z_4 = \frac{1}{N} \sum_1^N (d_i - u_i - q_i)_+ \tag{233}$$

We can still prepare a chart similar to the one given in Fig. 17, but the vertical axis would represent z_4, the expected number of unfilled demand.

In our analysis so far, we have assumed that the costs associated with inventory carrying or with ordering or with the occurrence of a shortage are all unknown, and have relied on managerial judgment in selecting the optimum ordering rule. Suppose, now, that both the inventory carrying cost and the ordering cost are known. Let us denote the inventory carrying cost for each article (per period) by α and the cost of ordering by β. We can compute the combined inventory carrying and ordering costs (per period) with the aid of the formula

$$z_5 = \alpha z_1 + \beta z_2 \tag{234}$$

Here, z_5 is a dollar measure of effectiveness which replaces the previous z_1 and z_2. We still assume that we do not know the cost of a shortage. However, we can replace the chart in Fig. 17 by a single curve shown in Fig. 18, which gives the relationship between (1) the combined inventory and ordering cost z_5 and (2) the probability of a shortage. Here, then, the manager will apply his judgment in determining what sort of combined inventory and ordering cost would be tolerated for a given level of protection. Owing to the fact that we know both the inventory carrying costs and the ordering costs, there is no need for managerial decision in balancing inventories against the number of orders. However, as we do not know the cost of a shortage, judgment must be exercised in determining what the probability of a shortage should be.

---

* George J. Feeney, "Strategic Decisions in Inventory Control Operations," *Management Science*, October, 1955, Vol. 2, No. 1, pp. 69–82.

Finally, if the cost of a shortage is known too, then the three meas-ures of effectiveness z_1, z_2, and z_3 can be replaced by a single cost figure, and with the aid of retrospective analysis the values of s and S can be selected so that this combined cost becomes the lowest possible; no advanced mathematics is necessary.

So far, we have assumed that both s and S are determined only once for all. A more elaborate procedure would involve a forecast R for the next period, and then the values of s and S could be influenced by this

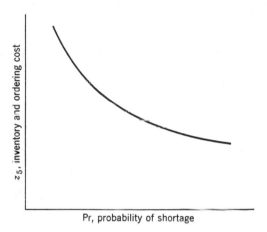

FIG. 18   Relationship between combined inventory and ordering cost, z_5, and probability of shortage, Pr.

forecast. For instance, we could say that the level of replenishment S and the reorder level s are given by

$$S = R + \xi \sqrt{R} \qquad\qquad (235)$$

$$s - \eta \sqrt{R} \qquad\qquad (236)$$

where the parameters ξ and η are to be determined. (We use the square root formula, as we have learned previously that this type of relationship is often appropriate.) How do we select the best values of the parameters ξ and η? We assume various combinations of numeri-cal values for ξ and η, and then compute the measures of effective-ness of the inventory control system. If there is no single measure of effectiveness, then managerial judgment needs to be applied to select the best method of control. On the other hand, if all the costs are known, then a single measure of effectiveness can be developed and we can compute the optimum s and S.

Let us finally point out that, under certain conditions, the S-s inventory ordering rule might not be the best. In order to demonstrate this, we proceed to describe a hypothetical inventory situation. Let us consider a two-stage inventory control problem, and focus on the economics of the second stage (as we did with the problem of ordering bread in a supermarket at noontime). Let us assume that there is an initial inventory of u units as a carryover from the first stage. Depending on the value of u, we might or might not order to meet the demand during the second stage. Let us denote by q the quantity ordered. Then v, the quantity at hand at the beginning of the second stage, is given by $v = u + q$. We assume that the inventory carrying cost is \$1 for each unit, or $(u + q)$ dollars total. We further assume that there is an ordering cost of \$100, and that the cost of a shortage is \$300. The loss function can be written as

$$W(u, q, d) = (u + q) + 100 \text{ In } \{q > 0\} + 300 \text{ In } \{u + q < d\} \quad (237)$$

where q is the ordering quantity and d is the demand. Let us assume that the demand in the afternoon is of the wholesale type: half the time the demand is 100 units, the other half 200 units.

Let us begin the analysis of this problem by assuming that we have no units at hand, or $v = 0$. We are certain to get some orders and, therefore, certain to suffer the loss of \$300. This is shown in Fig. 19 by point A. Suppose, now, on the other hand, that $v = 99$ and that there was no ordering. The loss is higher now because we are certain to lose both the \$300 and the inventory carrying cost of \$99. We have a total loss of \$399 as shown by point B in Fig. 19. Let us assume, now, that $v = 150$ and that still there was no ordering. Half the time the demand is 100, and there is no penalty. The other half the time the demand is 200, and there is a penalty of \$300. This means that on the average the penalty is \$150. In order to get the total expected loss we have to add the \$150 inventory carrying cost; this leads to a total expected loss of \$300 as shown by point C in Fig. 19. With the aid of similar computations, we can determine the loss for any valve of v, as shown in Fig. 19. The solid line shows the expected loss when we do not order; the dotted line when we do. As an illustration, point D represents the situation when we replenish to 100 units. Here, we have an inventory carrying cost of \$100, an ordering cost of \$100, and an expected penalty of \$150; this gives a total expected loss of \$350.

It can be deduced from Fig. 19 that, if the initial inventory u is less than 100 units, then the best thing to do is to order and, in particular, to replenish to 200 units. For if we do not order the solid line indicates a loss between $300 and $400, but if we replenish to 200 units the broken line indicates a loss of $300.   On the other hand, if the initial inventory u is more than 100 units but less than 150 units, then the best thing is not to order.   If initially, we have more than 150 units and less than 200 units, then the best thing to do is to replenish to 200 units.   Finally, if initially we have more than 200 units, then, of course, we do not order.   We observe, therefore, that when the initial inventory is between 100 and 150 units we are "betting" on a 100-unit sale, whereas when the initial inventory is less than 100 units or the inventory is between 150 and 200 units we are "betting" on a 200-unit

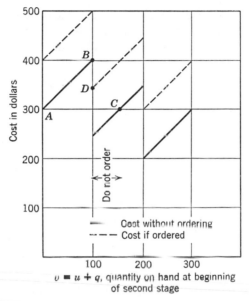

FIG. 19.   Illustration of a non-S-s type of inventory control.

sale.   In the first case we do not order; in the second case we replenish to 200 units.

The purpose of this somewhat artificial illustration is to show that the s-S policy is not always the best.   What is the optimum ordering rule under such general conditions?   This is a very difficult problem to solve, and not much work has been done on it yet.   The reader who is interested is referred to the original literature in the field of the theory of inventory control.*

* K. J. Arrow, T. Harris, and J. Marschak, "Optimal Inventory Policy," *Econometrica*, Vol. 16, July, 1951, pp. 250–272.   A. Dvoretzky, J. Kiefer, and J. Wolfowitz, "The Inventory Problem," *Econometrica*, Vol. 20, April, 1952, pp. 187–222; *ibid.*, July, 1952, pp. 450–466.

14. ORDERING RULES FOR THE CONTROL OF LARGE NUMBERS OF PARTS

In all our studies of inventory control, so far, we assumed that we are to determine the ordering rule for each part separately. In a business organization controlling thousands of parts, it might become impractical to carry through such an analysis. Therefore, "universal" ordering rules that can be applied to each individual part are needed. We propose to develop such universal ordering rules with the aid of retrospective analysis.

First of all, let us recall the economic lot size formula equation (142). We do not wish to assume that the inventory carrying cost p or the ordering cost A is known, but will use for the ordering quantity the equation

$$q = \xi \sqrt{Y/C} \tag{238}$$

where Y is the yearly forecast of demand, C is the cost of the part, and ξ is to be determined yet.

As far as the reorder level is concerned, we propose to use a formula that gives a fixed level of protection, or a fixed probability of a shortage, say, for each year. From previous experience (see equation (199)) we know that, if R denotes the forecast of demand for the replenishment period, then a protective stock which is proportional to $\sqrt{R}$ gives approximately the fixed level of protection during this replenishment period. If we want fixed protection for each year, we should use a protective stock proportional to $(Y/q) \sqrt{R}$, where Y/q is the expected number of orders per year. If we denote by L the length of the replenishment period, then Y/L can be used as the forecast of demand R for the replenishing period. Consequently, it makes good sense to investigate a protective stock of

$$w = \eta \frac{Y}{q} \sqrt{\frac{Y}{L}} \tag{239}$$

where the proportionality factor η is to be determined yet. This last equation can be written with the aid of equation (238) as

$$w = \frac{\eta}{\xi} Y \sqrt{\frac{C}{L}} \tag{240}$$

The reorder quantity is determined by adding the expected demand Y/L and the protective stock level w.

In summary, we propose an inventory control system where the ordering quantity is given by equation (238) and the protective stock level by equation (240). The question is how to determine the parameters ξ and η such that this inventory control system becomes optimum.

As we said before, we can obtain an answer to this problem by retrospective simulations. For various numerical combinations of the parameters ξ and η we compute, say, the average inventory level, the number of purchasing (or production) orders per year, and the shortages. The results of such computations can be presented graphically with the aid of a chart similar to the one shown in Fig. 17. However, the important point is that now we do not get a chart for each part but instead we get a single chart for all the parts. An enormous reduction in the computational work results from this substitution of a single chart for many different charts. The selection of the best values of the parameters ξ and η can be made with the same type of argument we used in connection with Fig. 17. Managerial judgment is required to determine what sort of a probability of a shortage and how many purchasing (or production) orders per year can be tolerated.

So far, we have assumed that the cost of carrying inventory, the cost of a shortage, and the cost of ordering are all unknown. If any two of these costs are known, then these two measures of effectiveness can be combined into a single one, and we can determine a curve similar to the one shown in Fig. 18. (This single curve applies simultaneously to all parts.) However, if all costs are known, then for each value of ξ and η, a single measure of effectiveness results and the optimum value of ξ and η can be obtained by selecting the lowest cost.

There are some limitations to this method. We have assumed that inventory carrying costs are proportional to the cost of the price of the part. This neglects the possibility, for instance, that the rate of obsolescence is different from each part. We have also assumed that the loss suffered from a shortage is the same for every part; this again might not be true. However, it can readily be seen that, if more detailed cost information is available, then the theory can be extended to include more cost information.

Moreover, the method has certain advantages. Instead of requiring advanced mathematics, it calls for only a certain amount of numerical computation. A further advantage is that, although inventory records for a single part may not be statistically significant, the records for all the parts may represent statistically important information.

Finally, we note that, if we have many thousands of parts, it might be satisfactory to choose a sample, determine the ordering rule for this sample, and then to apply the ordering rule to all parts.   This approach may represent a considerable reduction in the amount of computational work required.

15.   EMPLOYMENT AND PRODUCTION STABILIZATION THROUGH INVENTORY CONTROL

In the inventory control problems discussed in this chapter, we assumed that the reason for keeping an inventory is either to have protection against uncertainty in demand or to cut down the number of production (or purchase) orders.   However, earlier we studied a problem in a manufacturing operation (Chapter 8, Section 4) where we used inventories as a method of stabilizing employment.   Increasing or decreasing production is expensive; the cost of hiring, training, or laying off workers is high too.   We should expect, therefore, that such costs have an important effect on inventory control methods in manufacturing.   For instance, the type of inventory rule where we replenish to a certain level may not be practical in a manufacturing firm, as this rule does not take into account the problem of changing production levels.   In the problems we have studied so far, we have tacitly assumed that we are manufacturing a large number of parts and that the ordering rule does no upset production levels.   Now we will study situations where a few major products are manufactured, and develop ordering rules that result in smooth patterns of production.

To give an example, let us assume that a plant is manufacturing a single major type of product and that we are planning ahead for N production periods.   Let us denote by q_i the number of units to be produced in the ith production period, and let E_i denote the employment level in the same production period.   In order to put our problem in quantitative terms, we assume that the cost associated with any production plan is known.   Let us assume that E^* is the maximum number of people we can employ on regular time, and that if employment goes above this level we have to use a second shift.   Labor costs can be written in the form

$$z_1 = A_1 E_i + A_2(E_i - E^*)_+ \qquad (241)$$

where the first term on the right-hand side expresses regular time production, and the second term gives the cost of producing on second shift.   (This last term is 0 when the number of people employed is below the level of regular time employment).   The cost of hiring or firing can be written in the form

$$z_2 = A_3(E_i - E_{i-1})_+ + A_4(E_{i-1} - E_i)_+ \tag{242}$$

where A_3 is the cost of hiring and A_4 is the cost of laying off a worker. The inventory carrying cost is given by

$$z_3 = \frac{A_5}{2}[u_i + (u_i + q_i - d_i)_+] \tag{243}$$

Finally, we assume that there is a penalty for a shortage which can be expressed by

$$z_4 = A_6(d_i - u_i - q_i)_+ \tag{244}$$

Here, u_i is the inventory at the beginning of the ith period, and d_i is the demand in the same production period. Our problem is to determine a rule which gives the order quantity q_i and the employment level E_i such that the sum of all these costs (equations (241) through (244)) over all the production periods becomes the lowest possible.

Let us ask what factors the order quantity q_i should depend on. Let R_i be the forecast for the next production period; it is natural to assume that, if R_i is large, then q_i is large too. When R_i is small, then q_i should be small. Similarly, if the forecast Y_i for the next year increases, we would expect q_i to increase; whereas, if Y_i gets smaller, then q_i should get smaller too. If our inventory u_i is large, then we need less and expect q_i to go down; if the inventory u_i is small, we expect q_i to go up. Again, we expect the employment level E_i to behave in a similar way. Consequently, it is not unreasonable to assume that linear ordering rules similar to equation (204) might work in our problem here. Specifically, we will study ordering quantities which can be expressed as

$$q_i = \alpha_1 Y_i + \beta_1 R_i + \gamma_1 E_{i-1} - \delta_1 u_i + \epsilon_1 \tag{245}$$

$$E_i = \alpha_2 Y_i + \beta_2 R_i + \gamma_2 E_{i-1} - \delta_2 u_i + \epsilon_2 \tag{246}$$

In these equations, the forecasts R_i and Y_i appear with a positive sign, and u_i, the inventory level, appears with a negative sign. The employment level of the last production period E_{i-1} appears with a positive sign. (If employment during the last production period is high, then in order to smooth production we expect to have a relatively high production level in the next production period too.) The constants ϵ_1 and ϵ_2 are introduced to improve the effectiveness of these formulae.

How do we determine the coefficients α, β, γ, δ, and ϵ in these equations? We use retrospective analysis, as we have done in our other inventory control problems. Let the past demand be denoted by $d_1, d_2, \cdots, d_N$, the initial inventory by u_1, and the initial employment level by E_0. Let us assume that some sort of a forecasting method for R and Y is available. Then we are to select a numerical set of values for α, β, γ, δ, and ϵ, and with the aid of equations (245) and (246) compute a hypothetical past history of past employment and production level. The cost associated with this hypothetical past production plan should also be computed. If we repeat this whole computation for many numerical combinations we can select a solution with the least cost, and so we can evolve an optimum production plan. This sort of approach involves a great deal of numerical work, and it is fortunate that an alternate approximate method of analysis is available which avoids this large amount of computational work.* The method consists of replacing the cost equations (241) through (244) by *quadratic cost* functions.

Let us consider, first, the labor cost as expressed by equation (241). Such a cost function can be described graphically by the solid line in Fig. 20a, where E^* denotes the maximum regular time employment. The graph shows that, as long as employment is below E^*, labor costs can be represented by the straight line OA. If employment is above E^*, then we use the second shift at a premium cost and, consequently, the cost can be represented by another straight line AB. A *quadratic* approximation to this cost can be written in the form

$$z_{1,i} = C_1(E_i - C_2 E^*)^2 + C_3 E_i - C_4 E^* \tag{247}$$

and this relationship can be represented graphically by the broken line is Fig. 20a. The coefficients C_1, C_2, C_3, and C_4 in this equation are determined so that the broken line is close to the true (solid) cost line.

Figure 20b gives a graphical representation of hiring and firing costs (equation (242)). A quadratic approximation to this cost can be written as

$$z_{2,i} = C_5(E_i - E_{i-1})^2 \tag{248}$$

where the coefficient C_5 is adjusted such that the broken line representing the approximate cost stays close to the true cost.

The approximation of the costs of keeping inventories and suffering shortages (equations (243) and (244)) is more complicated. Let us, for the moment, focus our attention on a single production period, say the ith production period. Suppose for the moment that the inventory level at the beginning of this production period u_i is fixed, and that the order quantity q_i is fixed too. With the aid of equations (243) and

* See C. C. Holt, F. Modigliani, and H. A. Simon, "Linear Decision Rule for Production and Employment Scheduling," *Management Science*, Vol. 2, No. 1, October, 1955, p. 30.

(244) we can determine the combined inventory carrying and shortage costs for any value of the unknown demand d_i, and we can represent these costs by the solid lines in Fig. 20c.   If the demand is above $u_i + q_i$, we get the cost-line AB; if the demand is below $u_i + q_i$, the

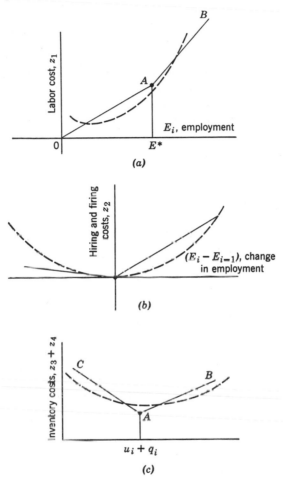

(a)

(b)

(c)

FIG. 20.   Quadratic cost functions.

cost is represented by AC.   We recognize, now, that for different production periods these graphs will change, making it difficult to develop an approximation.   However, we can attempt to replace these costs by a quadratic function as shown by the broken line.   Mathematically speaking, we approximate these costs by a quadratic function

$$z_{3,i} + z_{4,i} = C_6(u_i - C_7)^2 + C_8 \qquad (249)$$

The coefficients C_6, C_7, and C_8 are to be determined such that we get a fair approximation. With the aid of these approximations, the total cost can be written as

$$z = \sum_1^N \{[C_1(E_i - C_2E^*)^2 + C_3E_i - C_4E^*] + C_5(E_i - E_{i-1})^2$$
$$+ [C_6(u_i - C_7)^2 + C_8]\} \quad (250)$$

We could compute the cost with this formula using retrospective analysis, but we might as well compute the original cost as given by our original equations. The point is that a quadratic cost function can be minimized without numerical retrospective analysis.

Before we proceed to explain this new method of analysis, we introduce one further simplification. We assume that the inventory level at the end of each production period is given by

$$u_{i+1} = u_i + q_i - d_i \quad (251)$$

This formula might result in a negative inventory, and we will consider negative inventories as back orders.

We can state our problem now in a mathematical form. Let us consider the quantities u_i, E_0, d_1, d_2, $\cdots$, d_N given, and assume that production orders, employment levels, and inventories, are computed with the aid of equations (245), (246), and (251). We will also assume that definite forecasting formulae are available to compute the R's and Y's. The problem is to determine the α's, β's, γ's and ϵ's such that the cost function, equation (250), becomes a minimum.

A more elaborate ordering rule would use not only a forecast R for the next production period, and Y for the next year, but a forecast for each of the next 12 production periods. (See Equation (205).) Using the same notation as in equation (205) we get for the order quantity

$$q_i = \sum_{k=0}^{\infty} \alpha_k r_{i+k,i} + L_1E_{i-1} + M_1 - N_1u_i \quad (252)$$

and for the employment level

$$E_i = \sum_{k=0}^{\infty} \beta_k r_{i+k,i} + L_2E_{i-1} + M_2 - N_2u_i \quad (253)$$

We should expect that the rules expressed by equations (252) and (253) are superior to the ones described by equations (245) and (246), as the new rules are more sensitive to forecasts. The coefficients in the new equations could be determined by retrospective analysis, though we recognize that the amount of numerical work necessary may be prohibitive. However, as we said before, the use of quadratic cost functions represents a short cut and makes the completion of such an analysis possible.

There is one further important remark here. We said that equations (245) and (246) represent ordering and employment rules that make good sense. We said that equations (252) and (253) are even better. But we have no assurance that these types of rules are the best. Determining the best coefficients in equations (252) and (253) assures only that we select the best of the class of rules that can be expressed by relations of the type of equations (252) and (253). However, Holt, Modigliani, and Simon have shown that, even if one considers all possible types of ordering and employment rules, the ones given by equations (252) and (253) result in optimum ordering and employment.

This is quite a remarkable theorem, if we recognize that it is easy to conceive ordering systems which are different from the one given by equations (252) and (253).

Holt, Modigliani, and Simon have studied in detail the production smoothing problem for a certain paint factory and have shown that equations (252) and (253) take the form

$$q_i = 0.993E_{i-1} + 153 - 0.464u_i + 0.463r_{i,i} + 0.234r_{i,i+1}$$
$$+ 0.111r_{i,i+2} + 0.046r_{i,i+3} + 0.013r_{i,i+4} - 0.002r_{i,i+5}$$
$$- 0.008r_{i,i+6} - 0.010r_{i,i+7} - 0.009r_{i,i+8} - 0.008r_{i,i+9}$$
$$- 0.007r_{i,i+10} - 0.005r_{i,i+11} \quad (254)$$

and

$$E_i = 0.743E_{i-1} + 2.09 - 0.010u_i + 0.0101r_{i,i} + 0.0088r_{i,i+1}$$
$$+ 0.0071r_{i,i+2} + 0.0054r_{i,i+3} + 0.0042r_{i,i+4} + 0.0031r_{i,i+5}$$
$$+ 0.0023r_{i,i+6} + 0.0016r_{i,i+7} + 0.0012r_{i,i+8} + 0.0009r_{i,i+9}$$
$$+ 0.0006r_{i,i+10} + 0.0005r_{i,i+11} \quad (255)$$

The forecast for 12 production periods is used because there is a seasonal pattern of demand. The coefficients in the equations show that it is most important to have the forecast for the next three months. Forecasts for later periods have only a small influence on the ordering quantity and employment.

We also want to mention the forecasting procedure used by Holt, Modigliani, and Simon. First, a forecast for next year's demand is made; then the past seasonal pattern is studied and superimposed. This way, a forecast is obtained for each coming month. For further details of this theory, we refer to the original paper.

We will conclude our discussion of this section by presenting a simplified production smoothing method that has been developed by the same authors. This simpler method specifies the order quantity as

$$q = \tfrac{1}{12}Y - \xi(u - u^*) \qquad (256)$$

where u^* is the "ideal" inventory level. This ideal level is determined by first assuming that production is at a constant level throughout the year. If this assumption is made, then because of the seasonal variations in the demand there is a seasonal variation in inventories; consequently, at a certain time (say, during the summer), a minimum inventory level is reached. In order to get a given level of protection, we compute what this minimum inventory level should be. Working backwards from this minimum level, we can figure out what the "ideal" inventory level should be for each month. Returning now to equation (256), we can see that if the actual inventory is equal to the "ideal" inventory, then production is simply 1/12 of next year's demand. On the other hand, if we have too much inventory, then the second term in equation (256) gives a negative number and, therefore, we produce less. If our inventory is low, then the second term is positive and we produce more. The coefficient ξ is a measure of how fast we liquidate our inventory if it is above the "ideal" inventory, or how fast we make up for deficiencies. The authors used a value of 0.2 for ξ, which means that 20% of the surplus is liquidated or 20% of the deficiency is made up in each production period. The important thing here is that, when the actual inventory deviates from the ideal inventory, we do not suddenly adjust for the entire deviation, but only 20% of it. With the aid of retrospective analysis, best value of the parameter ξ could be determined. However, experience shows that the exact value of ξ is not very important.

As we already mentioned, the mathematical derivation is somewhat complicated and will not be included in this book. However, in order to give a hint of how such a derivation can be carried through, we will discuss a simplified case in the next section.

16. PRODUCTION SMOOTHING THROUGH INVENTORY CONTROL

We will outline briefly the mathematical details involved in deriving the results of the last section. In order to make things simpler, we will consider the somewhat restricted case where the quantity produced, x, is proportional to the level of employment, E, or

$$x = kE \qquad (257)$$

This means that we are not considering overtime (or a second shift), but that we smooth production by relying exclusively on inventory. We will again assume that we deal with N production periods, that the initial production level x_0 is given, and also that both the final inventory level u_N and production level x_N are given. Our problem is now to determine the quantities to be produced, $x_1, x_2, \cdots, x_{N-1}$, such that the total cost of production becomes a minimum. In agreement with our concept of using quadratic cost functions, we will assume that the combined inventory and shortage cost is given by

$$z_I = C_I \sum_{n=1}^{N} (u_n - C^*)^2 \qquad (258)$$

Here, each term represents a cost similar to the one given by equation (249). The cost of changing production, and the cost of changing employment, is a function of the change in production level, or

$$z_E = C_E \sum_{n=1}^{N+1} (x_n - x_{n-1})^2 \qquad (259)$$

In addition, there is a fixed labor cost associated with the number of units we produce, but we are not concerned with this as it cannot be changed. Consequently, the problem is to minimize the variable cost as given by

$$z = C_I \sum_{n=1}^{N} (u_n - C^*)^2 + C_E \sum_{n=1}^{N+1} (x_n - x_{n-1})^2 \qquad (260)$$

For completeness, we add the formula for the inventory level at the end of each production period

$$u_{n+1} = u_n + x_n - D_n \qquad n = 1, 2, \cdots, N-1 \qquad (261)$$

where D_n is the demand for the nth production period. Mathematically speaking, our problem is to minimize the cost as given by equation (260) under the side condition of equation (261). The unknowns are $u_2, u_3, \cdots, u_{N-1}$ and $x_1, x_2, \cdots, x_{N-1}$. In total we have $2N - 3$ unknowns and in order to determine these unknowns, we need $2N - 3$ equations. We recognize that relation (261) represents $N - 1$ equations, and consequently, we need $N - 2$ more equations. These equations must come from the fact that we want to minimize the cost as represented by equation (260). The partial derivatives of this expression with respect to the unknown inventory levels $u_2, u_3, \cdots, u_{N-1}$ must be zero, and this gives the $N - 2$ additional equations. In order to determine these equations, let us take the partial derivative of the cost with respect to the unknown inventory level u_k.   We get

$$\frac{\partial z}{\partial u_k} = 2C_I \sum_{n=1}^{N} (u_n - C^*) \frac{\partial u_n}{\partial u_k}$$

$$+ 2C_E \sum_{n=1}^{N+1} (x_n - x_{n-1}) \frac{\partial}{\partial u_k} (x_n - x_{n-1})$$

$$k = 2, 3, \cdots, N - 1 \quad (262)$$

We recognize now that

$$u_n = u_{n-1} + x_{n-1} - D_{n-1} \quad (263)$$

and, consequently, that

$$x_n - x_{n-1} = (u_{n+1} - 2u_n + u_{n-1}) + D_n - D_{n-1} \quad (264)$$

For purposes of this computation we will consider the inventory levels to be independent variables, and, therefore, the derivative of one inventory level with respect to another inventory level is zero, or

$$\frac{\partial u_n}{\partial u_k} = \begin{cases} 0 & \text{when } n \neq k \\ 1 & \text{when } n = k \end{cases} \quad (265)$$

(Here we recognized that the derivative of a variable with respect to itself is 1.)   With the aid of this last relationship we get

$$\frac{\partial (x_n - x_{n-1})}{\partial u_k} = \frac{\partial u_{n+1}}{\partial u_k} - 2 \frac{\partial u_n}{\partial u_k} + \frac{\partial u_{n-1}}{\partial u_k} \quad (266)$$

from which it follows that

$$\frac{\partial (x_n - x_{n-1})}{\partial u_k} = \begin{cases} +1 & \text{when } n = k + 1 \\ -2 & \text{when } n = k \\ +1 & \text{when } n = k - 1 \end{cases} \quad (267)$$

With the aid of this last equation, we can get from equation (262) the partial derivatives

$$\frac{\partial z}{\partial u_k} = 2C_I(u_k - C^*) + 2C_E[(x_{k+1} - x_k) - 2(x_k - x_{k-1})$$

$$+ (x_{k-1} - x_{k-2})] \quad (268)$$

These partial derivatives must all be 0, and consequently

$$\frac{C_I}{C_E}(u_k - C^*) + (x_{k+1} - 3x_k + 3x_{k-1} - x_{k-2})$$
$$= 0 \qquad k = 2, 3, \cdots, N-1 \quad (269)$$

As an illustration let us write this equation out in detail for $k = 2$. We get

$$\frac{C_I}{C_E}(u_2 - C^*) + (x_3 - 3x_2 + 3x_1 - x_0) = 0 \qquad (270)$$

In this last equation, x_1, x_2, x_3, and u_2 are the unknowns. The systems of equations given by equation (269), represent $N - 2$ linear equations, and so together with equation (261) we have $2N - 3$ equations for the $2N - 3$ unknowns; our problem is to solve for these equations. There are many ways of solving a system of linear equations, and we do not wish to go into the details of how such a solution is obtained. However, we do wish to point out that we expect that the unknowns depend linearly on the known quantities x_0, x_n, u_0, u_n, and D_1, D_2, $\cdots$, D_N. Therefore, we expect that the solution for (say) x_1 is given by a formula of the following type:

$$x_1 = \sum_{k=1}^{N} \alpha_k D_k + A x_0 - B u_0 + C u_N + D x_N \qquad (271)$$

When dealing with an actual problem, the system of linear equations must be solved numerically, and the coefficients in the above equation must be computed. We could also derive similar expressions for x_2, x_3, and so on. However, we may not elect to do this. When we make our next computation at the beginning of the next production period, we should look ahead again for twelve months and repeat the computation as before.

Let us speculate now about the coefficients in equation (271). If N is large, that is, if we are dealing with a large number of production periods, then we would expect that the final inventory u_N and the final production level x_N have a minor influence. Consequently, we expect that C and D are to be small. If we are planning for a sufficiently large number of production periods, then the formula for x_1 should simplify to

$$x_1 = \sum_{k=1}^{N} \alpha_k D_k + A x_0 - B u_0 \qquad (272)$$

Let us compare this equation with equation (252). Say we are considering the ith production period. In our new terminology q_i, the quantity to be produced in the ith production period is

$$q_i = x_i \tag{273}$$

The forecast for k period ahead made during the ith production period is given by

$$D_k = r_{i+k,i} \tag{274}$$

With this notation, equation (272) becomes

$$q_i = \sum_{k=0}^{\infty} \alpha_k r_{i+k,i} + A q_{i-1} - B u_{i-1} \tag{275}$$

This is the same type of equation as (252), the only difference being that the employment level E does not enter into the formula. (This is due to our assumption that the employment level is proportional to the production level.)

We see, then, that we have indeed shown that equation (275), represents an optimum rule. It is emphasized again that the approach is an approximate one, because the quadratic cost function is only an approximation to true costs.

The use of quadratic cost functions may become a powerful tool as it requires less numerical work than the more general retrospective method of analysis.

17. STATISTICAL DECISION THEORY AND METHODS OF INVENTORY CONTROL

The inventory control theory developed in this chapter is conceptually complex and abstract. The theory is still tentative as, so far, applications are not numerous. We want to finish this chapter by saying a few words about the nature of this inventory control theory. We also want to generalize and to show the relationship between this theory and the statistical theory of decisions.

Perhaps the best way to look at this inventory control theory is to consider it as a highly refined and extended form of the traditional concept of the ordering rule. The more conventional method is to examine past records and to develop some sort of a feel (or judgment) for what to order. We have seen that past records can be analyzed by statistical methods and that probability distribution functions can efficiently summarize some of the important characteristics of past demand. The probability distribution function may be normal or Poisson, or again may be of a new type. The probability distribution function concept is a refined way of examining some of the important regularities of past demand.

Whatever inventory control method is used, we need to have a way to compare one inventory control system with another in order to determine which one is superior. We make such comparisons by introducing the concept of the measure of effectiveness. If we have an overall cost associated with the system, then this is the measure to use. However, there are many business situations where a unique measure of effectiveness (such as the overall cost), is not available. In such situations, we accept such measures of effectiveness as the average inventory level, the number of shortages, or the number of purchase (or production) orders. The amount of overtime work (or night shift) may be considered as an additional measure of effectiveness. The theory brings into focus the fact that such measures must be established in order to select the best inventory control method.

We touched upon the fact that, in order to develop these inventory control systems, past records must be studied and forecasts must be made. We have attempted to put forecasting into a precise form by developing appropriate mathematical expressions. We have seen that under certain conditions the use of linear predictors is promising, and have shown techniques of determining optimum linear predictors.

We studied the problem of smoothing employment (or production levels) and obtained an optimum control method utilizing a single forecast of future demand. This approach may have its limitations, and possibly the theory will have to be extended to utilize the statistical behavior of forecasts. We have not included in the theory of forecasting "outside" factors (such as overall economic conditions), though such "extrinsic" factors may be included into the theory.

In conventional inventory theory, we talk about ordering rules, whereas here we write ordering rules in mathematical form. This brings the factors into focus on which the order quantity must depend. An ordering quantity can depend on past information such as the employment level during the last (production) period and also on the forecast of demand. We have seen that sometimes it is useful to restrict the form of the ordering rule (say an S-s rule, or a linear rule) and determine the coefficients.

There are many inventory control problems which can be treated best with the aid of simulation techniques. One of the important simulation techniques is the Monte Carlo method.* Another impor-

* A. Vazsonyi, "Electronic Simulation of Business Operations," (The Monte Carlo Method), presented to the Second Annual West Coast Engineering Management Conference of the American Society of Mechanical Engineers, May 27–28, 1957, Los Angeles.

tant technique is retrospective simulation, which has been treated with some detail in this chapter.   Here, a certain hypothetical ordering rule is predicated and past performance is computed under the assumption that inventory was controlled by this ordering rule.   We have seen that, when dealing with ordering rules with unknown coefficients, retrospective simulation can yield numerical values for the coefficients. When there is an overall cost associated with the system, we can directly compare different ordering rules.   However, if such an overall cost is not available, we need to deal with a number of different measures of effectiveness as we have done in the case of S-s rule.   Some general statements can be made about problems where no single measure of effectiveness is available.*   Say that we have two measures of effectiveness, the inventory level and the number of shortages.   Suppose that we have an ordering rule, and that an alternate second ordering rule is proposed that leads to higher inventories and to more shortages.   As our selection is made on the basis of these two measures of effectiveness, we will reject the second ordering rule.   Let us call an ordering rule an *efficient* one if no ordering rule can be developed which is superior to it in the sense we are describing here.   Mathematical theory allows the separation of efficient ordering rules from nonefficient ones, and the determination of the class of efficient ordering rules. This represents the limit we can go to with this type of analysis.   If these different measures of effectiveness cannot be compared with each other, all we can do is to ask for managerial judgment in choosing among the efficient ordering rules.   The advantage of this approach is that it clearly delineates the limit to which we can go on the basis of the theory; it shows where judgment comes into the picture.   The techniques we have developed under the name of imputed costs imply that often a further re-examination of the facts leads to a unification of some of the measures of effectiveness.   If this be the case, then the role of judgment can be reduced and that of quantitative techniques extended.

The problem of establishing measures of effectiveness is a very fundamental one.   We often take a restricted point of view and say that we are planning for next year, and that we wish to minimize costs or maximize profits.   However, it is clear that businessmen do not plan to operate only for next year, and that in fact they must consider many years in advance.   Then they must decide whether to maximize next year's profit or the profit for the average next five years, or, perhaps, to develop a plan such that the lowest profit during the next five years

* See George J. Feeney, footnote on p. 356.

will be the highest possible. (This last calls for a minimum-maximum principle similar to the one used in game theory.)

In summing up, then, in inventory control we are faced with making decisions under uncertainty; this is the subject matter that statistical decision theory deals with. An ordering rule is a statistical decision function which specifies how much to order or manufacture. The problem of deciding what should be the measures of effectiveness, and what should be maximized, is again a problem in statistical decision theory. G. J. Feeney* refers to these overall problems as the strategic problems, as distinguished from the daily decision of how much to order, which he calls tactical problems. The theory of inventory control we have developed in this book is much influenced by statistical decision theory, and it will be interesting to see how such theories influence business operations. The reader who has further interest in the subject is referred to the literature.†

* G. J. Feeney, footnote on p. 356.

† D. Blackwell and M. A. Girshick, *Theory of Games and Statistical Decisions*, John Wiley & Sons, 1954.

CHAPTER 11

ASSEMBLY LINE
FLOW SCHEDULING

1. THE CONCEPT OF SCHEDULING FUNCTIONS

In the previous chapter, we concentrated on problems where uncertainty predominates; now we will return to problems where uncertainty takes a secondary role. The first problem we want to study is scheduling production on a single assembly line. Let us consider a simple hypothetical case that can be described with the aid of Table 1. We are producing on an assembly line with seven work stations, 1, 2, 3, 4, 5, 6, and 7. Table 1 shows the day that each assembly enters the assembly line and how it moves on the assembly line from one work station to another. The first assembly enters the assembly line at the first work station on day 8, the second assembly on day 9, and so on; the fourteenth assembly enters the assembly line on day 21. At this time, production is speeded up as the fifteenth assembly enters the line on day 21.5, (middle of the twenty-first day). From then on, assemblies enter the line twice a day. The table also shows that the first assembly, serial number 1, moves from work station 1 to work station 2 on day 9, from station 2 to station 3 on day 10, and so on. The table specifies the dates of movements of assemblies through the work stations.

The motion of each assembly on the assembly line may be visualized with the aid of the diagram on the next page. Let us imagine, that periodically a whistle is blown. At each whistle, every assembly moves up one step. A completed assembly leaves the line, and a new

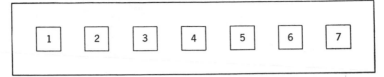

one is started. Now we proceed to put into mathematical form the rules governing the motion of the assemblies on this assembly line.

First, we will introduce a notation for the assemblies. We will denote the first assembly by A^1, the second by A^2, and so on, and the nth assembly by A^n. We say that assembly A^n enters station i on day t_i^n. For instance, assembly A^3 enters the fourth station at time t_4^3, which, according to Table 1, is 13. This means that on the thirteenth day A^3 enters station 4.

Assume for the moment that we are dealing with a steady rate of production of one assembly per day. The start days are given by

$$t_i^n = n + i + 6 \qquad (1)$$

Let us check, for instance, the time that A^6 enters the third station. For $i = 3$, $n = 6$, equation (1) gives the value of 15. We can check Table 1 and find that this is, indeed, the correct value.

So far we have assumed that we have a steady-state production of 1 unit per day and also that production starts on the eighth day. To formulate this problem under more general conditions, let us denote by t_1^1 the start date of the first assembly, and let σ denote the time spent by the first assembly on the first station. Then we can write

$$t_i^n = t_1^1 + (n + i - 2)\sigma \qquad (2)$$

In our particular case, $t_1^1 = 8$, and $\sigma = 1$, and by substituting these values into equation (2) we may verify equation (1). Note that, in Table 1, the diagonals going from a lower left corner to a top right-hand side corner all have the same dates. To discuss this in detail, consider what happens on the fifteenth day. The second assembly enters the seventh station, the third assembly enters the sixth station, the fourth assembly enters the fifth station, and so on. Mathematically speaking, this can be written as

$$t_i^n = t_{i-1}^{n+1} \qquad (3)$$

We can verify the validity of this last equation for steady-state production by using equation (2).

Table 1 is a convenient tabular presentation of the schedule for this assembly line. Sometimes it is more convenient to use the graphical

TABLE 1. Illustration of Assembly Flow Schedule [a]

	Station Number	Serial Number of Assembly																	
		1	2	3	4	5	6	7	8	9	10	11	12	13	14	15	16	17	18
Start Dates	1	8	9	10	11	12	13	14	15	16	17	18	19	20	21	21.5	22	22.5	23
	2	9	10	11	12	13	14	15	16	17	18	19	20	21	21.5	22	22.5	23	23.5
	3	10	11	12	13	14	15	16	17	18	19	20	21	21.5	22	22.5	23	23.5	24
Station Number	4	11	12	13	14	15	16	17	18	19	20	21	21.5	22	22.5	23	23.5	24	24.5
	5	12	13	14	15	16	17	18	19	20	21	21.5	22	22.5	23	23.5	24	24.5	25
	6	13	14	15	16	17	18	19	20	21	21.5	22	22.5	23	23.5	24	24.5	25	25.5
	7	14	15	16	17	18	19	20	21	21.5	22	22.5	23	23.5	24	24.5	25	25.5	26
Completion Dates		15	16	17	18	19	20	21	21.5	22	22.5	23	23.5	24	24.5	25	25.5	26	26.5

[a] The number t_i^n is the time when assembly serial number n enters station i. For instance, assembly A^6 enters station 3 at day 15 (t_3^6).

representation given in Fig. 1. The left-hand line shows the start days of the assemblies, that is, the dates when the assemblies enter the line. The right-hand line shows the completion date, which is the date that the assemblies leave the assembly line. (From the point of

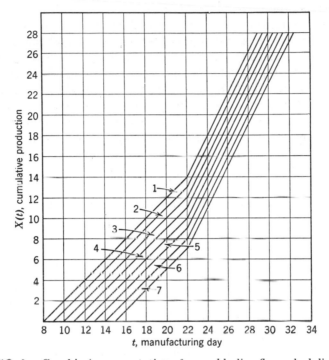

FIG. 1. Graphical representation of assembly line flow scheduling.

view of overall scheduling, these are the most important dates.) We denote by l^n the start date of assembly A^n and write

$$l^n = t_1{}^n \tag{4}$$

We denote by $\bar{l}^n$ the completion date of assembly A^n and write

$$\bar{l}^n = t_S^{n+1} \tag{5}$$

where S denotes the number of work stations on the assembly line. (In our example, S has the value 7, as we have 7 stations.) With the aid of equation (2) and remembering that start date is when the assembly enters the first station, we can write

$$l^n = t^1 + (n - 1)\sigma \tag{6a}$$

The time when an assembly leaves the line (station S) is the completion date of the assembly, and, therefore, for steady-state production

$$\bar{t}^n = t^1 + (n + S - 1)\sigma \qquad (6b)$$

So far, we have developed a mathematical notation to describe start dates, completion dates, or the dates when an assembly enters a particular work station; often another type of notation is more convenient. In Fig. 1, the left-hand side represents start dates, and the right-hand side represents completion dates. Consequently, by writing the equations of these lines, we can describe start and completion dates. Let t denote the time (which in our example is measured in manufacturing days), and let X denote the number of assemblies that are started by day t. We can say, then, that $X(t)$ represents the cumulative start dates, as shown by the left-hand line in Fig. 1. We recognize that at day t^n the nth assembly is started, and, consequently,

$$X(t^n) = n \qquad (7)$$

As an illustration, the function describing start dates for steady-state production is given by

$$X(t) = \frac{t - t^1}{\sigma} + 1 \qquad (8)$$

For instance, in Fig. 1, $t^1 = 8$, $\sigma = 1$. Which assembly is started on day 16 ($t = 16$)? Equation (18) gives the value of $X = 9$, and it can be verified, in Fig. 1 or in Table 1, that the ninth assembly is started on day 16.

It is seen, then, that the motion of assemblies on an assembly line can be described by two different methods. One employs start and completion dates; the other employs the function that gives the serial number of the assembly (as a function of time). How do we get from the second method of representation to the first?

Here, we need to introduce the mathematical concept of an inverse function. Let us consider, for instance, a simple quadratic function

$$y = x^2 \qquad (9)$$

For each value of x, there is a value of y. However, we can invert this function and say that for every value of y there is a value of x.

$$x = \sqrt{y} \qquad (10)$$

(In fact, both $+\sqrt{y}$ and $-\sqrt{y}$ will do.) The square root function is the inverse function of the square function. In general, if we deal with a function, $f(x)$, then for each value of x there exists a value of y which is given by $f(x)$.   Conversely, for each value of y we can determine one or more values of x such that $f(x)$ is equal to y.   The mathematical notation for the inverse function is the following:

$$x = f^{-1}(y) \qquad (11)$$

Let us now ask at what time the nth assembly is to be started.   For the moment, denote this time by u, then

$$X(u) = n \qquad (12)$$

as the left-hand side of the equation denotes the serial number of the assembly that is started at time u.   Returning to the previous notation of denoting by t^n the time when the nth assemgly is started, we have $u = t^n$ and the above equation can be written the following way

$$X(t^n) = n \qquad (13)$$

With the aid of the inverse function this can be written in the form

$$t^n = X^{-1}(n) \qquad (14)$$

This is, then, the mathematical expression which determines the start date from the serial number function.   As an illustration for steady-state production, it follows from equation (8)

$$t = (X - 1)\sigma + t^1 \qquad (15)$$

This gives the time of starting an assembly as a function of the serial number of the assembly.   For instance, when $X = 12$, we obtain from equation (15) $t = 11 + 8 = 19$, which means that the twelfth assembly is to be started on the nineteenth day, as can be verified either from Table 1 or Fig. 1.

With the aid of the inverse function notation, equation (15) can also be written as

$$X^{-1}(n) = (n - 1)\sigma + t^1 \qquad (16)$$

So far, we have developed the mathematics only for steady rate of production.   However, the example given in Table 1 and Fig. 1 involves an acceleration of production on manufacturing day 21.   The scheduling function for start dates in this production plan can be written as

$$X(t) = t - 7 \qquad 7 \le t < 21 \qquad (17)$$

and

$$X(t) = 2t - 28 \qquad 21 \le t \qquad (18)$$

These equations describe the (piecewise linear) line shown on the left-hand side of Fig. 1.   We propose to use the start date function $X(t)$

(straight or curved) as the fundamental scheduling function of our theory.

It is not sufficient to know the time the assemblies are started; we also need to know completion dates. Therefore, we introduce $\bar{X}(t)$, the schedule of completion dates. This function is represented in Fig. 1 by the line shown on the right-hand side. The equation of this (piecewise linear) line is given by

$$\bar{X}(t) = t - 14 \qquad 14 \leq t < 21 \qquad (19)$$

and

$$\bar{X}(t) = 2t - 35 \qquad 21 \leq t \qquad (20)$$

These two scheduling functions, the start scheduling function and the completion scheduling function will form the mathematical basis

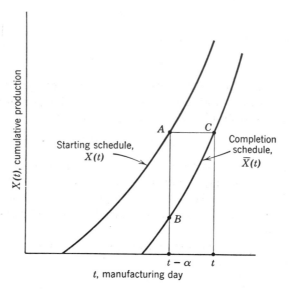

FIG. 2. Concept of manufacturing band.

of our scheduling system. Often it is unnecessary to go into the details of describing the motion of assemblies, station by station, and when this is so it is sufficient to work exclusively with these scheduling functions. Basically we conceive an assembly line schedule as shown in Fig. 2. The left-hand side shows the schedule of starting the assemblies, and the right-hand side shows the schedule of completing them. For instance, point A represents the start date of an assembly of serial number X and point C represents the completion date of the same assembly. The distance from A to C represents the time that this assembly spends on the assembly line.   Let us denote by α the time spent by an assembly on the assembly line, or the distance between the starting schedule and the completion schedule.   It will be shown later that for some important types of production this "make span" α is a constant and so the width of the "band" shown in Fig. 2 is fixed.   In general, the make span α is a function of the manufacturing day t and as illustrated in Fig. 2 the make span does vary.

Since the number of units completed at time t is the same as the number of units started at time $t - \alpha$, the relationship between the completion and starting schedule is given by

$$\bar{X}(t) = X[t - \alpha(t)] \tag{21}$$

In the case of the production schedule shown in Table 1 (or Fig. 1), the make span can be written in the following form

$$\alpha(t) = 7 \qquad\qquad \text{for} \quad 7 \le t < 14 \tag{22}$$

$$\alpha(t) = 7 - \tfrac{1}{2}(t - 14) \quad \text{for} \quad 14 \le t < 20 \tag{23}$$

$$\alpha(t) = 3.5 \qquad\qquad \text{for} \quad 20 \le t \tag{24}$$

We recognize that up through the twentieth day the production rate is 1 unit per day, whereas from the twenty-first day on the rate is 2 units per day.   This acceleration of production is accomplished by moving the assemblies faster on the assembly line, and not by introducing new work stations.   (In Fig. 1 the number of work stations does not change.)

Now we wish to derive the mathematical expression for the rate of production.   The rate of starting assemblies is given by the slope of the start schedule or, mathematically speaking, by the derivative of the start schedule.   Let us denote by $R_s(t)$ the rate of starting assemblies at time t.   Then

$$R_s(t) = dX/dt \tag{25}$$

Let us denote by $R_c(t)$ the rate of completion of assemblies.   Then

$$R_c(t) = d\bar{X}/dt \tag{26}$$

How many assemblies are on the assembly line at time t?   Obviously, this is given by the difference between the assemblies started and completed or

$$N(t) = X(t) - \bar{X}(t) \tag{27}$$

We now want to introduce two types of scheduling systems for later discussion.   Let us consider first a scheduling system where N, the

number of assemblies on the assembly line, is fixed. According to
equation (27)

$$\bar{X}(t) = X(t) - N \tag{28}$$

where N is not a function of time but a fixed quantity. A graphical
representation of such a scheduling system is given in Fig. 3. The
start schedule $X(t)$ and the completion schedule $\bar{X}(t)$ are represented
by similar curves, and the first is obtained from the second by a vertical
displacement specified by the quantity N. The rate of starting and

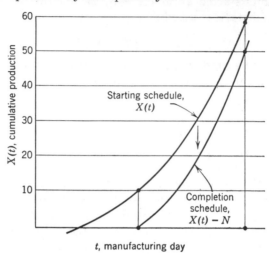

FIG. 3.   Manufacturing band with fixed rate of production.

completing assemblies can be computed from equations (25) and (26).
These rates are the same and are given by

$$R_s(t) = R_c(t) = dX/dt \tag{29}$$

The slopes at a given manufacturing day are the same because one curve
is obtained from the other by moving it vertically. Also, if we accelerate production as shown in Fig. 3, then the make span decreases. We
can verify this in Fig. 1, and we note that the make span indeed
becomes shorter. We can summarize this type of production by stating that there are the same number of assemblies on the line but that
they move faster and faster.

Acceleration of production is often experienced during the learning
stage when workers get accustomed to their work and improve their
efficiency. Another way to accelerate the line is to employ more
workers. Then it takes less time for an assembly to move through the
line, and so the whole assembly line is accelerated.

A different sort of production scheme is obtained when it is specified that each assembly must spend the same amount of time on the assembly line. Such a plan is shown in Fig. 4, where α, the make span, is a constant. According to equation (21) completion and starting schedules are related by

$$\bar{X}(t) = X(t - \alpha) \tag{30}$$

where α is a fixed number. The starting schedule and the completion schedule are represented by the same curve (this is true when there are a fixed number of assemblies on the line), except that the curves are

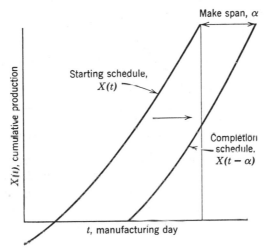

FIG. 4. Manufacturing band with fixed make span.

shifted horizontally (not up and down). We emphasize that with this type of production it is possible to accelerate, and, for instance, Fig. 5 shows that production is doubled. Such a production scheme is obtained, for instance, when each work station is split into two new stations and when new workers are assigned to man the new stations. Here, the make span remains constant but the number of work stations doubles. It is also apparent that, at the time we double the rate of starting assemblies, we have not yet changed the rate of completion. This occurs at a later time and we see that production is doubled through a step by step transition process.

In Section 4 of this chapter, a more general production scheme is presented which includes both of these scheduling systems as special cases.

Let us now summarize the accomplishments of this section. We have introduced the concepts of the scheduling functions and start and completion dates. These concepts allow a mathematical description of some of the scheduling problems in assembly line production.

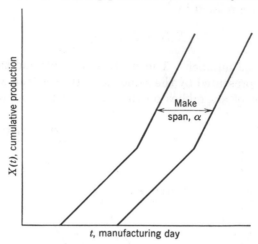

FIG. 5. Doubling production rate with constant make span.

These functions give the make span (the time spent by each assembly on the assembly line), the rate of production, and also the in-process inventory (the number of assemblies on the assembly line). Section 2 of this chapter shows how the manpower requirement can be computed with the aid of these scheduling functions.

2. MANPOWER REQUIREMENTS FOR A SINGLE ASSEMBLY LINE

We are to develop a mathematical model that includes considering the number of workers employed on an assembly line. As an illustrative example, let us consider Table 1 (or Fig. 1). There are 7 stations on the assembly line here. During the first twenty days, every second work station is manned; from the twenty-first day on every work station is manned (production rate is doubled). We introduce the $E^{(1)}(t)$ function which gives the number of people working on assembly serial number 1 at time t. Assembly number 1 enters the line on day 8 at station number 1; we assume that only stations numbers 2, 4, 6, and so on are manned and that, prior to day 8, there are no workers employed. We can write

$$E^{(1)}(t) = 0 \qquad t \le 9 \qquad (31)$$

On the ninth day, assembly serial number 1 enters station number 2. We assume that there is one man employed on station number 2. We write this in a mathematical form as

$$E^{(1)}(t) = 1 \qquad 9 \leq t < 10 \qquad (32)$$

On the tenth day assembly serial number 1 leaves station number 1.

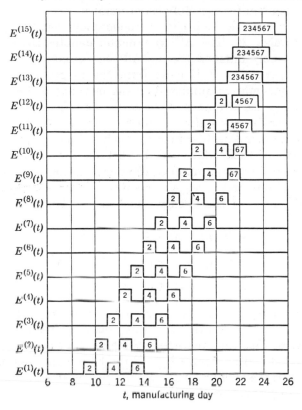

FIG. 6. Labor expenditure functions and manpower requirement.

Consequently, no work is being done on the tenth day on assembly serial number 1. Therefore,

$$E^{(1)}(t) = 0 \qquad 10 \leq t < 11 \qquad (33)$$

A graphical representation of the $E^{(1)}(t)$ function is given in the bottom line of Fig. 6. It can be seen that the value of this function is 0 before day 9; the value is 1 on the ninth day; on the tenth day the value becomes 0 again. The diagram also shows that on the eleventh day there is one man working on assembly number 1, that no one is working on the assembly on the twelfth day, that on the thirteenth day there is a man working on this assembly again, and that from then on the employment level on this assembly stays 0. The diagram also shows that on the ninth day there is employment on station number 2, on the eleventh day on station number 4, and on the thirteenth day on station number 6. Thus the $E^{(1)}(t)$ function does indeed describe the manpower required for assembly serial number 1.

Similarly, we can develop $E^{(2)}(t)$, the employment level needed for assembly number 2. The $E^{(3)}(t)$ function denotes the employment level for assembly number 3, etc. All these functions are shown in Fig. 6. For instance, it is clear from the diagram that assembly number 9 enters station number 6 on the morning of the twenty-first day, and that in the afternoon of the same day this assembly moves to station number 7 (work station number 7 is manned on the twenty-first day). The mathematical formula for each of these employment level functions can be easily determined. Let us, for instance, compute $E^{(15)}(t)$. Assembly serial number 15 enters station number 2 on the twenty-second day and moves twice a day. It leaves station number 2 in the afternoon of the twenty-fourth day. Therefore, $E^{(15)}(t)$ is given by:

$$E^{(15)}(t) = 0 \quad \text{for} \quad t \leq 22 \tag{34}$$

$$E^{(15)}(t) = 1 \quad \text{for} \quad 22 \leq t < 25 \tag{35}$$

$$E^{(15)}(t) = 0 \quad \text{for} \quad 25 \leq t \tag{36}$$

Let us now determine the total labor expended on a certain assembly. It is easy to see that the $E^n(t)$ functions describe the rate of labor and, therefore, that the area under these curves represents the total labor expended. If we denote by $\tau^{(1)}$ the labor expended on the first assembly, then the area under the $E^{(1)}(t)$ curve can be computed with the aid of integral calculus as

$$\tau^{(1)} = \int_9^{14} E^{(1)}(t) \, dt \tag{37}$$

This can also be written as

$$\tau^{(1)} = \int_{-\infty}^{+\infty} E^{(1)}(t) \, dt \tag{38}$$

because the employment level is 0 outside of the start and completion dates. In general, if we denote the labor expended on the nth assembly by τ^n then

$$\tau^n = \int_{-\infty}^{+\infty} E^n(t) \, dt \tag{39}$$

What is the employment level at time t on the whole assembly line? Workers work on the first, on the second, on the third, etc., assembly. If we denote by $E(t)$ the total employment level at time t, then this can be obtained by adding the employment levels for each of the assemblies. In a mathematical form

$$E(t) = E^{(1)}(t) + E^{(2)}(t) + \cdots + E^{(n)}(t) + \cdots \qquad (40)$$

This can be written as:

$$E(t) = \sum_{n=1}^{\infty} E^n(t) \qquad (41)$$

In our example each assembly takes exactly three days to complete, and τ^1, τ^2, and so on, are all equal to three man-days. In general, the labor expended on different assemblies may be different. There may be many reasons for this, but the most important one is that at the beginning workers are untrained, and that as time goes on they learn and can do the same job more efficiently. (We will have an opportunity later to discuss learning curves.) The total employment level in our example starts with one man, then goes to two men, and so on, until the assembly line is fully manned and six workers are employed.

Suppose we want to know the cumulative labor expended on this assembly line by manufacturing day t? The $E(t)$ function describes the labor expended at time t, and, therefore, the area under this curve represents the cumulative labor. With the aid of integral calculus, this area can be expressed as

$$\int_{-\infty}^{t} E(x)\, dx = \text{Cumulative labor expended} \qquad (42)$$

We have developed here a detailed mathematical model to deal with labor expenditure on an assembly line. It is often impractical (or unnecessary) to make an analysis with this degree of detail, and so there is a need for an approximate method of analysis. Let us assume that we use only start and completion schedules. From this, α^n, the make span for the nth assembly can be determined. Let us denote by τ^n the labor to be expended on the nth assembly. We do not know how this τ^n labor is expended during this α^n make span, but we assume that the labor is expended at a uniform rate. This means that, on the nth assembly between the start date and completion date (on the average), τ^n/α^n number of workers are employed. Consequently, the labor level function $E^n(t)$ can be approximated in the following simple way: Before starting an assembly, there are no workers employed, and, therefore,

$$E^n(t) = 0 \quad \text{for} \quad t \leq t^n \tag{43}$$

Between start and completion date, the rate of labor is τ^n/α^n:

$$E^n(t) = \tau^n/\alpha^n \quad \text{for} \quad t^n < t \leq \bar{t}^n \tag{44}$$

Finally, after the completion date, $\bar{t}^n$, the employment level is 0 again and, therefore,

$$E^n(t) = 0 \quad \text{for} \quad \bar{t}^n < t \tag{45}$$

We can develop an approximation for the total labor requirement by multiplying the rate of production by the labor requirement. This can be written as

$$E(t) = \frac{dX}{dt} \cdot \tau^n \qquad X = n \tag{46}$$

We want to say a few words now about learning (or time reduction) curves which are widely used in the aircraft industry. Let us denote by T^n the cumulative labor expended on the first n assembles. This can be written as

$$T^n = \tau^{(1)} + \tau^{(2)} + \cdots + \tau^n \tag{47}$$

Learning curves deal with the average labor expended on the first n assemblies. This average can be written as

$$\frac{T^n}{n} = \frac{\tau^{(1)} + \tau^{(2)} + \cdots + \tau^n}{n} \tag{48}$$

Suppose we employ an 80% learning curve. This implies that the average labor expended on the first, say, 200 assemblies is 80% of the average expended on the first 100 assemblies. This can be written as

$$\frac{\frac{1}{200} T^{(200)}}{\frac{1}{100} T^{(100)}} = 0.80 \tag{49}$$

Speaking in more general terms, an 80% learning curve specifies that the average time to make the first $2n$ assemblies is 80% of the average time required to make the first n assemblies, or

$$\frac{\frac{1}{2n} T^{2n}}{\frac{1}{n} T^n} = 0.80 \tag{50}$$

It is convenient to write the right-hand side of equation (50) in a different form, namely,

$$\frac{\dfrac{1}{2n}\, T^{2n}}{\dfrac{1}{n}\, T^{n}} = \frac{1}{2^{k}} \tag{51}$$

The exponent in the denominator on the right-hand side is computed so that we have the proper per cent figure on the right-hand side. For instance, for an 80% time reduction curve the value of k is 0.322, (very close to $\frac{1}{3}$).

We need to compute, say, on an 80% learning curve the cumulative labor expenditure T^{n}. This is given by the formula

$$T^{n} = T_{n}^{\,1-k} \tag{52}$$

where T denotes the time required to make the first assembly. For instance, for an 80% time reduction curve, the labor required to make the first n assemblies is given by

$$T^{n} = Tn^{0.678} \sim Tn^{\frac{2}{3}} \tag{53}$$

In order to verify equation (52), or its special case (53), we substitute T^{n} into equation (51) and see that equation (51) does hold.

Let us develop a formula for the average labor required to manufacture the first n assemblies. This average can be computed by taking equation (52) and dividing both sides by n. For intance, for an 80% time reduction curve,

$$\frac{1}{n}\, T^{n} \sim Tn^{-\frac{1}{3}} \tag{54}$$

If T^{n} or $(1/n)T^{n}$ is plotted on logarithmic paper (Fig. 7), we obtain a straight line.

Let us compute τ^{n}, the labor requirement for the nth assembly. We take the cumulative labor requirement for the first n assemblies and subtract the cumulative requirement for the first $(n-1)$ assemblies, or

$$\tau^{n} = T^{n} - T^{n-1} = T[n^{1-k} - (n-1)^{1-k}] \tag{55}$$

It is easy to show that, for large values of n, we can use the approximation

$$n^{1-k} - (n-1)^{1-k} \sim 1 - k/n^{k} \tag{56}$$

As an illustration let us take an 80% learning curve and $n = 10$. In this case, $k = \frac{1}{3}$, and

$$10^{\frac{2}{3}} - 9^{\frac{2}{3}} = 3.15 \qquad \frac{1 - \frac{1}{3}}{10^{\frac{1}{3}}} = 3.09$$

We see, then, that this approximation is within 2% of the exact result. With the aid of this approximation, the labor requirement for the nth assembly τ^n can be expressed as

$$\tau^n = T \frac{(1 - k)}{n^k} \tag{57}$$

We can also compute the labor requirement $E(t)$ for the entire assembly

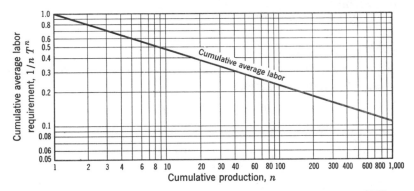

FIG. 7.   Eighty per cent time reduction curve: $(1/n)T^n = n^{0.322}$.

line by using equations (46) and (57), as follows:

$$E(t) = T(1 - k) \frac{dX}{dt} [X(t)]^{-k} \tag{58}$$

As an illustration, consider an 80% learning curve. Here, k has the value of $\frac{1}{3}$. Equation (58) becomes

$$E(t) = \frac{2}{3} T \frac{dX}{dt} [X(t)]^{-\frac{1}{3}} \tag{59}$$

Let us apply this last formula under the assumption that the same number of workers are employed on the assembly line. Mathematically speaking, the problem is to determine the $X(t)$ scheduling function such that, on the left-hand side of equation (58), the $E(t)$ function stays a constant. This is a problem in the theory of ordinary differential equations and can easily be solved. The result is that

$X(t)$ is given by

$$X(t) = 1 + \left(\frac{t - t^1}{\sigma}\right)^{1/(1-k)} \tag{60}$$

where t^1 is the start date of assembly serial number 1, and σ is the time spent by the first assembly at the first station. If we schedule on an

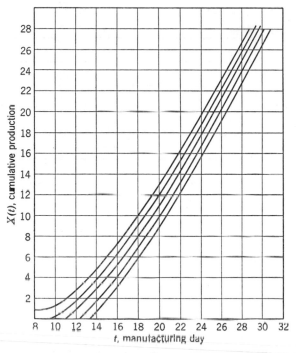

FIG. 8.   Assembly line producing on an 80% learning curve.

80% learning curve, then k has the value of $\frac{1}{3}$, and

$$X(t) = 1 + \left(\frac{t - t^1}{\sigma}\right)^{3/4} \tag{61}$$

How do we get the start date, say, for assembly serial number 2? Assembly serial number 1 is started at time t^1; it leaves the first station σ time later; this is the time when assembly serial number 2 is started. Therefore, the start date for assembly serial number 2 is obtained by adding to t^1 the value of σ or $t^2 = t^1 + \sigma$. We get from equation (61)

$$X(t^2) = 2 \tag{62a}$$

Assembly serial number 3 is started at time t^3, and we must have

$$X(t^3) = 3 \tag{62b}$$

As an illustration, let us compute a schedule when the first assembly is started on day 8 or $t^1 = 8$, when there are four work stations on the

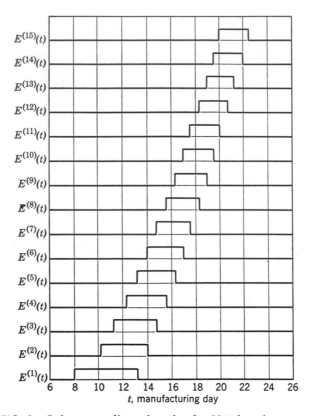

FIG. 9.   Labor expenditure function for 80% learning curve.

assembly line, and when the first assembly spends $\sigma = 2.15$ days on the first work station.   According to our formula we get

$$X(t) = 1 + \left(\frac{t - 8}{2.15}\right)^{3/2} \tag{63}$$

The scheduling functions are shown in Fig. 8.   This schedule represents an 80% learning curve and the employment of a fixed number of workers.   The labor expenditure functions, $E^{(1)}(t)$, $E^{(2)}(t)$, and so on, are shown in Fig. 9.

3. MULTIPLE ASSEMBLY LINE PRODUCTION

We will now develop a mathematical model which describes production on many assembly lines which feed into a single main assembly line. In order to be specific we consider the manufacture of a single main assembly, A_1, and of three subassemblies, A_2, A_3, and A_4. Figure 10 gives a schematic representation of the work stations. Line 1 represents the main assembly line. Lines 2 and 3 feed into the main assembly line at different work stations. Assembly A_4 is made on line 4, and this line feeds into line 3. Completion dates for the main assemblies are given in the first column of Table 2. It is seen that the first A_1 is to be completed on manufacturing day 200, the second on day 205, etc. The rate of production for the first five of A_1 is 1 per five days. Then the assembly line is speeded up to a production rate of 1 unit of A_1 per two days. In terms of our mathematical notation, the first column in Table 2 represents $\bar{X}_1(t)$, the completion schedule of assembly A_1. Therefore,

$$\bar{X}_1(T^n) = n \qquad (64)$$

where T^n is the completion date of the nth assembly A_1. Let us compute the start days for assembly A_1. It is seen in Fig. 10 that there are 9 work stations on the main assembly line. Therefore, the tenth A_1 enters the line at the same time that the first A_1 is completed, or

$$t_1{}^{10} = T^1 \qquad (65)$$

where $t_1{}^{10}$ denotes the start day of the tenth A_1, and T^1 denotes the completion date of the first A_1. More generally, the nth A_1 is to be started on day $t_1{}^n$, where

$$t_1{}^n = T^{n-9} \qquad (66)$$

What must be done if there are more than 9 work stations on the main assembly line? Let us denote by S_1 the number of work stations on the main assembly line. Then

$$t_1{}^n = T^{n-S_1} \qquad (67)$$

where $t_1{}^n$ is the start date for the nth A_1. How do we get $t_1{}^1$, the start day of the first A_1? According to equation (66) this is given by T^{-8}, but so far we do not have values assigned to T^{-8}. Let us assume that the values for T^{-1}, T^{-2}, T^{-3}, and so on are given in Table 2 in the top row. Here T^1, the completion date of the first A_1, is 200. T^0 is 195, T^{-1} is 190, $\cdots$, T^{-8} is 146 (tenth number in the top row). Now the

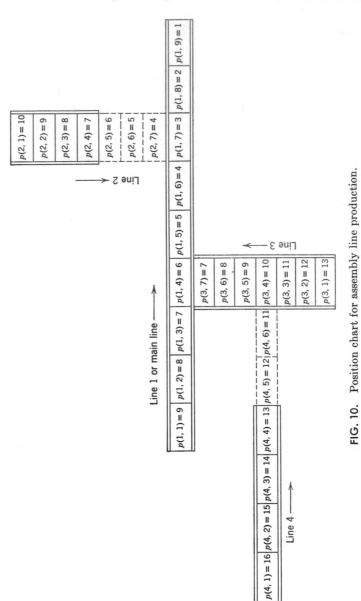

FIG. 10.   Position chart for assembly line production.

TABLE 2. Assembly Flow Schedule, Position versus Serial Number Matrix

Serial Number = n	Position Number = p															
	1	2	3	4	5	6	7	8	9	10	11	12	13	14	15	16
1	200	195	190	185	180	175	170	162	154	146	138	128	118	108	98	88
2	205	200	195	190	185	180	175	170	162	154	146	138	128	118	108	98
3	210	205	200	195	190	185	180	175	170	162	154	146	138	128	118	108
4	215	210	205	200	195	190	185	180	175	170	162	154	146	138	128	118
5	220	215	210	205	200	195	190	185	180	175	170	162	154	146	138	128
6	222	220	215	210	205	200	195	190	185	180	175	170	162	154	146	138
7	224	222	220	215	210	205	200	195	190	185	180	175	170	162	154	146
8	226	224	222	220	215	210	205	200	195	190	185	180	175	170	162	154
9	228	226	224	222	220	215	210	205	200	195	190	185	180	175	170	162
10	230	228	226	224	222	220	215	210	205	200	195	190	185	180	175	170

start date for the first A_1 is given by

$$t_1{}^1 = T^{-8} = 146 \qquad (68)$$

It is seen, then, that start and completion schedules for A_1 are specified by the numbers in the first column and top row in Table 2.

Let us turn our attention now to scheduling assembly A_3 on assembly line number 3. We note (Fig. 10) that assembly line number 3 feeds into the main line at the sixth work station, and that assembly line number 3 has 7 work stations. Consequently, we say that line number 3 is 13 positions back from the completion date of the main assembly. More specifically, the fourteenth A_3 enters on line number 3 when the first A_1 is completed. In the general case, we say that $t_3{}^n$, the start day of the nth A_3, is given by

$$t_3{}^n = T^{n-13} \qquad (69)$$

The number 13 in the superior on the right-hand side relates to the statement that A_3 starts 13 positions back from the completion date of A_1. Furthermore, say the seventh A_3 leaves line 3 at the time when the first A_1 is completed. Then the seventh A_3 is completed at time

$$\bar{t}_3{}^7 = T^1 \qquad (70)$$

where $\bar{t}_3{}^7$ denotes the completion date of the seventh A_3. More generally, the nth assembly A_3 is completed when the $(n-6)$th A_1 is completed or

$$\bar{t}_3{}^n = T^{n-6} \qquad (71)$$

The number 6 appears in the superior on the right-hand side because line 3 feeds into the sixth position of the main line. Equations (69) and (71) give start and completion dates for A_3, and these equations form the mathematical model for scheduling on this assembly line.

Let us turn our attention now to assembly line 2 as shown schematically in Fig. 10. This assembly line has four work stations plus three fictitious work stations introduced between assembly line 2 and the main assembly line. These fictitious work stations are introduced to allow time to transport completed assemblies from line 2 to the main line. (Also, these three fictitious stations allow an in-process inventory of three A_2's.) The first work station on line 2 is in the tenth position with respect to the main line, or nine positions behind the last position on the main line. The start dates of the nth assembly of A_2 are given by

$$t_2{}^n = T^{n-9} \qquad (72)$$

Similarly, we can develop an equation for the completion dates of A_2.

In fact, we can assign a position number to each work station on each assembly line as shown in Fig. 10. We denote by $p(i, j)$ the position number of the jth work station on assembly line i. For instance, $p(3, 6)$ is the position number of the sixth work station on the third assembly line. (In Fig. 10, $p(3, 6) = 8$.) Each assembly, whether on the main or on another assembly line, has a serial number, and we say that a certain serial number "completes out of a position" at a certain time. Let us denote by $\theta_p{}^n$ the time when the nth assembly completes out of position p. Then

$$\theta_p{}^n = T^{n-p+1} \tag{73}$$

For instance, as an illustration, let us determine the time that the first A_1 is completed. We see from Fig. 10 that A_1 completes out of the first position and, therefore, $p = 1$. We have $n = 1$, and so we need $\theta_1{}^1$. According to our equation this is given by T^1, and from Table 2 T^1 equals 200. This is, indeed, the completion date of the first A_1. Let us determine, say, when the first A_3 is completed. The last work station on line number 3 is in position $p = 7$, and, therefore, this completion date is given by $T^{-5} = 170$.

In summary, then, we see that the $\theta_p{}^n$ numbers specify the schedules of all these assemblies. In the aircraft industry, these numbers are referred to as the position-serial numbers. Values of $\theta_p{}^n$ for our example are given in Table 2. Suppose we want to determine the schedule for assembly A_3. Figure 10 shows that A_3 is completed in a position number 7. Consequently, completion dates for A_3 are given in the seventh column of Table 2. For instance, the first A_3 is completed on day 170, the second on day 175, the third on day 180, and so on. Assembly A_3 starts in position 13, and completion dates for position 13 are given in the thirteenth column of Table 2. Start dates for position 13 are the same as the completion dates for position 14; these are shown in the fourteenth column of Table 2. It is seen, then, that the first A_3 enters the line on day 108, the second on day 118, and so on.

We proceed now to give a more formal description of this position-serial number type of scheduling. Let us denote the assembly lines by $L_1, L_2, \cdots, L_i$ the number of work stations on assembly line L_i by ξ_i, and the fictitious station on L_i by η_i. Let us say that assembly line L_i feeds into a position number π_i on the next assembly line. For instance, in our example, L_4 feeds into L_3 at position 10 and, therefore, $\pi_4 = 10$. Finally, let us denote the number of stations on line L_i by S_i including real and fictitious stations. (S_i is the sum of ξ_i and η_i.) Now we can determine the start date for the nth A_i by writing

$$t_i{}^n = T^{n-\pi_i-S_i} \tag{74}$$

Similarly, the completion date for A_i is given by

$$\bar{l}_i^n = T^{n-\pi_i-\eta_i} \tag{75}$$

For the sake of completeness, we state that

$$\xi_i + \eta_i = S_i \tag{76}$$

For the main assembly line L_1 we will use the convention that $\pi_1 = 0$. If there are no fictitious stations on the main assembly line, then $\eta_1 = 0$.

So far, we have worked with start and completion dates. Now we turn our attention to determining both the start and completion scheduling functions. The basic scheduling function used here is the scheduling function for completing the main assemblies. If we denote this function by $\bar{X}(t)$, then

$$\bar{X}(T^n) = n \tag{77}$$

In accordance with the previous notation, let us denote by $X_i(t)$ the start scheduling function of assembly A_i, and by $\bar{X}_i(t)$ the completion scheduling function of A_i. The completion scheduling function for the main assembly A_1 is given by

$$\bar{X}_1(t) = \bar{X}(t) \tag{78}$$

The relationship between the start scheduling function and the completion scheduling function is given by

$$\bar{X}_i(t) = X_i(t) - \xi_i \tag{79}$$

Let us recognize that there are ξ_i number of assemblies on assembly line L_i.

How do we get the relationship between the completion schedule for A_i and the completion schedule of the main assembly? A_i is $\pi_i + \eta_i$ number of positions behind the completion of A_1, and, consequently,

$$\bar{X}_i(t) = \bar{X}_1(t) + \pi_i + \eta_i \tag{80}$$

As a numerical verification of these formulas, let us consider our example. According to Table 2, the third A_1 completes on day 210 and, therefore,

$$\bar{X}(210) = 3 \tag{81}$$

According to Fig. 10, A_3 completes out of position 7. From equation 80 we get for the completion schedule of A_3

$$\bar{X}_3(210) = 3 + \pi_3 + \eta_3 \tag{82}$$

From Fig. 10 $\pi_3 = 6$, as L_3 feeds into the sixth position of L_1. Also, $\eta_3 = 0$, as there is no fictitious station on L_3. Consequently, the right-hand side of equation (82) has the value 9. The formula indicates then that on day 210 the ninth A_3 is completed. Let us compare this with Table 2. The last work station on L_3 is in the seventh position, and, consequently, the seventh column in Table 2 gives completion dates for A_3. The ninth unit in the seventh column is completed on day 210, and this is indeed in agreement with equation (82).

Let us now compute the start schedule of A_i. We get with the aid of equations (79) and (80)

$$X_i(t) = \bar{X}(t) + S_i + \pi_i \qquad (83)$$

We observe that A_i starts $S_i + \pi_i$ days ahead of the completion of the main assembly A_1.

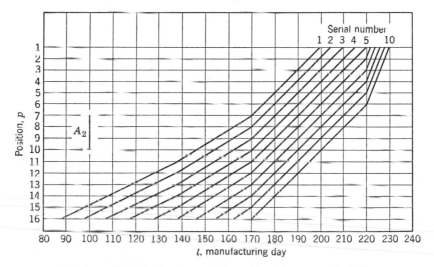

FIG. 11.   Graphical representation of position-type scheduling.

It is often useful to have a graphical representation of position-type scheduling as shown in Fig. 11. The left-hand line shows the schedule of assemblies which have the serial number 1. Assembly A_2 is in position 7 to 10 as shown by the short vertical line in Fig. 11. We can now read directly that the first A_2 is to be started on day 146 and completed on day 170, that the fifth A_2 is to be started on day 175 and completed on day 190.

This type of scheduling is a generalization of the scheduling system for a single assembly line described by equation (28). We have the

fixed number of assemblies on each assembly line, and, therefore, the
rate of production is the same on all assembly lines. Acceleration of
production is accomplished by speeding up the motion of assemblies on
the lines. As time goes on, assemblies spend less and less time on the
assembly lines. For instance, Fig. 11 shows that the first A_2 spends
24 days on the assembly line, whereas say the fourth A_2 spends only
15 days. The type of scheduling system described here is widely used
in the aircraft industry, where it is possible both to increase the number of workers at stations and to apply learning curves.

Let us now compute the manpower required for assembly L_i. With
the aid of equation (58) this can be written as

$$E_i(t) = T_i(1 - k) \frac{d\bar{X}_i}{dt} [\bar{X}_i(t)]^{-k} \tag{84}$$

where T_i denotes the labor required to make the first assembly A_i.
It follows from equations (79) and (80) that

$$\frac{d\bar{X}_i}{dt} = \frac{d\bar{X}}{dt} \tag{85}$$

Consequently, we get the labor requirement for line L_i

$$E_i(t) = T_i(1 - k) \frac{dX}{dt} [\bar{X}(t) + \pi_i + \eta_i]^{-k} \tag{86}$$

The important point here is that during the same manufacturing day
assemblies are made which may have different serial numbers. Therefore, these assemblies may be at different points on the learning curve.
By the time the first final assembly is completed, some subassemblies
have been being manufactured for a long time, and, consequently,
these subassemblies are produced with high efficiency.

The total manpower requirement is obtained by adding the man-
power required for each of the assemblies, and so we get

$$E(t) = \sum_i E_i(t) \tag{87}$$

Carrying out this summation with the aid of equation (84) leads to a
rather complicated formula, and in order to have a simple way to forecast labor requirements it is useful to develop an approximation. This
can be obtained by assuming an "average" learning rate. We get
for the labor requirement

$$E(t) = \left(\sum_i T_i \right) (1 - k) \frac{d\bar{X}}{dt} [\bar{X}(t)]^{-k} \tag{88}$$

where the first factor is the sum of the labor requirements for all of the first assemblies. (This is the total labor required to make the first main assembly and all subassemblies that are required for it.)

4. MATHEMATICAL MODEL OF ASSEMBLY LINE PRODUCTION

So far, we have considered two types of assembly line production. In one of these the number of assemblies on each assembly line remains constant, and in the other one the make span (that is, the time that an assembly spends on an assembly line) is fixed. Now we propose to develop a more general mathematical model which includes these two types as special cases.

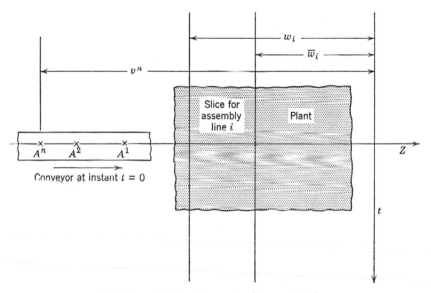

FIG. 12.   Model of assembly line production.

Let us consider the production system described graphically in Fig. 12. The conveyor shown on the left-hand side keeps moving towards the plant which is represented by the shaded area. Dummy assemblies are placed on this conveyor and transported into the plant. All assemblies with serial number 1 are represented by the dummy A^1 on the conveyor, and all assemblies with serial number 2 are represented by A^2, etc. For each assembly A_i there is a "slice" designated in the plant. As the conveyor moves toward the plant, the dummy assemblies enter and then leave this slice. We specify that the first

A_i is to be started when the dummy A^1 reaches its slice, and is to be completed when A^1 leaves this "slice."   The second A_i is to be started when A^2 reaches its slice, and is to be completed when A^2 leaves the slice.   It is seen, then, that (1) if the position of dummies is specified on the conveyor, (2) if the motion of the conveyor is specified, and (3) if we have a slice assigned to each A_i, we can generate a well-defined production schedule.   The slices in the plant must be placed in such a way that, when A_i feeds into A_j, the slice for A_i is on the left of the slice for A_j, and sufficient space must be allowed between the slices for transportation time (and in-process inventory).   Also, the schedule depends on the placing of the dummy assemblies on the conveyor and on the motion of the conveyor, as we do not assume that the conveyor moves at a constant speed.

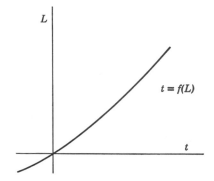

FIG. 13.   The conveyor motion function, $L(t)$.

In order to put this scheduling system into a mathematical form, the following appropriate notations are introduced.   On the far right-hand side of Fig. 12 an arbitrary zero line is established.   We say that the beginning of the slice for A_i is a distance w_i from the zero line, and that the end of the slice is a distance $\bar{w}_i$ from the zero line.   (These distances from the zero line need to be given for every assembly.) The next thing is to introduce a notation for the placing of the dummies on the conveyor.   Figure 12 shows the dummy assemblies at 0 time ($t = 0$).   Thus, at instant $t = 0$, A^n (the nth dummy) is at a distance of v^n from the zero line.   Distances are positive to the right-hand side of the zero line, and therefore we say that A^n has the coordinate $-v^n$.

The nth assembly A_i is to be started when A^n reaches the left-hand side of the appropriate slice.   Suppose that in time t the conveyor moves a distance L.   The conveyor motion function $L(t)$ shown in Fig. 13 specifies the motion of the conveyor.   At 0 time, A^n has the coordinate $-v^n$, and during time t it moves by $L(t)$; therefore, the coordinate $Z^n(t)$ of the nth dummy at time t is given by

$$Z^n(t) = -v^n + L(t) \qquad (89)$$

How do we determine $t_i{}^n$, the start time for the nth A_i? According to our scheduling scheme at time $t_i{}^n$, the nth dummy A^n reaches the left-hand side of the slice that is a distance of w_i from the zero line. Consequently, we must have

$$Z^n(t_i{}^n) = -w_i \qquad (90)$$

Similarly, the completion time $\bar{t}_i{}^n$ of the nth A_i must satisfy the following equation

$$Z^n(\bar{t}_i{}^n) = -\bar{w}_i \qquad (91)$$

With the aid of equation (89) we get

$$-v^n + L(t_i{}^n) = -w_i \qquad (92)$$

$$-v^n + L(\bar{t}_i{}^n) = -\bar{w}_i \qquad (93)$$

There are two ways to look at the curve in Fig. 13: we can consider L as a function of t (the $L(t)$ function), or time t as a function of L, which leads to the inverse function $t^{-1}(L)$. In order to avoid confusion, this inverse function is denoted by $f(L)$. To each value of the distance L there is a time t assigned. With the aid of this $f(L)$ function start and completion dates may be computed as

$$t_i{}^n = f(v^n - w_i) \qquad (94)$$

$$\bar{t}_i{}^n = f(v^n - \bar{w}_i) \qquad (95)$$

It is of some use to represent the spatial distribution of the dummies on the conveyor in a graphical fashion. Figure 14 shows for each serial number n (horizontal axis) the distance v^n (the vertical axis). A continuous curve drawn between the dots provides a curve of the spatial distribution v as a function of the serial number X. The curve shown in Fig. 14 is designated by $v(X)$. We also need the inverse function, that is, we need to determine X (the serial number of the assembly) as a function of the distance v. We denote this inverse function by $g(v)$. This is the function that, for any value of the distance v, gives the serial number X (or n). In accordance with this definition we have

$$g(v^n) = n \qquad (96)$$

With the aid of these functions it is possible to determine the scheduling functions $X_i(t)$ for each assembly. At time $t_i{}^n$ the nth assembly A_i is started, and, therefore,

$$X_i(t_i{}^n) = g(v^n) \qquad (97)$$

(According to the definition of the $g(v)$ function, the right-hand side is n.) From this equation it follows, with the aid of equation (92), that

$$X_i(t_i{}^n) = g[L(t_i{}^n) + w_i] \tag{98}$$

and, more generally, that

$$X_i(t) = g[L(t) + w_i] \tag{99}$$

We see that, if the two functions, the conveyor motion function (as shown in Fig. 13) and the spatial distribution function (as shown in Fig. 14), are given, then we can schedule with the aid of equation (99).

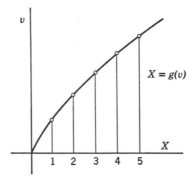

FIG. 14. Spatial distribution function $v(X)$.

For any given t we get the value of L from Fig. 13, then we compute $L(t) + w_i$ (which equals the proper value of v), and finally, from Fig. 14, the serial number X is determined. We recognize that our schedule depends on the shape of the curves shown in Figs. 13 and 14. In order to get a better understanding of this scheduling system, we will now present two illustrations.

 First, let us assume that the conveyor moves with a constant velocity. This means that the conveyor motion function is a straight line. Then

$$L(t) = \frac{l}{\tau} t \tag{100}$$

and the inverse function is given by

$$f(L) = \frac{\tau}{l} L \tag{101}$$

This implies that in time τ the conveyor moves a distance l. We get the start days with the aid of equation (94) as

$$t_i{}^n = \frac{\tau}{l} v^n - \frac{\tau}{l} w_i \tag{102}$$

The completion dates are given by

$$\bar{t}_i{}^n = \frac{\tau}{l} v^n - \frac{\tau}{l} \bar{w}_i \qquad (103)$$

Let us ask how much time the nth A_i is to spend on the assembly line. Figure 12 shows that this make span equals the time it takes for the nth dummy to move from the left-hand side to the right-hand side of the slice. Owing to the fact that the conveyor is moving with a constant speed, the first, second, or nth dummy spends the same amount of time within this slice. Therefore, we are dealing here with a scheduling system where the make span is constant. We can compute the make span $\alpha_i{}^n$ from equations (102) and (103).

$$\alpha_i{}^n = \bar{t}_i - t_i{}^n = \frac{\tau}{l}(w_i - \bar{w}_i) \qquad (104)$$

Here we see that the quantity on the right-hand side is indeed independent of the serial number of the assembly. Therefore, the only way we can accelerate production is by putting the dummy assemblies on the conveyor closer together. This means that in Fig. 14 the spatial distribution function must be a curve that bends downward. With the aid of equations (99) and (100) the start schedule may be obtained:

$$X_i(t) = g\left(\frac{l}{\tau} t + w_i\right) \qquad (105)$$

If A_1 denotes the main assembly and $X_1(t)$ the start schedule for the main assembly, we get

$$X_1(t) = g\left(\frac{l}{\tau} t + w_1\right) \qquad (106)$$

Consequently, the start schedule $X_i(t)$ for assembly A_i is given by

$$X_i(t) = X_1(t + w_i - w_1) \qquad (107)$$

Thus the schedule for assembly A_i is obtained from the schedule of A_1 by moving the scheduling function along the axis horizontally to the left-hand side. This is the type of scheduling discussed for a single assembly line in Section 1 of this chapter, (Fig. 4). We see that this scheduling system is a generalization of scheduling with a fixed make span. Let us denote by ϕ_i the width of this shift to the left (the width of the manufacturing band in Fig. 4). Then,

$$\phi_i = w_i - w_1 \qquad (108)$$

and

$$X_i(t) = X_1(t + \phi_i) \qquad (109)$$

In summary, equation (109) gives a scheduling system where the schedule of each assembly is given by a left-hand shift of the schedule for the main assembly. (It is to be emphasized that this scheduling system is quite different from the one discussed in Section 3 of this chapter, where each assembly line had a fixed number of work stations.)

Let us consider now another type of scheduling system where the spatial distribution function is straight. Here the dummy assemblies are spaced at equal distances on the conveyor, and the conveyor moves at a variable speed. The spatial distribution function is straight, and, therefore,

$$v(X) = lX \qquad (110)$$

From this it follows that

$$v^n = ln \qquad (111)$$

Start and completion dates are given by

$$t_i{}^n = f(ln - w_i) \qquad (112)$$

$$\bar{t}_i{}^n = f(ln - \bar{w}_i) \qquad (113)$$

(Remember that the f function is the inverse function of the conveyor motion function.) A further simplification can be made by assuming that the slices are located according to the equations

$$w_i = M_i l \qquad (114a)$$

$$\bar{w}_i = \bar{M}_i l \qquad (114b)$$

where M_i and $\bar{M}_i$ are integers. (It will be seen later that this offers a simplification in the computation of the scheduling functions.) Start and completion dates are given by

$$t_i{}^n = f[l(n - M_i)] \qquad (115)$$

$$\bar{t}_i{}^n = f[l(n - \bar{M}_i)] \qquad (116)$$

Let us now introduce

$$f(lM) = T^M \qquad (117)$$

The inverse conveyor motion function is used only for integer values of M, and, therefore, we can replace this function by a sequence of numbers $\cdots, T^{-1}, T^0, T^1, \cdots$. With the aid of this notation the start and completion dates can be expressed as

$$t_i{}^n = T^{n-M_i} \qquad (118)$$

$$\bar{t}_i{}^n = T^{n-\bar{M}_i} \qquad (119)$$

These equations are of the same type as equations (74) and (75);

we are concerned here with position-type scheduling. We see that, indeed, our mathematical model of assembly line production described here includes constant make span, and position-type scheduling.

We can proceed to determine the start and completion schedules. From equation (110)

$$X = \frac{v}{l} \tag{120}$$

and, consequently, the inverse spatial distribution function is given by

$$g(v) = \frac{v}{l} \tag{121}$$

The scheduling functions from equation (99) are

$$X_i(t) = \frac{L(t) + w_i}{l} \tag{122}$$

$$\bar{X}_i(t) = \frac{L(t) + \bar{w}_i}{l} \tag{123}$$

How many assemblies A_i are on an assembly line? Let N_i denote this number; then

$$N_i = X_i(t) - \bar{X}_i(t) = \frac{w_i - \bar{w}_i}{l} = M_i - \bar{M}_i \tag{124}$$

We recognize here that we have a fixed number of assemblies on each assembly line, as there should be with position-type scheduling. (This is a consequence of the fact that the dummies are spaced equally on the conveyor.)

We see, then, that our mathematical model of assembly line production includes these two cases as special ones. We can schedule with a constant make span or with a fixed number of assemblies on the line. This latter type of scheduling leads to fixed in-process inventories. On the other hand, if the make span is fixed, then inventories are proportional to the rate of production. The important point to make is that we can specify the conveyor motion and spatial distribution functions and thereby manipulate manpower requirements and also in-process inventories. This is necessary in actual assembly line production, and, therefore, the mathematical model described here is useful in dealing with such real-life situations.

CHAPTER 12

MACHINE SHOP SCHEDULING

1. A TWO-STAGE PROBLEM

In the previous chapter, a mathematical model was developed to describe production on assembly lines; now, we turn our attention to machine-shop-type scheduling. In particular, we wish to describe job-shop-type production. With this type of production, various lots of parts are being manufactured but these lots are not made in a continuous fashion. In order to get a clear understanding of the type of problems we want to discuss, we will begin with an exceedingly simple problem.

A particular machine shop is confronted with the problem of producing five lots of different parts, and each of these lots is to be machined on two different types of machines. Moreover, every lot of these parts has to go through the first type of machine first, and then finished on the second type of machine.* In order to prepare a production schedule we need to know the length of time that it takes to manufacture these lots. Let us say that A_1, the first operation on the first lot, takes 8 days, and that B_1, the second operation on the first lot, takes 7 days. We can put the labor requirements into the tabular form given on page 411. For instance, A_4, the first operation on the fourth lot, takes 6 days; the second operation on the same lot takes 10 days. The total labor required on machine 1 to complete the first

* S. M. Johnson, "Optimal Two- and Three-Stage Production Schedules with Set-Up Time Included," *Naval Research Logistics Quarterly*, Vol. 1, No. 1, March, 1954, p. 61–68.

operation on all five lots is 29 days; the second operation on machine 2 requires 26 days.   This means, then, that there is a total of 55 days of labor to be performed.   However, we do not know how many days will elapse before we can complete the manufacture of these lots, and we do not know in what sequence they should be manufactured.

	A_i	B_i
1	8	7
2	4	1
3	9	5
4	6	10
5	2	3

The top part of Fig. 1 shows a possible solution to the scheduling problem.   This top part specifies making the first lot first, the second lot the second, the third lot the third, and so on.   It can be seen that on the eighth day the first operation on the first lot is finished, and that on the ninth day we begin the second operation on the first lot.   The first operation on the second lot is completed on the twelfth day, and we could start the second operation on the second lot on the thirteenth day.   However, machine 2 is not available on the thirteenth day, as (on the thirteenth, fourteenth, and fifteenth days) it is still busy performing the second operation on the first lot.   On the sixteenth day we can start the second operation on the second lot, and so on.

This first solution of our scheduling problem requires a total make span of 40 days.   We have two machines, and, therefore, there is a total of 80 days of machine time involved.   Out of these 80 days, 55 days are productive; this results in a 69% machine utilization.   Is this solution the one which requires the shortest make span?   Is this the one with the highest machine utilization?   We could answer this question by trying all possible combinations of schedules and selecting the best one.   An easy computation shows that there are 600 different combinations, and to construct all these 600 schedules and compare them would be quite a lot of work.   Moreover, if we had more than five lots (perhaps 20), then the number of combinations would be astronomical and it would be utterly impractical to select the shortest make span by a survey of all possible schedules.   What we need is a short-cut method which leads directly to a solution.

Let us consider the last operation in this schedule B_5, that is, the

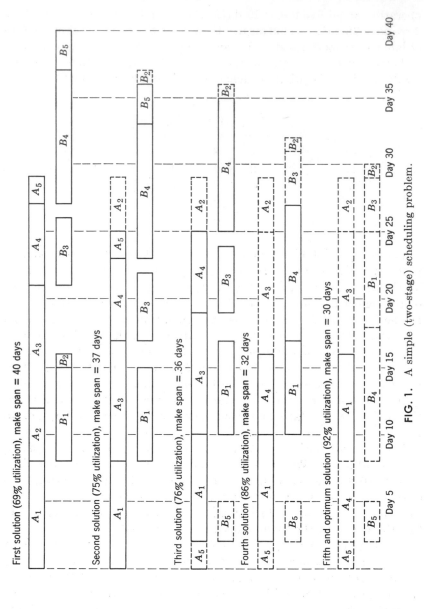

FIG. 1. A simple (two-stage) scheduling problem.

second operation on the fifth lot.   This operation takes 3 days.   Now, if we had a schedule ending with another lot so that the last operation would take less than 3 days, then we could shorten our total make span.   We recognize that B_2, the second operation on the second lot, takes only 1 day; therefore, if we made the second lot the last lot, we could shorten our make span.   Let us, therefore, extract the second lot from the schedule and collapse the rest; that is, let us handle the lots in the following sequence: first lot, third lot, fourth lot, and fifth lot.   This would save us 4 days in the manufacturing span, as the new schedule can be obtained from the original schedule by moving the schedules for the third, fourth, and fifth lots to the left in a block. Now we still have to add the second lot at the end; this adds 1 day to our schedule, as it takes 1 day to complete the second operation of the second lot.   (The first operation takes 4 days, but this does not add to the total make span.)   This way, we can save a total of 3 days in the manufacturing span and obtain the second solution as shown in Fig. 1.   The manufacturing make span is 37 days, resulting in a 75% machine utilization.   Is this the shortest make span?

By inspecting the second solution in its graphical form, we recognize that A_1, the first operation on the first lot, takes 8 days, and that during these 8 days the second machine is idle.   Can something be done about this?   If we started with a lot where the first operation takes less time, we would be better off.   It is the fifth lot that has the shortest first operation, as this lot takes only 2 days on the first machine.   Let us, therefore, omit the fifth lot from our schedule, collapse the remainder, and put the manufacture of the fifth lot at the beginning.   Now we have the third solution to our problem, with a manufacturing span of 36 days, and with a 76% machine utilization.   Is this the best solution?

Let us consider the manufacture of the third lot.   If we handle this lot not last, but next to last, as shown in the fourth solution, we could cut down the manufacturing span to 32 days and improve machine utilization to 86%.   However, this is still not the best possible solution. If we handle the fourth lot ahead of the first lot, but after the fifth lot, we get a solution shown in Fig. 1 which has only a 30-day make span and a machine utilization of 92%.   A little thought on the part of the reader will convince him that there is no way to improve this solution, and that, therefore, it has the shortest possible make span and the highest machine utilization.

In this particular problem, we discussed a scheduling problem where there were five lots and two machines.   S. M. Johnson, in his paper, found a solution to the problem with any number of lots.   However, he still has to assume that there are only two machines, and that every lot goes through the first machine first and through the second machine second.   He established the following six steps in obtaining a solution:

Step 1

List the labor requirements in two columns:

i	A_i	B_i
1	A_1	B_1
2	A_2	B_2
3	.	.
4	.	.
.	.	.
.	.	.
.	.	.
n	A_n	B_n

Step 2

Select the shortest labor requirement.

Step 3

If the shortest labor requirement is that of the first machine (that is, an A_i), place the corresponding lot first.

Step 4

If it is that of second machine (that is, B_i), place the corresponding lot last.

Step 5

Remove this lot from the table.

Step 6

Repeat the steps on the remainder of the lots, continue the process, and work from both ends toward the middle.

The reader who is interested in the mathematical proof of the validity of this rule is referred to the original paper by S. M. Johnson (footnote, p. 410).

So far, we have considered only a special case of the machine shop scheduling problem. Now we will establish a mathematical model for a more general case.

2. MORE GENERAL FORMULATION OF THE PROBLEM

Let us consider a machine shop manufacturing lots of four different parts P_1, P_2, P_3, and P_4. These parts are manufactured on three machines, M_1, M_2, and M_3. A manufacturing analysis of these parts shows in what sequence they have to go through these machines. This information can be put in the following tabular form:

	P_1	P_2	P_3	P_4
M_1	1	2	1	2
M_2	2	1	2	1
M_3	3	3	3	3

The top horizontal numbers refer to the parts and the first column to the machines; for instance, it can be seen that P_2 goes to M_2 first, as shown by the sequence number 1. The same part goes to M_1 second, as shown by the number 2, and to M_3 third, as shown by the number 3. Now, we put into tabular form the time required to make these lots. Each machine has to be set up to make the part, and the setup time can be put into the tabular form shown below:

	P_1	P_2	P_3	P_4
M_1	2.0	1.0	1.0	2.0
M_2	0.5	3.0	1.0	1.0
M_3	1.0	1.0	2.0	1.0

For instance, when P_2 goes on M_1, this machine has to be set up; this takes 1 hour. Finally, we need to know how long it takes to make these parts. This can be put into a tabular form by showing the production time for each part:

	P_1	P_2	P_3	P_4
M_1	0.20	0.10	0.25	1.00
M_2	0.05	0.30	0.25	0.50
M_3	0.10	0.10	0.50	0.50

For instance, P_2 on M_1 takes one-tenth of an hour, as shown by the number 0.10 in the first row, second column.

Now we have the basic manufacturing information, and we can develop various schedules. Let us assume that we wish to make 90 of P_1, 40 of P_2, 36 of P_3, and 18 of P_4. Let us focus our attention on the problem of constructing some sort of a schedule. Suppose that we decide to make P_1 first. We know that P_1 goes on machine M_1 first. We can also determine that a total of 20 hours is required, as there is a setup of 2 hours and a run time of 90 times 0.2 hours. We propose to use a graphical representation of our schedule. In Fig. 2a the horizontal axis represents manufacturing days; to each machine M_1, M_2, and M_3 we allocate the particular part to be made. We denote the first operation on P_1 (which happens to be on M_1) by $\Omega_{1,1}$; as shown by its horizontal bar in Fig. 2a, it extends for 20 days. The second operation on P_1 is on M_2; we denote this operation by $\Omega_{1,2}$. This operation requires $0.5 + 90(0.05) = 5.0$ hours. However, it requires time to transport the lot from M_1 to M_2. We allow a fixed 3 hours transportation time for moving a production lot from one machine to another. So we begin $\Omega_{1,2}$ not at hour 20, but at hour 23. A simple computation gives the requirement for the third operation on P_1, that is, for $\Omega_{1,3}$, as shown in Fig. 2a.

Now we can proceed to construct a schedule for P_2. The first operation on the second lot $\Omega_{2,1}$ is on M_2, and this can be started at zero hour. The second operation $\Omega_{2,2}$ is to be performed on M_1, but, as M_1 is busy until the twentieth hour, we can start this second operation on P_2 only after the twentieth hour. We proceed now, step by step, and complete the schedule as shown in Fig. 2a. This schedule is constructed under the hypotheses that the priority list of the parts is P_1, P_2, P_3, and P_4.

Is this the best solution? More specifically, is this solution the one with the shortest possible make span? In Fig. 2b we show a solution with a priority list of P_2, P_1, P_3, and P_4. We recognize that this solution has a longer make span than the first one. Figure 2c represents a solution with the priority list of P_3, P_1, P_2, and P_4. This solution is better than the first or the second one.

Is this the solution with the shortest make span? If not, how do we get a solution with the shortest make span? What we need here is a rule similar to the one that Johnson developed for the two-stage problem. However, such a rule is not available; here we have an unsolved problem.

Perhaps, we could survey all possible combinations and select the one with the shortest make span. We could set up a priority list for the first machine, then one for the second machine, and finally one for the third machine. It can be shown that this leads to a total of 30,824

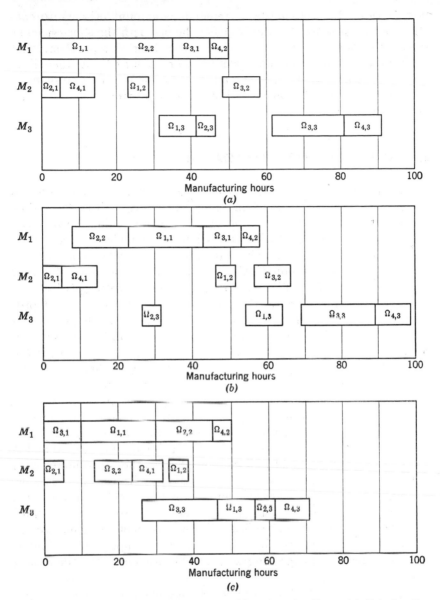

FIG. 2. Graphical representation of machine shop loading. (a) Priority list: P_1, P_2, P_3, P_4. (b) Priority list: $P_2\ P_1, P_3, P_4$. (c) Priority list: P_3, P_1, P_2, P_4.

possibilities. It is obviously a tremendous amount of work to construct all these schedules and to select the one with the shortest make span. Furthermore, this is still a very special sort of a problem; what do we do when we have hundreds of parts or machines? As there is no exact mathematical solution available, we must rely on approximate methods, and we will now show how such approximate methods can be developed.

3. THE PROBLEM OF SHOP LOADING

We have seen in the previous section that we do not know how to "solve" the problem of machine shop scheduling. In spite of this, important guides in machine shop scheduling can be developed. The purpose of this section is to show a mathematical model that can help.* We will again present an illustrative example and assume that a machine shop is confronted with the problem of manufacturing four parts, P_1, P_2, P_3, P_4. Plans are made for manufacturing periods 5, 6, 7, 8, and 9. Figure 3a shows the requirements for each part in each production period. We can see that in the fifth and sixth production periods, that is, in π_5 and π_6, no parts are required. In the seventh production period π_7 there is a requirement of 30 for P_1, 10 for P_2, 30 for P_3, and 10 for P_4. The rest of the columns in Fig. 3a show the requirements in the eighth and ninth production periods. It will be convenient to work with the cumulative schedules shown in Fig. 3b. The cumulative requirement for instance for P_1 is 30 by the seventh production period, 40 by the eighth, and 60 by the ninth period. In order to schedule, we need to know how much labor is required and is available for each machine. Figure 3c specifies the run time for each part. For instance, P_1 takes 4 hours on M_2. With the aid of Fig. 3c, we can compute the run time required for any production schedule. However, we do not know the setup time, and also we do not know the time the machines will be idle. We know from our previous studies in this chapter that idle times can be of great importance. This is the point where we make an important assumption in our mathematical model.

Suppose we have had a great deal of experience in the manufacture of these parts, and we know that we can count on a 75% utilization on the second machine, M_2. More explicitly, we assume that 75% of the time the machines are producing, and 25% of the time the machines

---

* A. Vazsonyi, "Economic Lot Size Formulas in Manufacturing," *Journal of the Operations Research Society of America*, Vol. 5, No. 1, 1957.

are under setup or idle. Suppose that in every production period we have 200 hours available on M_2. As we can expect only a 75% utilization, we say that 150 productive hours will be available on M_2. We can repeat this argument for each of the machines and prepare a table like the one shown in Fig. 3d. This figure shows the available productive hours in each production period for each machine. In Fig. 3d we have the same number of hours available on each machine in different production periods, though in general this might not be the case. (That is, it is possible that we are buying or retiring machines, and then the schedule of the available hours will vary from period to period.)

Let us remind ourselves that this schedule of available productive hours is an idealized concept. If we knew how to solve the problem presented in the first two sections of this chapter, we could predict how much idle time and how much setup time is required. However, as we do not know how to solve the problem, we will make the assumption that from past statistics we can predict machine utilization. This assumption may hold as long as new schedules are not too different from old ones. However, if we face radically new schedules, then the assumption of maintaining machine utilization becomes questionable and our method of analysis may be in error.

Our problem now is to develop a schedule that meets the requirements specified in Fig. 3a, and is within the productive machine hours specified in Fig. 3d. Let us denote by $x_i{}^m$ the number of parts P_i made in production periods π_m. How many hours of labor are imposed on each of the machines in each of the production periods? As an example, let us compute the load on M_1 in the eighth period. We are to make $x_1{}^8$ of P_1, $x_2{}^8$ of P_2, $x_3{}^8$ of P_3, $x_4{}^8$ of P_4. According to Fig. 3c, each P_1 takes 2 hours on M_1, and therefore P_1 puts a load of $2x_1{}^8$ hours on machine M_1. Each P_2 takes 3 hours on machine M_1, and, therefore, we have $3x_2{}^8$ hours imposed on machine M_1. Part P_3 puts no load on M_2 according to Fig. 3c as M_2 is not involved in making P_2. Each P_4 puts a load of 1 hour on M_1, and, therefore, we have $x_4{}^8$ hours. Let us denote by $h_1{}^8$ the hours imposed on M_1 in the eighth production period; then

$$h_1{}^8 = 2x_1{}^8 + 3x_2{}^8 + x_4{}^8 \tag{1}$$

Let us denote in general by $h_n{}^m$ the hours imposed on machine M_n in production period π_m. Then

$$h_n{}^m = \sum_i \tau_{n,i} x_i{}^m \tag{2}$$

where each P_i requires $\tau_{n,i}$ labor hours on M_n. This schedule will be acceptable if the machine hours imposed are within available productive hours. Let us denote by $\bar{h}_n{}^m$ the number of productive hours available on machine M_n in production period π_m. (These are the numbers shown in Fig. 3d.) We will be within capacity if

$$h_n{}^m \leq \bar{h}_n{}^m \tag{3}$$

With the aid of equation (2), this can be written as

$$\sum_i \tau_{n,i} x_i{}^m \leq \bar{h}_n{}^m \tag{4}$$

Let us denote by N the number of machines (three in the present case),

$\diagdown\!\!\!\!\!\!\!{}^{k}_{j}$	π_5	π_6	π_7	π_8	π_9
P_1	0	0	30	10	20
P_2	0	0	10	20	30
P_3	0	0	30	10	30
P_4	0	0	10	20	10

(a) Matrix $[r]$

$\diagdown\!\!\!\!\!\!\!{}^{k}_{j}$	π_5	π_6	π_7	π_8	π_9
P_1	0	0	30	40	60
P_2	0	0	10	30	60
P_3	0	0	30	40	70
P_4	0	0	10	30	40

(b) Matrix $[R]$

$\diagdown\!\!\!\!\!\!\!{}^{j}_{i}$	P_1	P_2	P_3	P_4
M_1	2	3	0	1
M_2	4	0	2	2
M_3	0	5	5	2

(c) Matrix $[\tau]$

$\diagdown\!\!\!\!\!\!\!{}^{k}_{i}$	π_5	π_6	π_7	π_8	π_9
M_1	100	100	100	100	100
M_2	150	150	150	150	150
M_3	200	200	200	200	200

(d) Matrix $[\bar{h}]$

$\diagdown\!\!\!\!\!\!\!{}^{k}_{i}$	π_5	π_6	π_7	π_8	π_9
M_1	0	0	60	20	40
M_2	0	0	120	40	80
M_3	0	0	0	0	0

(e) Matrix $[y^m_{n,1}]$

FIG. 3.   Computation of machine shop loading.

and by M the number of production periods (five in the present case). Then there are NM number of inequalities in equation (4). The unknown schedule of parts must satisfy these inequalities in order to stay within machine capacities.

This is, however, not sufficient. We must also meet the schedule as specified in Fig. 3b. Let us denote by R_i^m the number of P_i's that are required by the mth production period π_m. (This is the cumulative requirement.) Let us, furthermore, denote by X_i^m the cumulative schedule of part P_i in production period π_m. Then

$$X_i^m = \sum_{k=1}^{m} x_i^k \tag{5}$$

The cumulative schedule of parts must be more or at least equal to the cumulative requirement, and, consequently, we must have

$$X_i^m \geq R_i^m \tag{6}$$

Let us denote by I the number of parts (four in the present case); then there are IM number of equations described by equation (5) and IM number of inequalities described by equation (6).

$\,^k_i$	π_5	π_6	π_7	π_8	π_9
M_1	100	100	40	80	60
M_2	150	150	30	110	70
M_3	200	200	200	200	200

(f) Matrix $[z_{n,1}^m]$

$\,^k_j$	π_5	π_6	π_7	π_8	π_9
P_1	0	0	30	10	20
P_2	0	5	10	25	20
P_3	0	20	15	15	20
P_4	5	35	0	0	0

(g) Matrix $[x]$

$\,^k_j$	π_5	π_6	π_7	π_8	π_9
P_1	0	0	30	40	60
P_2	0	5	15	40	60
P_3	0	20	35	50	70
P_4	5	40	40	40	40

(h) Matrix $[X]$

$\,^k_i$	π_5	π_6	π_7	π_8	π_9
M_1	5	50	90	95	100
M_2	10	110	150	70	120
M_3	10	195	125	200	200

(i) Matrix $[h]$

FIG. 3 ($continued$)

Now we have a mathematical statement of the problem we wish to solve: Let us find the positive x's such that equations (4), (5), and (6) are satisfied.   How many equations do we have in a realistic problem? Suppose the number of parts I is 500, the number of production periods M is 10, and the number of machines N is 50.   We have IM or 5,000 unknowns.   (These unknowns represent the schedule of parts in each production period.)   Equation (4) represents 500 inequalities, equation (5) represents 5,000 equations and, finally, equation (6) represents another 5,000 inequalities.   We can see that we have a tremendous number of equations.

So far, we have not specified what is to be considered as an optimum solution.   We need a method of evaluating schedules, and, more specifically, we need some sort of a cost function.   Then we have a problem with 5,000 unknowns and 10,500 relationships, and the problem is to find a solution which minimizes the cost.   If the cost function is linear, we have a linear programming problem.   However, the solution of linear programming problems of this size is beyond the capability of the largest computing machines of today.   Furthermore, even if at the expense of a great deal of labor we could solve this problem, there is the question of whether it is worth while to compute an accurate answer here.   Let us remember that our analysis is approximate, because of the assumption on machine utilization.   However, it is often adequate to get a solution to the system of equations (4), (5), and (6), without being concerned whether the solution is an optimum one.   We will now show how such a (not necessarily optimum) solution can be obtained.

Let us first ask why we cannot make the schedule the same as the requirements.   Or why we cannot put

$$x_i{}^m = r_i{}^m \tag{7}$$

This schedule meets the requirement, but does it stay within available productive machine hours?   There is no reason to believe that this is the case.   As an illustration, let us compute the machine load on M_1 in production period π_9.   We need to apply equation (2) in order to get $h_1{}^9$;

$$h_1{}^9 = \tau_{1,1} r_1{}^9 + \tau_{1,2} r_2{}^9 + \tau_{1,3} r_3{}^9 + \tau_{1,4} r_4{}^9 \tag{8}$$

By substituting the numerical values we get a machine load of 140 hours.   But we have only 100 productive hours available, and, consequently, this schedule is not within the capacity of M_1.   We must manufacture some of the parts earlier than the seventh production period in order to meet the requirements and stay within available capacities.

Our method of solution consists of a step by step computation starting at the last production period. Let us consider for the moment only the schedule for P_1. By the end of the ninth production period, we need 60 P_1's, whereas by the end of the eighth production period we need 40 P_1's. If we do not manufacture anything else but P_1's, how many of these parts can we make in the ninth production period? In order to answer this question, we need to know the machine loads imposed in the ninth production period. These are given by

$$h_1{}^9 = 2x_1{}^9 \qquad\qquad (9a)$$

$$h_2{}^9 = 4x_1{}^9 \qquad\qquad (9b)$$

$$h_3{}^9 = 0 \qquad\qquad (9c)$$

We must stay within capacities, and, therefore, we must have

$$h_1{}^9 \leq 100 \qquad\qquad (10a)$$

$$h_2{}^9 \leq 150 \qquad\qquad (10b)$$

$$h_3{}^9 \leq 200 \qquad\qquad (10c)$$

From these it follows that

$$x_1{}^9 \leq 50 \qquad\qquad (11a)$$

$$x_1{}^9 \leq \tfrac{150}{4} \leq 37 \qquad\qquad (11b)$$

We can see that we cannot make more than 37 P_1's in the ninth production period. However, we need only 20 and, consequently, we specify 20 or put $x_1{}^9 = 20$. Let us carry out the same argument in the eighth production period. It is easy to compute that we could make 37 P_1's, but we need only 10; therefore, we specify 10, that is, make $x_1{}^8 = 10$. Similarly, in the seventh production period, we could make 37 of P_1 but we need only 30 and so we put $x_1{}^7 = 30$. This concludes the schedule of P_1, and so far we follow the schedule of requirements. Let us turn our attention to scheduling P_2.

We must take into consideration that we have already scheduled P_1, and so we do not have the total productive hours available as shown in Fig. 3d. In order to determine how many hours we still have, let us compute the hours imposed by the schedule of P_1. This is shown in Fig. 3e, which was computed with the aid of Fig. 3c, which shows machine hour requirements. Now we take the hours expended (Fig. 3e), subtract them from the hours originally available (Fig. 3d), and get the hours still available for P_2 (Fig. 3f).

Now we can ask how many P_2's we can make in the ninth production period. The load imposed on M_1 must be within capacity, or we must have

$$3x_2{}^9 \leq 60 \tag{12}$$

P_2 does not involve machine 2, and, therefore, there is no restriction there. However, we must stay within capacity on M_3, and, consequently, we must have

$$5x_2{}^9 \leq 200 \tag{13}$$

From this we conclude that we cannot make more than 20 of P_2 in the ninth production period. Let us inspect now Fig. 3b, the cumulative requirements for P_2. We note that by the end of the ninth production period we need 60 parts, whereas by the end of the eighth production period we need 30. This means, then, that if we had only 30 by the end of the eighth production period, we would have to make another 30 to keep our schedule. However, this is beyond our machine capacity; we cannot make more than 20 parts. Therefore, we specify that we will make 20 of P_2 in the ninth production period and will assume that we will have a cumulative 40 of P_2 by the end of the eighth production period. Consequently, we have $x_2{}^9 = 20$. We also have the cumulative schedules for the ninth and eighth periods as

$$X_2{}^9 = 60 \tag{14}$$

$$X_2{}^8 = 40 \tag{15}$$

Let us turn our attention now to the schedule of P_2 in the eighth production period. We must stay within machine capacities on M_1:

$$3x_2{}^8 \leq 80 \tag{16}$$

and M_3:

$$5x_2{}^8 \leq 200 \tag{17}$$

This means that we can make 26 of P_2 in the eighth production period. However, these parts are manufactured in lots of five and, consequently, we specify that we will make 25 units, which leads to

$$x_2{}^8 = 25 \tag{18}$$

The cumulative schedule for P_2 is

$$X_2{}^8 = 15 \tag{19}$$

With a similar argument we can compute the rest of the schedule for the P_2, and get

$$x_2{}^7 = 10, \ X_2{}^7 = 15, \ x_2{}^6 = 5, \ X_2{}^6 = 5$$

Now we have a schedule for P_1 and P_2. Next, we compute the machine load imposed by the schedule of P_2 and subtract from the originally available productive hours the combined load imposed by P_1 and P_2. This gives the hours available for the manufacture of P_3 and P_4. Then we compute the schedule for P_3, and compute the available machine hours for P_4 by subtracting the load imposed by P_1, P_2, and P_3. The computations are completed by determining the schedule for P_4. Figure 3g, shows the complete schedule, and Fig. 3h the cumulative schedule. By comparing Figs. 3b and 3h, we see that the schedule we have developed does, indeed, meet the requirements. In Fig. 3i, the total labor imposed, is shown and it is easy to observe that productive machine hours are indeed within the available productive hours (Fig. 3d).

We have developed a method to obtain a solution to our problem. As long as the problem is not too big, we can obtain a solution by hand computation. However, if the problem gets really big, for instance, if it is necessary to deal with 500 parts, 10 production periods, and 50 machines, then the hand computation becomes too laborious. Fortunately, this method of solution can be programmed on an electronic computer relatively easily. A good way to begin this electronic computer programming is to spell out the method of solution in a mathematical fashion. For this reason, we proceed to formalize the method.

First of all, we wish to replace equation (4) by an equation which uses only the cumulative schedules or

$$\sum_i \tau_{n,i}(X_i^m - X_i^{m-1}) \le \bar{h}_n^m \tag{20}$$

The problem is to find a positive solution to equation (20) under the restriction that

$$X_i^m \ge X_i^{m-1} \tag{21}$$

(This last equation means that the cumulative schedule does not decrease.) Our method begins by ignoring all other parts but P_1 and by taking the portion of equation (20) which refers to P_1. This leads to the inequality

$$\tau_{n,1}(X_1^m - X_1^{m-1}) \le \bar{h}_n^m \tag{22}$$

Assume that we do not plan to have a final inventory:

$$X_1^M = R_1^M \tag{23}$$

(If we planned for a final inventory, this last equation would have to be modified.) How do we get X_1^{M-1}? We determine the maximum number of P_1's that could be made by computing the hours imposed on the machines.   This leads to the inequality

$$X_1{}^M - X_1^{M-1} \leq \frac{\bar{h}_n{}^M}{\tau_{n,1}} \qquad n = 1, 2, \cdots, N \tag{24}$$

This same equation in a different form is

$$X_1{}^M - X_1^{M-1} \leq \min_n \left[\frac{\bar{h}_n{}^M}{\tau_{n,1}} \right] \tag{25}$$

This says that the left-hand side must be smaller than the smallest of the various terms on the right-hand side.   Let us compare this with our previous numerical example.   In equation (10) we had 100, 150, and 200 hours on each of the machines; then we divided by 2, 4, and 0 and got 50, 37, and infinity.   We took the smallest of these numbers as indicated by equation (25).   We can write equation (25) in a somewhat different form as

$$X_1^{M-1} \geq X_1{}^M - \min_n \left[\frac{\bar{h}_n{}^M}{\tau_{n,1}} \right] \tag{26}$$

This shows, then, that X_1^{M-1} has to be larger than the number shown on the right-hand side.   According to the requirements this number must also be larger than R_1^{M-1}, and so

$$X_1^{M-1} \geq R_1^{M-1} \tag{27}$$

Now, in our method we always took the largest possible $x_1{}^M$; this means that we take the smallest possible X_1^{M-1}.   In other words, we get X_1^{M-1} by taking the larger of the two numbers appearing on the right-hand side of equations (26) and (27).   Mathematically speaking, this can be written in the form

$$X_1^{M-1} = \max \left\{ \left[X_1{}^M - \min_n \frac{\bar{h}_n{}^M}{\tau_{n,1}} \right], R_1^{M-1} \right\} \tag{28}$$

In our particular numerical case we had

$$\min \left[\frac{\bar{h}_n{}^M}{\tau_{n,1}} \right] = 37 \tag{29}$$

The cumulative requirement for P_1 at the end of the ninth period was 60, and therefore

$$X_1{}^M = R_1{}^M = 60 \tag{30}$$

The cumulative requirement at the end of the eighth period was 40, and so

$$R_1^{M-1} = 40 \tag{31}$$

The cumulative schedule is obtained with the aid of equation (28), which in the present case becomes

$$\max\{[60 - 37], 40\} = 40 \qquad (32)$$

Consequently,

$$X_1^{M-1} = 40 \qquad (33)$$

We can see, then, that our equation (28) is indeed the same as the method we have already used. Similarly, the schedule for P_1 can be computed step by step by working backward with the aid of the following relationship:

$$X_1^{m-1} = \max\left\{\left[X_1^m - \min_n \frac{\bar{h}_n^{\,m}}{\tau_{n,1}}\right], R_1^{m-1}\right\}$$
$$m = M, M-1, M-2, \cdots \qquad (34)$$

Now we have a mathematical expression of the schedule for P_1. In order to compute the schedule for P_2 we need to compute the machine hours imposed by P_1. Let $y_{n,1}^m$ denote the load imposed on machine M_n in production period π_m. (The second index, 1, of y shows that this is the load imposed by scheduling only one part.) We have

$$y_{n,1}^m = \tau_{n,1} x_1^m \qquad (35)$$

The hours that are still available can be computed:

$$z_{n,1}^m = \bar{h}_n^{\,m} - y_{n,1}^m \qquad (36)$$

We can use a formula like equation (34), but we must replace the originally available productive hours by the remainder of the hours. We get

$$X_2^{m-1} = \max\left\{\left[X_2^m - \min_n \frac{z_{n,1}^m}{\tau_{n,2}}\right], R_2^{m-1}\right\} \qquad (37)$$

This is the schedule for P_2. Next, we compute the hours imposed on the machines by P_1 and P_2:

$$y_{n,2}^m = \tau_{n,1} x_1^m + \tau_{n,2} x_2^m \qquad (38)$$

The remainder of the available productive tours can be computed:

$$z_{n,2}^m = \bar{h}_n^{\,m} - y_{n,2}^m \qquad (39)$$

Now we are in a position to compute the schedule for P_3:

$$X_3^{m-1} = \max\left\{\left[X_3^m - \min_n \frac{z_{n,2}^m}{\tau_{n,3}}\right], R_3^{m-1}\right\} \qquad (40)$$

We can generalize this by saying that, after k steps (that is, after computing the schedule for P_1, P_2, $\cdots$, P_k), we impose on the machines the load

$$y_{n,k}^m = \sum_{j=1}^{k} \tau_{n,j} x_j^m \tag{41}$$

The still available productive hours are given by

$$z_{n,k} = \bar{h}_n^m - y_{n,k}^m \tag{42}$$

The schedule for P_{k+1} is given by

$$X_{k+1}^{m-1} = \max \left\{ \left[X_{k+1}^m - \min_n \frac{z_{n,k}^m}{\tau_{n,k+1}} \right], R_{k+1}^{m-1} \right\} \tag{43}$$

In summary, we have here a system of equations, an algorithm, which, step by step, gives the solution to the scheduling problem. Our problem of putting machine shop scheduling on an electronic computer can be solved by programming this algorithm for a particular computer.

In our method of solution, we computed first the schedule of P_1, then the schedule of P_2, and so on. An alternate method of computation is to start with the schedule of P_1 for the last production period, then get the schedule for P_2 for the last production period, and so on, completing the schedules for all the parts in the last production period. Then proceed to the next to last production period and compute the schedule there, and so on. The amount of computation required in both methods is the same. However, there might be some practical reason to prefer one of the two methods. If this computation is performed on an electronic computer, one of the two methods might be preferred because of some special characteristics of the computer.

Thus we see that, although the problem of machine shop scheduling cannot be solved exactly, important approximate information can be obtained. In the last chapter we will take up production scheduling again and describe some further guides that can be of great use in the scheduling of machine shop operations.

CHAPTER 13

A MATHEMATICAL MODEL
OF
PRODUCTION SCHEDULING

1. THE PROBLEM OF PARTS LISTING; THE GOZINTO THEOREM*

So far, we have considered the problem of assembly line flow scheduling and machine shop scheduling as separate problems. However, most manufacturing firms are confronted with both of these problems. Therefore we now propose to discuss mathematical models that include both.

The hypothetical firm we will discuss is manufacturing assemblies, sub-assemblies, and detail† parts. Let us assume that three different assemblies are manufactured as shown in Fig. 1. The shippable (top) assemblies are called A_2, A_4, and A_9, as shown in the top row. Assembly A_2 is made up of two different subassemblies and of a single detail part, that is, A_2 requires one of assembly A_7, two of assembly A_8 and two of the detail part A_6. We see from the diagram that A_7 and A_8 are assemblies as they have other articles going into them, whereas A_6 is a detail part as there is no part going into A_6. The diagram shows how each of the assemblies is made up; for instance, A_8 takes one of A_1 and one of A_5, A_7 takes one of A_1 and two of A_5. (A Gozinto diagram may be very complicated for a manufacturing firm making many assemblies and parts.)

---

* The basic concepts presented in this section were developed by the celebrated Italian mathematician Zepartzat Gozinto. See Z. Gozinto, *Collected Works*, Vol. 3 (in preparation). Also A. Vazsonyi, "The Use of Mathematics in Production and Inventory Control," *Management Science*, Vol. 1, No. 1, and Vol. 1, Nos. 3–4, 1955.

† A detail part is machined but not assembled.

429

The first problem we wish to deal with is the determination of how many of each article are required to meet a given shipping schedule. Suppose we are to ship 20 of A_2, 40 of A_4, 80 of A_9, and also 50 of A_5 as spares.   How many A_1, A_5, A_7, and so on are required to meet this shipping schedule?   We recognize that this is not a simple question to answer.   Using the diagram shown in Fig. 1, we could compute requirements, but when this diagram gets more complicated (as it would in a realistic case) the determination of requirements gets complicated.

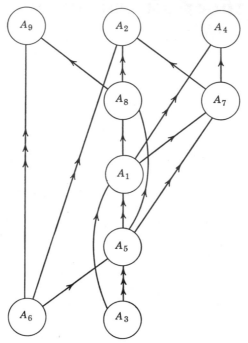

FIG. 1.   The Gozinto graph.

Therefore, what we propose to do now is to develop a mathematical model that is capable of answering the question of how many.

In order to be able to deal with the problem in a mathematical form, an appropriate notation must be introduced.   The graphical information of Fig. 1 can be put into a numerical form as shown in Fig. 2. This figure, the *next assembly quantity matrix*, shows how many of each assembly (or detail parts) are required "directly" in any other assembly.   For instance, according to Fig. 1, each A_2 takes two of A_8 "directly"; the second number in the eighth row in Fig. 2 shows the number 2.   Or the fifth number in the third row shows that each A_5 takes three A_3's directly (as can be verified in Fig. 1).   Let us denote the quantity shown in the ith row, jth column, by $N_{i,j}$. Our problem is to determine how many of each assembly (or detail parts) are required in total for each other assembly. For instance, we would like to know how many A_6's are required in total, say, for each A_2. Suppose for the moment that we have solved this problem and put the answers in a tabular form as shown in Fig. 3. For instance, 27 of A_3 are required for each A_4 as shown by the fourth number, third row. We call this figure the *total requirement factor matrix*, and our problem is to determine the total requirement factor matrix from the next assembly

	1	2	3	4	5	6	7	8	9
1	0	0	0	2	0	0	1	1	0
2	0	0	0	0	0	0	0	0	0
3	1	0	0	0	3	0	0	0	0
4	0	0	0	0	0	0	0	0	0
5	2	0	0	0	0	0	2	1	0
6	0	2	0	0	1	0	0	0	3
7	0	1	0	1	0	0	0	0	0
8	0	2	0	0	0	0	0	0	1
9	0	0	0	0	0	0	0	0	0

FIG. 2. The next assembly quantity matrix.

quantity matrix. We need a system of equations that relate the unknown numbers $T_{i,j}$ in the total requirement factor matrix to the known $N_{i,j}$'s in the next assembly quantity matrix.

In order to develop this system of equations, let us first try to answer how many A_5's are required for each A_2? With the aid of Fig. 1 we can say that:

Total number of A_5's required for each A_2]
    = [Number of A_8's going directly into each A_1]
        $\times$ [Total number of A_1's required for each A_2]
    + [Number of A_5's going directly into each A_7]
        $\times$ [Total number of A_7's required for each A_2]
    + [Number of A_5's going directly into each A_8]
        $\times$ [Total number of A_8's required for each A_2]

We can put this statement into a mathematical form with the aid of our notation:

$$T_{5,2} = N_{5,1} \cdot T_{1,2} + N_{5,7} \cdot T_{7,2} + N_{5,8} \cdot T_{8,2} \qquad (1)$$

There is a simple graphical pattern behind equation (1) as shown in Fig. 4. Let us compute $T_{5,2}$, the second number in the fifth row in the total requirement factor matrix. We recognize from equation (1) that this particular number (shown by the little square in the T table in Fig. 4) is obtained by combining the fifth row of the N (next assembly quantity) table and the second column of the T table. That is, the first number in the fifth row of the N table is to be multiplied by the top

	1	2	3	4	5	6	7	8	9
1	1	3	0	3	0	0	1	1	1
2	0	1	0	0	0	0	0	0	0
3	7	33	1	27	3	0	13	10	10
4	0	0	0	1	0	0	0	0	0
5	2	10	0	8	1	0	4	3	3
6	2	12	0	8	1	1	4	3	6
7	0	1	0	1	0	0	1	0	0
8	0	2	0	0	0	0	0	1	1
9	0	0	0	0	0	0	0	0	1

FIG. 3. The total requirement factor matrix.

number in the second column of the T table, and the second number in the fifth row of the N table is to be multiplied by the second number in the second column of the T table (this number happens to be zero). Then we multiply the third number in the fifth row of the N table by the third number in the second column of the T table, and so on. Finally, we add all these numbers. (This method of combining rows and columns is matrix multiplication.) We can write equation (1) in an abbreviated form as

$$T_{5,2} = \sum_k N_{5,k} \cdot T_{k,2} \qquad (2)$$

We recognize that this type of equation holds not only for $T_{5,2}$ but for any number in the T table, and consequently we have

$$T_{i,j} = \sum_k N_{i,k} \cdot T_{k,j} \qquad i \neq j \qquad (3)$$

Let us check this equation for $T_{6,2}$, which is the total number of A_6's required for each A_2. We write $i = 6$ and $j = 2$ in equation (3) and get:

$$T_{6,2} = N_{6,1}T_{1,2} + N_{6,2}T_{2,2} + N_{6,3}T_{3,2} + N_{6,4}T_{4,2} + N_{6,5}T_{5,2}$$
$$+ N_{6,6}T_{6,2} + N_{6,7}T_{7,2} + N_{6,8}T_{8,2} + N_{6,9}T_{9,2} \qquad (4)$$

By taking the numbers from Figs. 2 and 3, we get

$$T_{6,2} = (0)(3) + (2)(1) + (0)(33) + (0)(0) + (1)(10) + (0)(12)$$
$$+ (0)(1) + (0)(2) + (3)(0) \qquad (5)$$

By computing the terms on the right-hand side we get 12, and this is indeed the second number in the sixth row in Fig. 3.

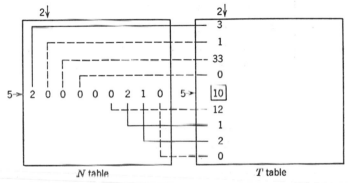

FIG. 4. Schematic representation of the equation $T_{5,2} = \sum_k N_{5,2}T_{k,2}$.

Incidentally, let us note that in Fig. 2, the next assembly quantity matrix, we have zeros in the diagonal. (By diagonal, we mean the first number in the first row, the second number in the second row, the third number in the third row, and so on.) On the other hand, in the diagonal of the total requirement factor matrix, we have 1's. The fact is that we are at liberty to select these numbers the way we wish, as the question of how many A_2's are required for each A_2 directly is not a sensible one, nor is the question of how many A_2's are required in total for each A_2. The convention of putting zeros into the diagonal of the next assembly quantity matrix, and 1's into the diagonal of the total requirement factor matrix, is a convenient one that leads to simple mathematics. In fact, in equation (5), we must make $T_{2,2}$ equal to 1 and $N_{6,6}$ to 0 in order to make the equations hold.

Let us note that equation (3) does not hold when $i = j$, or

$$T_{i,i} \neq \sum_k N_{i,k} T_{k,i} \tag{6}$$

That is, if article A_i does go directly into article A_k, then $N_{i,k}$ has a positive value but $T_{k,i}$ must be 0 as no A_i's are required for A_k. Furthermore, when $T_{k,i}$ is a positive number, then a certain number of A_k's are required for each A_i and then $N_{i,k}$, the number of A_i's going directly into A_k, must be 0. Consequently, every term on the right-hand side is 0, and so the sum must be 0 too. On the other hand,

1	0	0	0	0	0	0	0	0
0	1	0	0	0	0	0	0	0
0	0	1	0	0	0	0	0	0
0	0	0	1	0	0	0	0	0
0	0	0	0	1	0	0	0	0
0	0	0	0	0	1	0	0	0
0	0	0	0	0	0	1	0	0
0	0	0	0	0	0	0	1	0
0	0	0	0	0	0	0	0	1

FIG. 5. The unit matrix.

according to our convention, $T_{i,i}$ (an element in the diagonal in the total requirement factor matrix), is 1. It is seen that we cannot apply equation (3) for the diagonals.

We have already mentioned that the system of equations represented by equation (3) can be considered as matrix multiplication. The reader who is familiar with matrix multiplication will realize that equation (6) can be written in the form:

$$[T] = [N] \times [T] + [1] \tag{7}$$

Here each quantity in the brackets represents a matrix; the last matrix is the *unit matrix* shown in Fig. 5. The abbreviated notation of equation (7) is not too helpful, as the important fact is that we have a system of equations relating the known N's to the unknown T's. This system of equations must be solved for the unknown T's in order to answer the question of how many articles are required for each other article.   The reader familiar with matrix algebra will realize that the problem we want to solve here is matrix inversion.   That is, we can write equation (7) in the following form:

$$[1][T] - [N][T] = [1] \tag{8}$$

From this it follows that

$$[1 - N][T] = [1] \tag{9}$$

Finally, this can be written as

$$[T] = \frac{[1]}{[1 - N]} \tag{10}$$

However, matrix inversion does not help here as it requires a great deal of numerical work, and if we were dealing with thousands of parts we would have matrices with thousands of rows and columns.   Inversion of such matrices involves a prohibitive amount of computational work   Fortunately, in our problem we are dealing with special types of matrices, known as triangular matrices.   Such matrices can be inverted with relative ease.   As an illustration, we show how to compute the second column of the T matrix.

Let us first try to compute the top number in the second column of the T matrix, $T_{1,2}$.   It follows from equation (3) that

$$T_{1,2} = N_{1,4}T_{4,2} + N_{1,7}T_{7,2} + N_{1,8}T_{8,2} = 2T_{4,2} + T_{7,2} + T_{8,2} \tag{11}$$

We recognize that in this equation we do not know the terms on the right-hand side.   Therefore, we proceed to the second number in the second column of the T matrix.   This happens to be a diagonal, and, therefore, we can write that $T_{2,2} = 1$.   Now we proceed to the third number in the second column and write:

$$T_{3,2} = T_{1,2} + 3T_{5,2} \tag{12}$$

Unfortunately, we do not know all the terms on the right-hand side, so we proceed to the fourth term $T_{4,2}$.   We recognize by inspecting Fig. 2 that the fourth row is 0 in the N matrix.   Therefore, when the fourth row of the N matrix is combined with the second column of the T table we get 0 and, consequently, we have $T_{4,2} = 0$.

Now we proceed to $T_{5,2}$, and write:

$$T_{5,2} = 2T_{1,2} + 3T_{7,2} + T_{8,2} \tag{13}$$

Again we do not know the right-hand side, so we proceed to $T'_{6,2}$. We write:

$$T_{6,2} = 2T_{2,2} + T_{5,2} + T_{9,2} \qquad (14)$$

This is again of no help. We write the equation for $T_{7,2}$ as

$$T_{7,2} = T_{2,2} + T_{4,2} \qquad (15)$$

and for $T_{8,2}$ as:

$$T_{8,2} = 2T_{2,2} + T_{9,2} \qquad (16)$$

Neither of these is immediately useful as we do not know the right-hand side terms. The bottom term in the second column in the T matrix is $T_{9,2}$. We recognize that the ninth row in the next assembly quantity matrix is 0, and that consequently we have

$$T_{9,2} = 0 \qquad (17)$$

We see, then, that when we tried to compute the numbers in the second column of the T matrix we succeeded in computing the second, fourth, and ninth numbers; in the other cases we failed. However, we can now start again at the top and try again. We fail to get $T_{1,2}$ as we do not have the right-hand side of equation (11) yet. $T_{2,2}$ we already have. We try $T_{3,2}$ but fail as we do not have the right-hand side of equation (12) yet. Moving downward in the second column of the T table we reach $T_{7,2}$ and recognize from equation (15) that we do have the right-hand side, as we know that $T_{2,2} = 1$ and $T_{4,2} = 0$. Consequently, we get $T_{7,2} = 1$. (We can verify with the aid of Fig. 1 that A_7 goes directly into A_2 and that it does not go into A_2 through any other assembly.) The reason we could not get, say, $T_{6,2}$ is that A_6 goes directly into A_2 but also into A_5. We can also get $T_{8,2}$ from equation (16), as both $T_{2,2}$ and $T_{9,2}$ are known. Thus, we get $T_{8,2} = 2$. (We recognize from Fig. 1 that A_8 goes directly into A_2; this is the reason that we can compute $T_{8,2}$.) We now have values for $T_{2,2}$, $T_{4,2}$, $T_{7,2}$, $T_{8,2}$, and $T_{9,2}$.

Now we start our process again by working from the top to the bottom. With the aid of equation (11), we compute $T_{1,2}$ and get $T_{1,2} = 3$. We cannot yet get $T_{3,2}$, as in equation (12) we do not have $T_{5,2}$. However, from equation (13) we get $T_{5,2} = 10$. Finally, from equation (14) we get $T_{6,2} = 12$.

Now we start on the top again and compute the final $T_{3,2}$ from equation (12) and get $T_{3,2} = 33$. This completes the computation of the second column of the T matrix.

We recognize that this same method would work for any other column of the T matrix. In order to make the mathematics involved here clear, we show schematically the method of computation. Let us introduce the following notation:

$$T_{1,2} = x_6,\ T_{2,2} = x_1,\ T_{3,2} = x_9,$$
$$T_{4,2} = x_2,\ T_{5,2} = x_7,\ T_{6,2} = x_8, \tag{18}$$
$$T_{7,2} = x_4,\ T_{8,2} = x_5,\ T_{9,2} = x_3$$

Our system of equations can be written as follows:

$$x_1 + \qquad\qquad\qquad\qquad\qquad\qquad = 0$$
$$0x_1 + x_2 \qquad\qquad\qquad\qquad\qquad = 0$$
$$0x_1 + 0x_2 + x_3 \qquad\qquad\qquad\qquad = 0$$
$$x_1 + x_2 + 0x_3 - x_4 \qquad\qquad\qquad = 0$$
$$2x_1 + 0x_2 + x_3 + 0x_4 - x_5 \qquad\qquad = 0 \tag{19}$$
$$0x_1 + 2x_2 + 0x_3 + x_4 + x_5 + x_6 \qquad\qquad = 0$$
$$0x_1 + 0x_2 + 0x_3 + 3x_4 + x_5 + 2x_6 - x_7 \qquad = 0$$
$$2x_1 + 0x_2 + x_3 + 0x_4 + 0x_5 + 0x_6 + x_7 - x_8 \quad = 0$$
$$0x_1 + 0x_2 + 0x_3 + 0x_4 + 0x_5 + x_6 + 3x_7 + 0x_8 - x_9 = 0$$

We see now why such a system of equations is called triangular. The first equation has only x_1, and therefore there is no problem in determining x_1. The second equation relates x_1 and x_2, but as we already know x_1 we can get x_2. The third equation involves x_1, x_2, and x_3, but we have already determined x_1 and x_2 and, therefore, there is no problem in getting x_3. The fourth equation has the fourth unknown involved, but we already know the first three unknowns and so we can get the fourth unknown, and so on. This is the reason that our system of equations can be solved with ease.

However, we want to mention that the method of computing the total requirement factors described here might not be the most efficient method. We are certain that this method works, but there might be a short cut and, in an actual situation where thousands of articles are involved, such a short cut can be of great importance. We also want to mention that such computations would be most likely carried out with the aid of electronic computers.

We see, then, that we have a way to solve the problem of how many parts are required for each assembly. If we know how many assemblies we want to ship, we can compute how many assemblies and detail parts are required. Let us denote by $S_1, S_2, \cdots , S_9$, the shipping requirements for each of the articles. (Most of these S's will be 0, as only a few of the articles are shippable.)   Let us denote the total requirements for each article by $x_1, x_2, \cdots, x_9$.   The question is how to get the x's from the S's?   As an illustration, let us try to compute x_5, the total requirements for A_5.   We have:

$$x_5 = T_{5,1}S_1 + T_{5,2}S_2 + T_{5,3}S_3 + \cdots + T_{5,9}S_9 \tag{20}$$

Using the total requirement factors from Fig. 3, we get

$$x_5 = 2S_1 + 10S_2 + 8S_4 + S_5 + 4S_7 + 3S_8 + 3S_9 \tag{21}$$

Suppose, for instance, that there is a requirement of 20 A_2's, 30 A_4's, 80 A_9's, and 50 A_5's (the A_5's are required as spares).   The total number of A_5's required is given by

$$x_5 = 10(20) + 8(30) + 50 + 3(80) = 730 \tag{22}$$

Thus in order to meet this shipping requirement, we need 730 A_5's.

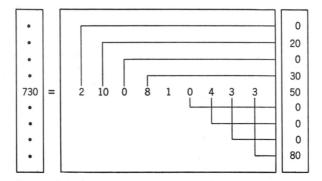

FIG. 6.   Schematic representation of the matrix multiplication $[x] = [T] \times [S]$.

More generally, we can determine the requirements for any shipping schedule with the aid of the formula

$$x_i = \sum_j T_{i,j}S_j \tag{23}$$

which is a generalization of equation (20).   The reader who is acquainted with matrix multiplication recognizes that we are dealing here with the matrix relationship:

$$[x] = [T][S] \tag{24}$$

where x is an unknown column matrix, S is a known column matrix giving the shipping schedule, and T is the total requirement factor matrix.   A schematic representation of equation (24) is shown in Fig. 6.   It is seen that we need to combine a row of the T matrix with the shipping schedule matrix (which is a column matrix). If equation (24) is combined with equation (10), we get

$$[X] = \frac{[I]}{[1 - N]} [S] \tag{25}$$

which can be written as:

$$[X] = \frac{[S]}{[1 - N]} \tag{26}$$

We see, then, that the problem of determining requirements for a given shipping schedule can be summarized in a very concise form with the aid of matrix algebra. It is quite interesting and perhaps not unnecessary to emphasize that the single matrix equation, (26), gives a complete answer to the problem we are discusssing here.

So far, we have discussed only the problem of how many assemblies and detail parts are required to meet a shipping schedule. The next problem we wish to take up is how to schedule the production of these articles.

2. PRODUCTION ON MANY ASSEMBLY LINES

In Chapter 11, we developed mathematical models for assembly flow scheduling when there was only a single final assembly. We propose now to extend this work to the production of many final assemblies. We also wish to include the possibility that the same part (or assembly) is required several times in some other assembly. Let us again consider a hypothetical factory that is manufacturing the articles for which the Gozinto graph is shown (Fig. 1). Shipping schedules are given for A_2, A_4, and A_9, and also perhaps for some spares, and we wish to determine the schedules for all assemblies and detail parts. In order to develop our mathematical model, let us assume first that we are only concerned with manufacturing the top assembly A_9 and that, therefore, we wish to determine schedules only for A_1, A_3, A_5, A_6, and A_8.

In Table 1, in the first column, we show the given shipping schedule $S_9(t)$ for A_9. For instance, it is seen that, by manufacturing day 130, a cumulative quantity of five units of A_9 must be shipped. A graphical representation of this schedule is given in Fig. 7; the horizontal axis is the manufacturing day, and the vertical axis shows the number of assemblies to be completed. The function $S_9(t)$ represents the completion schedule of the top assembly A_9. How do we get the start

schedule for A_9?   We propose to use the same scheduling system as
we used in Section 4 of Chapter 11; there, it was assumed that each
assembly spends a fixed amount of time on the assembly line.   We
assume that we need 5 days to complete each A_9.   When an assembly
is completed, it may not be ready for shipping and we allow a cushion of
3 days for getting ready to ship.   We say that the make span for A_9
is $\alpha_9 = 5$, the cushion for A_9 is $\beta_9 = 3$, and the total span is $\gamma_9 = 8$.
The start schedule $Y_9(t)$ for assembly A_9 is given by the equation

$$Y_9(t) = S_9(t + \gamma_9) \tag{27}$$

This means that the shipping schedule is to be shifted to the left by 8
days in order to obtain the start schedule (Fig. 7).

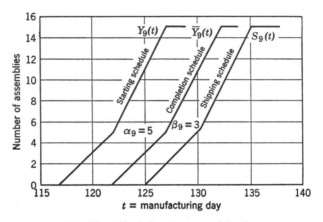

FIG. 7.   Scheduling for assembly A_9.

Let us now develop the completion schedule for assembly A_9.   This
schedule is obtained by shifting the shipping schedule 3 days to the left,
and, if we denote the completion schedule for assembly A_9 by $\bar{Y}_9(t)$,
we can write that

$$\bar{Y}_9(t) = S_9(t + \beta_9) \qquad \beta_9 = 3 \tag{28}$$

This completion schedule is shown in Fig. 7; both the completion and
start schedules are shown in Table 1 in the second and third columns.
(A shift to the left in Fig. 7 corresponds to an upward shift in Table 1.)
    So far, this is not very different from our discussion of scheduling
a single assembly (Chapter 11).   However, now we proceed to schedule the assemblies that go into A_9.   According to Fig. 1 we need A_6's
and A_8's for A_9; let us first schedule assembly A_8.   Let us denote by
$\bar{Y}_8(t)$ the availability schedule of A_8.   When does an A_8 need to be

TABLE I   Manufacturing Schedule of Assemblies[a]

t	(1) S_9	(2) $\bar{r}_9$	(3) r_6	(4) $\hat{r}_a$	(5) $\bar{r}_8$	(6) r_8	(7) $\hat{r}_1$	(8) $\bar{r}_1$	(9) r_1	(10) $\hat{r}_5^8$	(11) $\hat{r}_5^1$	(12) $\hat{r}_5$	(13) $\bar{r}_5$	(14) $\bar{r}_5$	(15) r_5	(16) $\hat{r}_6^5$	(17) $\hat{r}_6^9$	(18) $\hat{r}_6$	(19) $\hat{r}_n$	(20) $\bar{r}_6$	(21) r_6	(22) $\hat{r}_3^1$	(23) $\hat{r}_3^5$	(24) $\hat{r}_3$	(25) r_3	(26) $\bar{r}_3$	(27) r_3
101															0	0		0	0	0	0		0	0	0	0	10
102															0	0		0	0	0	0		0	0	0	0	20
103															0	0		0	0	0	6		0	0	0	10	30
104														0	3	3		3	6	6	12		9	9	10	20	40
105									0		0	0	0	0	6	6		6	12	12	18	0	18	18	20	30	50
106						0	0	0	0		0	0	0	0	9	9		9	18	18	24	0	27	27	30	40	60
107					0	0	0	0	0		0	0	0	3	12	12		12	24	24	30	0	36	37	40	50	70
108			0	0	0	0	0	0	1	0	2	2	0	6	15	15	0	15	30	30	42	1	45	47	50	60	90
109			0	0	0	1	1	1	2	0	4	4	6	9	21	21	0	21	42	42	54	2	63	66	90	70	110
110		0	0	0	1	2	2	2	3	0	6	6	9	12	27	27	0	27	54	54	66	3	81	85	110	90	130
111	0	0	1	1	2	3	3	3	4	1	8	8	12	15	33	33	3	33	66	66	78	4	99	104	130	110	150
112	0	0	2	2	3	4	4	4	5	2	10	10	15	21	39	39	6	39	78	78	90	5	108	115	150	130	150
113	0	1	3	3	4	5	5	5	7	3	14	15	21	27	45	45	9	45	90	90	90	7	135	144	150	150	150
114	1	2	4	4	5	7	7	7	9	4	18	20	27	33	45	45	12	45	90	90	90	9	135	146	150	150	
115	2	3	5	5	7	9	9	9	11	5	22	25	33	39	45	45	15	48	90	90		11	135	148			
116	3	4	7	7	9	11	11	11	13	7	26	30	39	45			21	51				13		150			
117	4	5	9	9	11	13	13	13	15	9	30	35	45	45			27	54				15		150			
118	5	7	11	11	13	15	15	15	15	11	30	37	45				33	57				15		150			
119	7	9	13	13	15	15	15	15	15	13	30	39	45				39	60									
120	9	11	15	15	15	15	15	15		15	30	41	45				35	66									
121	11	13	15	15				15		15	30	43	45				35	72									
122	13	15								15	30	45					35	78									
123	15	15								15	30	45						84									
124	15	15										43						90									
125	15																	90									
126																		90									
127																											
128																											
129																											
130																											
131																											
132																											
133																											
134																											
135																											
136																											
137																											
138																											
139																											
140																											

[a] The first column shows the manufacturing day, and the rest of the columns show the various start, completion, and consumption dates of the assemblies. As an example, observe that the cumulative number of A_1's to be started by manufacturing day 117 is eleven.

available? We need assembly A_8 in order to start assembly A_9. Therefore, the availability schedule of A_8 must be the same as the start schedule of A_9, or

$$\tilde{Y}_8(t) = Y_9(t) \tag{29}$$

The availability schedule for assembly A_8 is given in the fourth column of Table 1 and shown graphically in Fig. 8. Let us assume that the make span of assembly A_8 is $\alpha_8 = 2$, and that the cushion (transportation or other unforeseen events) is $\beta_8 = 1$. This gives, then, a total

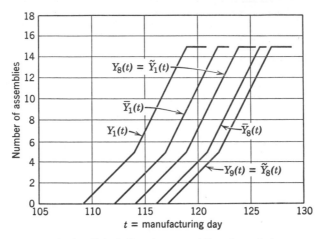

FIG. 8. Scheduling for assemblies A_1 and A_8.

make span of $\gamma_8 = 3$. The availability schedule of A_8 is related to the start schedule of A_8 by

$$Y_8(t) = \tilde{Y}_8(t + \gamma_8) \tag{30}$$

We can relate the start schedule of A_8 to the shipping schedule of A_9 with the aid of equation (29)

$$Y_8(t) = \mathcal{G}_9(t + \psi_8) \tag{31}$$

where ψ_8, the shift for A_8, is given by

$$\psi_8 = \gamma_8 + \psi_9 \tag{32}$$

The schedules for assembly A_8 are given in Table 1 and are shown graphically in Fig. 8.

We call ψ_8 the setback of assembly A_8. In order to have a uniform system of notation, we also introduce the setback ψ_9 for assembly A_9, where

$$\psi_9 = \gamma_9 \tag{33}$$

The start schedule of assembly A_9 now becomes

$$Y_9(t) = S_9(t + \psi_9) \qquad (34)$$

We proceed now to construct schedules, step by step, for each of the other assemblies. We determine the various setbacks or ψ's with the aid of the diagram shown in Fig. 9. The horizontal axis shows manufacturing days, and we allow a 3-day cushion and a 5-day make span for A_9; this results in an 8-day setback or $\psi_9 = 8$. On the other hand, the setback of A_8 is 11 days. The other setbacks in Fig. 9 are constructed in accordance with the Gozinto diagram shown in Fig. 1.

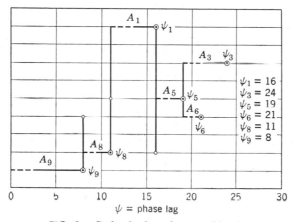

FIG. 9. Setback chart in assembly A_9.

We continue constructing the schedules by realizing that A_1 must be available when A_8 is started:

$$\tilde{\tilde{Y}}_1(t) = Y_8(t) \qquad (35)$$

We allow two days between completion and availability:

$$\tilde{Y}_1(t) = \tilde{\tilde{Y}}_1(t + \beta_1) \qquad \beta_1 = 2 \qquad (36)$$

Finally, the start schedule for A_1 is given by

$$Y_1(t) = \tilde{Y}_1(t + \gamma_1) \qquad \gamma_1 = \alpha_1 + \beta_1 = 2 \qquad (37)$$

We can relate this schedule to the shipping schedule of A_9 with the aid of the equation

$$Y_1(t) = S_9(t + \psi_1) \qquad \psi_1 = 16 \qquad (38)$$

(We can verify with the aid of the setback chart in Fig. 9 that $\psi_1 = 16$.) Figure 8 shows graphically the schedules for A_1, and Table 1 shows these schedules numerically.

Let us continue now and determine the schedule for A_5. We recognize that A_5 is used in both A_1 and A_8, as A_5 is a "multiple use" assembly. In order to deal with A_5 we introduce the concept of the consumption schedule. Let $\hat{Y}_5{}^8(t)$ denote the consumption schedule of assembly A_5 "in A_8." (These are the A_5's that are consumed by A_8.) This consumption schedule is the same as the starting schedule of A_8, or

$$\hat{Y}_5{}^8(t) = Y_8(t) \tag{39}$$

We need A_5's in A_1, but each A_1 takes two A_5's, and therefore we write

$$\hat{Y}_5{}^1(t) = 2\, Y_1(t) \tag{40}$$

The total consumption schedule for A_5 is given by

$$\hat{Y}_5(t) = Y_8(t) + 2\, Y_1(t) \tag{41}$$

The consumption schedule of A_5 is shown graphically in Fig. 10 by the

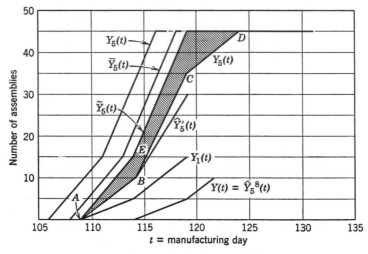

FIG. 10.   Schedules for assembly A_5.

line $ABCD$. We can relate this consumption schedule to the shipping schedule with the aid of equations (33) and (38):

$$\hat{Y}_5(t) = S_9(t + \psi_5) + 2\, S_9(t + \psi_1) \tag{42}$$

Now the availability schedule of A_5 may be the same as the consumption schedule of A_5, or

$$\tilde{Y}_5(t) = \hat{Y}_5(t) \tag{43}$$

However, we recognize that we can make A_5's for inventory, and, therefore, any schedule for A_5 for which

$$\hat{Y}_5(t) \geq \hat{Y}_5(5) \tag{44}$$

is a satisfactory schedule. For instance, the availability schedule given by

$$\tilde{Y}_5(t) = 3 \, S_9(t + \psi_1) \tag{45}$$

is satisfactory. This implies that we make all A_5's as if they were going into A_1's. We first consume the A_5's that do go into A_1's, and place the rest of the A_5's into in-process inventory. These A_5's are consumed later in assembly A_8. Our in-process inventory is given by

$$\tilde{Y}_5(t) - \hat{Y}_5(t) = S_9(t + \psi_1) - S_9(t + \psi_8) \tag{46}$$

This inventory is represented by the shaded area in Fig. 10. The advantage of this scheduling system lies in its simplicity; we can directly relate the schedule to the final shipping schedule and thereby simplify the computational procedure. The completion schedule for A_5, are given by

$$\bar{Y}_5(t) = \tilde{Y}_5(t + \beta_5) \qquad \beta_5 = 1 \tag{47}$$

The start schedule for A_5 is given by

$$Y_5(t) = \tilde{Y}_5(t + \gamma_5) \qquad \gamma_5 = 3 \tag{48}$$

The start schedule can be expressed directly with the aid of the final shipping schedule by writing

$$Y_5(t) = 3 \, S_9(t + \psi_5) \qquad \psi_5 = 19 \tag{49}$$

This equation can also be written as

$$Y_5(t) = T_{5,9} S_9(t + \psi_5) \tag{50}$$

Now we proceed to get the schedules for A_6. First, the consumption schedule is given by

$$\hat{Y}_6(t) = \hat{Y}_6{}^9(t) + \hat{Y}_6{}^5(t) = 3 \, Y_9(t) + Y_5(t) \tag{51}$$

which can be expressed with the aid of the shipping schedule as

$$\hat{Y}_6(t) = 3 \, S_9(t + \psi_9) + 3 \, S_9(t + \psi_9) \tag{52}$$

We can manufacture to inventory and simplify the scheduling procedure by writing

$$\tilde{Y}_6(t) = 6 \, S_9(t + \psi_5) \tag{53}$$

The completion schedule for assembly A_6 is given by

$$\bar{Y}_6(t) = \tilde{Y}_6(t + \beta_6) \qquad \beta_6 = 1 \tag{54}$$

The start schedule can be expressed with the aid of the shipping schedule by writing

$$Y_6(t) = T_{6,9} S_9(t + \psi_6) \tag{55}$$

where

$$T_{6,9} = 6 \qquad \psi_6 = 21 \tag{56}$$

The factor 6 in equation (53) is the total requirement factor which specifies how many A_6's are required (in total) for each A_9.   Figure

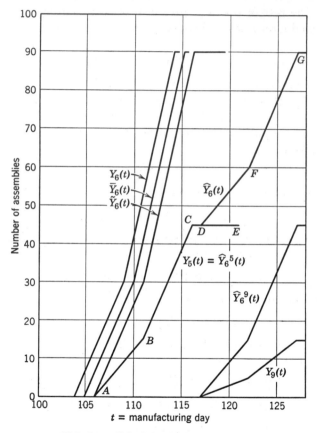

FIG. 11.   Schedules for assembly A_6.

11 shows these schedules graphically, and columns 16 to 21 of Table 1 show the schedules numerically.

Step by step, the schedules for each assembly or part can be determined.   Figure 12 gives the rest of the schedules in graphical form, and columns 22 to 27 of Table 1 show the schedules numerically.

So far, we have only considered shipping a single final assembly A_2. Let us now examine a more general situation with many shippable assemblies, denoting the shipping schedule for assembly A_k by $S_k(t)$. If, for the moment, we consider only assemblies (and parts) that are

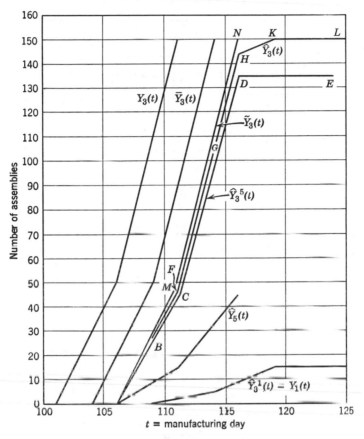

FIG. 12.   Schedules for assembly A_3.

required for shipping A_k, start dates are given by

$$Y_i(t) = T_{i,k} S_k(t + \psi_i) \tag{57}$$

completion dates by

$$\bar{Y}_i(t) = T_{i,k} S_k(t + \psi_i - \alpha_i) \tag{58}$$

and availability dates by

$$\tilde{Y}_i(t) = T_{i,k} S_k(t + \psi_i - \gamma_i) \tag{59}$$

However, this notation does not allow for the distinction between assemblies (and parts) that are made for A_k and articles that are made for other shippable assemblies. Let us denote by $X_{i,k}(t)$ the start schedule of those assemblies A_i which eventually end up in a shippable A_k. For instance, $X_{i,9}(t)$ represents the schedule of those A_i's that

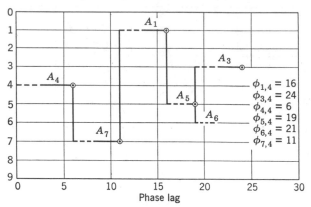

FIG. 13. Setback chart in assembly A_4.

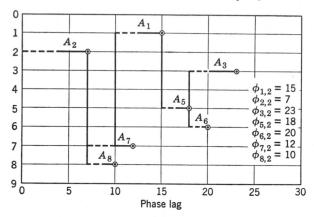

FIG. 14. Setback chart in assembly A_2.

go (directly or indirectly) into A_9, and therefore

$$X_{i,9}(t) = Y_i(t) \qquad (60)$$

With this notation then, equation (50) becomes

$$X_{5,9}(t) = T_{5,9} \, S_9(t + \phi_{5,9}) \qquad (61)$$

where $\phi_{5,9}$ is the same setback as ψ_5. Now we need to develop equations to meet the requirements for each of the shippable assemblies A_k.

In order to do this, we need setbacks "in" each of the shippable assemblies. These are shown graphically in Figs. 13 and 14 and numerically in Table 2. Therefore, the start schedule for those A_i's which eventually end up in a shippable A_k is given by

$$X_{i,k}(t) = T_{i,k} S_k(t + \phi_{i,k}) \tag{62}$$

Completion schedule for the same assembly is given by

$$\bar{X}_{i,k}(t) = T_{i,k} S_k(t + \phi_{i,k} - \alpha_i) \tag{63}$$

TABLE 2. Setback Matrix [ϕ]

	1	2	3	4	5	6	7	8	9
1	5	15	0	16	0	0	10	8	16
2	0	7	0	0	0	0	0	0	0
3	13	23	0	24	8	0	18	16	24
4	0	0	0	6	0	0	0	0	0
5	8	18	0	19	3	0	13	11	19
6	10	20	0	21	5	0	15	13	21
7	0	12	0	11	0	0	5	0	0
8	0	10	0	0	0	0	0	3	11
9	0	0	0	0	0	0	0	0	8

and availability schedule is given by

$$\bar{\bar{X}}_{i,k}(t) = T_{i,k} S_k(t + \phi_{i,k} - \gamma_i) \tag{64}$$

The consumption schedule is somewhat more complicated and is given by

$$X_{i,k}(t) = \sum_j \hat{X}^j_{i,k}(t) \qquad i \neq k \tag{65}$$

where

$$\hat{X}^j_{i,k} = N_{i,j} T_{j,k} S_k(t + \phi_{i,k}) \qquad i \neq k \tag{66}$$

In order to get the combined schedules for each of these articles and assemblies, we have to add the various schedules for A_i. Therefore,

$X_i(t)$, the start schedule for assembly A_i, is given by

$$X_i(t) = \sum_k T_{i,k} S_k(t + \phi_{i,k}) \tag{67}$$

Completion schedule is given by

$$\bar{X}_i(t) = \sum_k T_{i,k} S_k(t + \phi_{i,k} - \alpha_i) \tag{68}$$

and the availability schedule is given by

$$\tilde{X}_i(t) = \sum_k T_{i,k} S_k(t + \phi_{i,k} - \gamma_i) \tag{69}$$

The consumption schedule is somewhat more complicated and is given by

$$\hat{X}_i(t) = \sum_k \sum_j N_{i,j} T_{j,k} S_k(t + \phi_{i,k}) \tag{70}$$

Before leaving this topic, we wish to put our result in a somewhat different form. So far, it has been assumed that assemblies are scheduled for every day. However, it might be more useful to schedule for each production period (for each week or each month). Let us say that t (which previously noted manufacturing day) now denotes the production period under consideration. For instance, $t = 1$ is the first production period, $t = 2$ is the second production period, etc. We wish now to develop schedules for these production periods. Let us denote by $x_i{}^m$ the quantity of A_i to be made in the mth production period. We can write, with the aid of our previous notation,

$$x_i{}^m = X_i(m + 1) - X_i(m) \tag{71}$$

We denote by $s_i{}^m$ the number of A_i's that are to be shipped in the mth production period. Then

$$s_i{}^m = S_i(m + 1) - S_i(m) \tag{72}$$

With the aid of equation (67) (by taking differences) we find that

$$x_i{}^m = \sum_k T_{i,k} s_k^{m+\phi_{i,k}} \tag{73}$$

We see, then, that here we have a direct relationship between the quantity to be shipped and the quantity to be manufactured.

As an illustration, let us consider our example. We interpret t as the sequence number of the production periods and determine, say, the number of A_5's that must be made in the eleventh production period:

$$x_5{}^{11} = T_{5,1} s_1{}^{19} + T_{5,2} s_2{}^{29} + T_{5,4} s_4{}^{30} + T_{5,5} s_5{}^{14}$$
$$+ T_{5,7} s_7{}^{24} + T_{5,8} s_8{}^{22} + T_{5,9} s_9{}^{30} \tag{74}$$

Let us interpret the right-hand side of equation (74). The first term represents the A_1's which will be shipped in the nineteenth production period. As A_5's must be made eight production periods earlier than A_1's, we need to make A_5's in the eleventh production period. Each

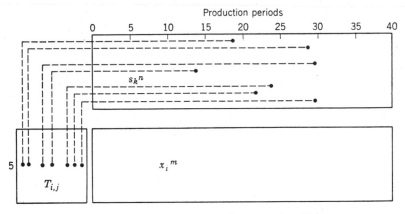

FIG. 15. Schematic representation of scheduling equation (74):

$$x_5{}^{11} = T_{5,1}s_1{}^{19} + T_{5,2}s_2{}^{29} + T_{5,4}s_4{}^{30} + T_{5,5}s_5{}^{14} + T_{5,7}s_7{}^{24} + T_{5,8}s_8{}^{22} + T_{5,9}s_9{}^{30}$$

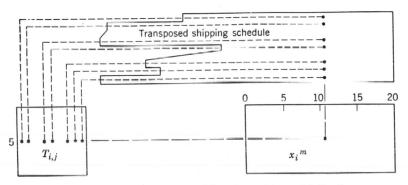

FIG. 16. Scheduling as a problem in matrix multiplication.

A_1 requires $T_{5,1}$ of A_5, and therefore $T_{5,1}S_1{}^{19}$ represents the number of A_5's required for A_1's to be shipped in the nineteenth production period. A schematic representation of equation (74) is shown in Fig. 15. We see that articles A_i are made in production period m with the intention of putting these articles into shippable assemblies at some later date. This is not matrix multiplication, as we do not combine a row of the T matrix with a column of the S matrix. The computation is more complicated: we combine a row of the T matrix with numbers in the S matrix, as shown by dots in Fig. 15. These dots, however, do not form a column. This computation can be expressed as matrix multiplication by transposing the shipping schedule. When we move each row of the shipping matrix as shown in Fig. 16, the dots in the shipping matrix form a column and equation (73) becomes matrix multiplication. For each article, A_i, however, the shipping matrix must be transposed as specified by the proper set-back chart. We have discussed this schematic representation of our scheduling equations in order to clarify the nature of the equations involved. The actual computations must be carried out as specified by equation (73).

In this section, we have developed a technique of scheduling assemblies and detail parts even when there are many shippable assemblies. Now we will extend this scheduling system to include the problem of scheduling in job-shop-type manufacturing.

3. SCHEDULING FROM THE POINT OF VIEW OF DECISION THEORY

In this chapter we have developed mathematical models to deal with the problem of scheduling assembly lines. Previously, we had discussed the problem of scheduling machine-shop-type production and saw that there is no precise mathematical solution to this type of problem. However, we developed certain guides for estimating the work load and certain techniques for scheduling in machine shops. Now, we propose to show that our method of assembly flow scheduling can be extended to include scheduling in machine-shop-type production, provided we do not insist on an exact solution to the problem.

In order to develop these further guides to machine-shop-type production, we propose to look at the scheduling problem from a different point of view.* Suppose we inspect the machines in a shop and observe which of the machines are productive and which are idle. We observe, for instance (Fig. 17), that machine 1 is productive, and that, in fact, three other lots (represented by circles) are waiting to get on machine 1. Machine 2 is in production; and there are four lots waiting for the machine. Machine 3 is either productive or not, but the diagram shows that there are no lots waiting for this machine. Machine 4 is productive, and there are two lots waiting to get on this machine. When a machine completes a lot, the foreman may be confronted with the problem of what to schedule next. If there are no parts to be worked on, there is no decision to make; if there is only one lot to be

* See A. Vazsonyi, "Operations Research in Production Control," *Journal of the Operations Research Society of America,* Vol. 4, No. 1, 1956.

worked on, then this is the lot that the foreman puts on the machine. However, if there are several lots to be worked on, then a decision has to be made as to which of these lots should be worked on first. This scheduling problem is a problem in decision making. What we need is a method whereby the foreman can make the right decision. In order to understand the problem better, let us discuss some possible decision rules.

One possible decision rule might be to assign a priority to each part and take the lot with the highest priority. This is a well-defined rule, but the difficulty with it is that parts with low priority have a tendency to be put off, and that some parts with low priorities might be permanently delayed. As every part is required in the manufacturing process, this means that the whole manufacturing process might come

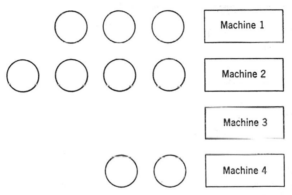

FIG. 17.   Shop loading as a problem in waiting lines.

to a standstill. This is the reason that a simple priority system is often unsatisfactory.

Another possible decision rule is to work on the lot that arrives at the machine first. This system makes it certain that no part is delayed indefinitely. However, if a part slows down in the manufacturing process, and is not given higher priority, it can stay in the shop for a very long time.

Finally, it is possible to class as a decision rule the use of a chance variable for scheduling. That is, we can imagine the chance variable as resulting from the use of a roulette wheel. Each time the foreman is to take on a lot, he runs the roulette wheel, which specifies which part to take on. Such a system would tend to equalize the in-process time for different parts.

Each of these decision rules has an important weakness. Usually, manufacturers must meet some shipping schedule, and none of these decision rules is based on this fact.   What we need is a decision rule that depends on the shipping schedule.   Let us consider a manufacturing firm that manufactures parts as shown by the Gozinto graph in Fig. 18.   The larger rectangles in the diagram represent assemblies,

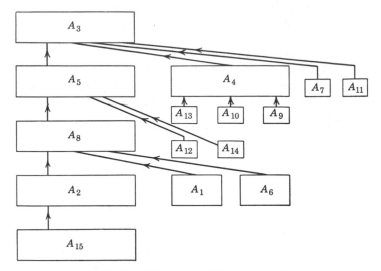

FIG. 18.   Hypothetical Gozinto graph.

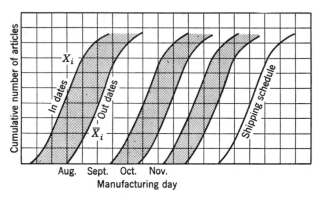

FIG. 19.   The concept of manufacturing bands.

and the smaller blocks represent detail parts.   Let us assume that schedules are established for each of these assemblies (or parts), forming a set of manufacturing bands as shown in Fig. 19.   As long as an assembly (or part) is made on a continuous assembly line, these manufacturing bands represent the start and completion schedules, and we have a scheduling system similar to the one described previously for assembly flow scheduling.   However, what do we do when parts are manufactured in lots?

Suppose that each week we manufacture a lot of a certain part, and that we specify that each of these lots be made within the manu-

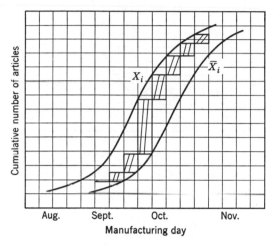

FIG. 20.   Weekly release of production lots.

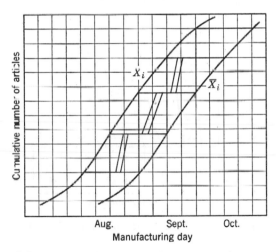

FIG. 21.   Biweekly release of production lots.

facturing band as shown in Fig. 20.   More precisely, we specify that each lot is to be started and completed so that the rectangle formed by the start and completion dates lies entirely within the manufacturing band.   For biweekly producton we will have a diagram like Fig. 21,

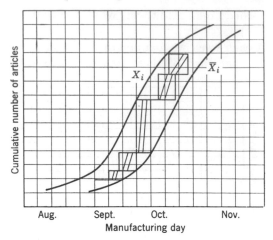

FIG. 22.   Variable release of production lots.

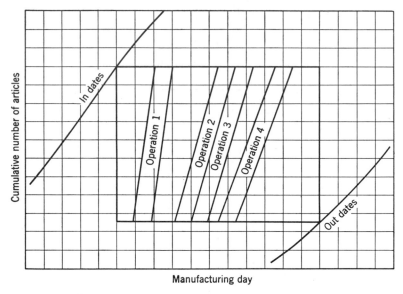

FIG. 23.   Actual production showing each operation.

and for a variable production cycle we have a diagram like Fig. 22.
A more precise interpretation of the concept of the manufacturing
band is given in Fig. 23.   A production part might go through many
machines and there might be many operations on each of these
machines.   The production part in Fig. 23 goes through four operations, and start and completion dates are given for each of these opera-

tions. The important thing is that all the starting dates and all the completion dates are within the manufacturing band.

Now we turn to the question of how to determine the manufacturing bands. Let us construct a setback chart (Fig. 24) in accordance with the Gozinto graph (Fig. 18) by allowing a fixed make span and cushion for each assembly (or part). As long as we deal with assemblies we have nothing new here. However, if we deal with parts that are made in lots, then we must decide what the make span should be.

The first thing to do is to make a manufacturing analysis of the part and to determine how much setup and run time is required for each

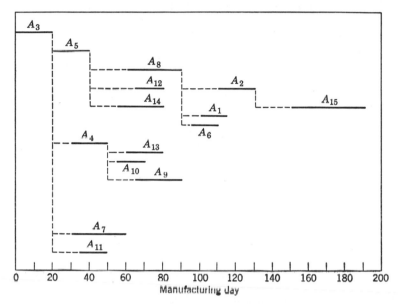

FIG. 24. Hypothetical setback chart.

individual lot. This does not give the make span, as we know that lots may be idle on the floor waiting to be worked on, and therefore that the total make span depends also on how much time a lot has to wait, as well as on setup and run time. If we had a complete solution to the scheduling problem in job-shop-type production, this idle time could be calculated. However, then we would not need to schedule with the aid of manufacturing bands. What we need is an approximate method to determine the width of the manufacturing bands.

One such method is to make an analysis of the operations in the shop and to establish a statistical rule which gives the make span of each part. It is often true that these parts can be classified so that the make

span of each group of parts follows a simple statistical rule.   For
instance, Fig. 25 shows a scatter diagram of make span versus number of operations to be performed on each part.   Let us denote by ω
the number of operations to be performed and by α the make span.
With the aid of a straight-line approximation, we get

$$\alpha = A\omega + C \tag{75}$$

where A is the slope of the straight line in Fig. 25, and C is the distance where the line intersects the vertical axis.   We note that we are
dealing with production parts whose make span is approximately independent of the labor hours required to make each part.

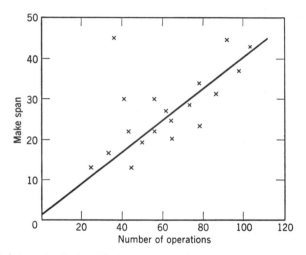

FIG. 25. Statistical relationship between number of operations and make span.

Under more general conditions we might be confronted with a situation where the make span does depend on the labor hours required.
Let us denote by τ the hours required to make a particular part.   Let
us assume that the make span, α, is a linear function of the number of
operations, ω, and the labor hours required, τ.   Then equation (75) is
to be replaced by

$$\alpha = A\omega + \beta\tau + C \tag{76}$$

This new equation is more general than equation (75) and has a wider
applicability.

We want to point out, though, that this method of correlating the
make span with the number of operations and the labor hours holds
only under special conditions.   In general, a detailed study must be
made to determine the make span for each part.   Let us assume now

that such a study has been made and that the make span is known, and ask how the foreman is to make his decision as to when to process a particular lot. So far, we have talked only in general terms about manufacturing bands as shown in Figs. 21, 22, and 23, but we have not specified in detail how the foreman is to use them. Under some conditions it might be adequate to suggest to the foreman that he stay within the bands and delegate the authority to him to accomplish this. However, we want to go one step further and set up detailed rules to guide the foreman.

Specifically, let us consider a foreman who is confronted with the problem of deciding which of seven lots he should work on. According to the first column of Table 3, the first lot involves 50 operations, the second lot 60 operations, and so on. The second column of Table 3 shows the make span for each of these lots; for instance, the fourth lot has a make span of 45 days. With the aid of the manufacturing bands that have been computed in advance, the foreman notices that, the fourth lot has an in date of 246 and an out date of 291. The left-hand side of the manufacturing band is formed by in dates, and the right-hand side by out dates. (These make spans were computed with the aid of equation (75), where the values of $A = 2$, and $C = 5$ were used.) Let us inspect the information on the first and second lot closely. Which of these lots should he process first? The foreman observes that 20 operations are completed on the first lot, and that the twenty-first operation is to be performed next. On which manufacturing day should those 20 operations have been completed? The in date for the first lot is 195, and we allow 2 days $(A = 2)$ for each operation, that is, 40 days for the first 20 operations. We also allow $C = 5$, that is, we allow 5 days for handling. If we denote by t^* the manufacturing day on which the first N operations should have been completed, we get

$$t^* = T + (2N + 5) \qquad (77)$$

where T is the in date. From this equation we deduce that on manufacturing day 240 the 20 operations should have been completed. The foreman observes that the current manufacturing day t is 250; this shows that this lot is 10 days late. Let us compare the urgency of the first lot with that of the second lot by carrying out a similar computation for the second lot. We observe that the second lot is 10 days late. However, the first lot is 10 days late out of a total make span of 105 days, whereas the second lot is 10 days late out of a total make span of 125 days. We conclude that the first lot is more delinquent than the second one and decide to give priority to the first lot. We can

TABLE 3. Machine Shop Scheduling with the Aid of a Decision Function
(t = 250)

	Number of Operations ω	Make Span α	In Date T	Out Date $\overline{T}$	Operations Completed N	t^*	Lateness $t = t^*$	Decision Parameter λ	Decision Function δ
1	50	105	195	300	20	240	10	0.095	0.095
2	60	125	185	310	25	240	10	0.080	0.080
3	100	205	210	415	10	235	15	0.066	0.066
4	20	45	246	291	7	265	−15	−0.79	−0.79
5	25	55	277	332	19	320	−70	−1.27	−1.00
6	10	25	195	220	5	210	40	1.6	1.6
7	15	35	321	356	2	330	−80	−2.3	−1.00

put this reasoning into a mathematical form by stating that we compute the ratio

$$\lambda = \frac{t - t^*}{\bar{T} - T} \tag{78}$$

where t is the current date, t^* is the date where the lot "should be," T is the in date, and $\bar{T}$ is the out date. (We get for the first lot $\lambda_1 = 0.095$, and for the second lot $\lambda_2 = 0.080$.) Here λ is a decision parameter, and the foreman is to take the lot for which the decision parameter takes the largest value. This applies not only to the first and second lot but to all seven lots. Table 3, column t^*, shows the manufacturing day where the particular lot should be; the next column shows the lateness of each lot. Under column λ we have the decision parameter computed; it can be seen that the sixth lot has the largest decision parameter, and therefore that this is the lot the foreman should take first. It is apparent that this sixth lot should have been started on day 195. The make span for it is 25 days. Out of 10 operations, 5 have been completed, and it follows from equation (77) that $t^* = 210$. This means that the sixth lot is 40 days late. Consequently, the value of the decision parameter λ is 1.6.

We visualize our scheduling system as follows. Every time a lot is completed on a machine, the foreman surveys the lots that are waiting, computes the decision parameter for each lot, and selects the lot with the largest decision parameter.

We recognize that we have a scheduling system here that removes decision making from the foreman. Under the former system the foreman had too many decisions to make; now he might not have enough opportunity to exercise his judgment. One way to get around this difficulty is to introduce a decision function as shown in Fig. 26. For each value of the parameter λ, there is a value of δ

$$\delta = f(\lambda) \tag{79}$$

Here, we schedule not with λ but with δ, and the foreman is to select the lot for which the parameter δ takes the largest value. The decision function shown in Fig. 26 can be described mathematically by saying that

$$\delta = -1 \quad \text{for} \quad \lambda \leq -1 \tag{80}$$

and

$$\delta = \lambda \quad \text{for} \quad \lambda > -1 \tag{81}$$

In the last column of Table 3 we list these values of the decision parameter δ. We note again that the sixth lot is to be made first because the decision function δ has the largest value here. However, we note that there is a tie between the fifth and seventh lots as δ has the value -1 for each; these lots are ahead of schedule. The foreman must make the decision as to which of these parts should be processed first.

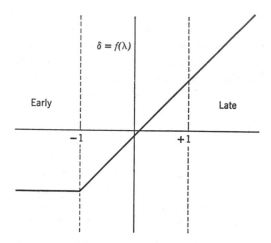

FIG. 26.   Decision function for production control.

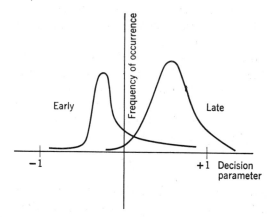

FIG. 27.   Statistical distribution of the decision parameter.

In summary, then, with this decision function the foreman has no choice on late parts but he does have a choice of early parts. The decision function could be of a different shape, depending on the nature of the problem, or of a different type. The important point is that, with the aid of decision functions, preciseness and flexibility can be introduced in the scheduling system.

A further use of these decision functions is shown in Fig. 27.   Suppose we inspect the shop, compute the decision function for each of the lots waiting to be worked upon, and prepare a frequency diagram as shown in Fig. 27.   If most of the decision functions have a positive value and the distribution function looks like the one shown on the right-hand side of Fig. 27, then most of the parts are late and the shop as a whole is late.   On the other hand, if we get a curve, as shown on the left-hand side, then the shop as a whole is ahead of schedule.   If the decision parameters do not vary much, we get a narrow distribution curve as the one shown in Fig. 28.   This indicates that the parts

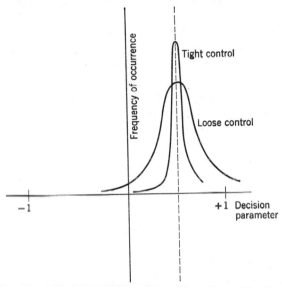

FIG. 28.   Statistical distribution of the decision parameter.

are late but that they are tightly controlled (they are behind schedule by the same amount).   On the other hand, if the curve is wide, as shown in Fig. 28, the shop is late but the parts are controlled loosely. The statistical distribution of the decision function gives important information on the operation of the shop.

The use of decision functions in scheduling is new, and we suggest this approach only as a possibility.   In order to put such a scheme in use, it will be necessary to study various decision functions and determine which of them is more suitable for the particular manufacturing operation.   It will probably be difficult to answer the problem of how to select the best decision function.   We can only suggest here that, a few decision functions should be assumed and a retrospective analysis made in order to determine which of the decision functions would be more desirable. (Another approach would be to use the Monte Carlo method.) We mention again here that, in order to select an optimum decision function, measures of effectiveness must be developed first, and this (as we have seen before), is difficult. Dollar values must be assigned to such factors as the ability of meeting schedules, the efficient use of available machines, and the ability of keeping a low inprocess inventory.

4. SCHEDULING LABOR, INVENTORIES, COSTS, AND RECEIPTS

In Section 2 of this chapter, we developed mathematical models for scheduling production on assembly lines. In the last section, this scheduling system was extended, with the aid of the concept of manufacturing bands, to parts that are manufactured in lots. Now we can use our method of assembly line scheduling to handle both assembly line and job-shop-type production. In particular we can say that our scheduling system as expressed by equations (67) to (70) is applicable in both cases. Consequently, we can proceed to develop the associated labor requirements, inventories, and costs. We begin by extending equation (2) of Chapter 12 to man-power requirements. Let us denote by $H_n(t)$ the cumulative labor requirements of day t in labor class n. Then

$$H_n(t) = \sum_i \tau_{n,i} X_i(t) \tag{82}$$

where $\tau_{n,i}$ is the hours required of labor class n to make a single article A_i. Here it is assumed that all labor is expended at the start schedule. If the manufacturing band is too wide, then it is better to assume that the labor is expended halfway between start and completion schedules. Then we can write

$$H_n(t) = \frac{1}{2} \sum_i \tau_{n,i} \frac{X_i(t) + \bar{X}_i(t)}{2} \tag{83}$$

(If more labor is expended in the first half of the manufacturing band than in the second half, it is better to introduce another type of weighting between the start and completion schedules.) If we wish to relate the labor requirements to the shipping schedules we can combine equations (82) and (67) and get

$$H_n(t) = \sum_i \sum_k T_{i,k} \tau_{n,i} S_k(t + \phi_{i,k}) \tag{84}$$

This last equation relates man-power requirements directly to the shipping schedules.

The computations involved in equation (84) are somewhat complicated, and from the practical point of view it is convenient to use this equation in a slightly different form. Therefore we write

$$H_n(t) = \sum_k \sum_\phi L_{k,n}(\phi)\, S_k(t + \phi) \tag{85}$$

where

$$L_{k,n}(\phi) = \Sigma T_{i,k} \tau_{n,i} \tag{86}$$

for those i's for which $\phi_{i,k} = \phi$. We can interpret $L_{k,n}(\phi)$ as the work load imposed on labor class n by the manufacture of a single shippable assembly A_k and its associated subassemblies and detail parts.

TABLE 4. Labor Loading Function $L(\phi)$

ϕ	A_3	A_5	A_4	A_8	A_{15}	Misc.	$L_3(\phi)$
0							0
10	25					5	30
20	25					5	30
30		50				5	55
40		50	10			5	65
50			10			5	15
60						5	5
70				0		5	5
80						5	5
90						5	5
110					40	5	45
120					40	5	45
130					40	5	45
140						5	5
150							

Total 360

In order to illustrate this computational technique, let us compute man-power requirements for the manufacture of the articles shown in the Gozinto diagram, Fig. 18. (The setback system is shown in Fig. 24.) We assume for the time being that we are scheduling the single assembly A_3 and compute only total man-power requirements. Table 4 shows the labor loading function $L(\phi)$, which specifies the labor required in each production period for each article. For instance,

A_4 requires 20 hours, and these hours are expended in equal proportions at manufacturing day 40 and 50. Table 4 also shows that 65 hours of labor are expended evenly during the entire manufacturing process. The labor loading function $L(\phi)$ is shown graphically in Fig. 29. Let us denote by $S(t)$ the delivery schedule of assembly A_3. How do we get the cumulative man-power requirement? We have to take the labor loading function $L(\phi)$ as shown in Fig. 29, shift it in time,

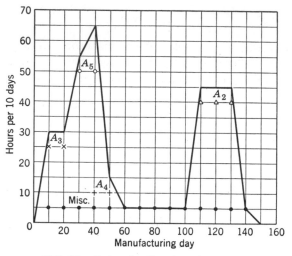

FIG. 29. Labor loading function $L(\phi)$.

and multiply it by the number of assemblies A_3 to be shipped. In a mathematical form, the cumulative manpower requirement is given by

$$H(t) = \sum_{\phi} L(\phi)\, S(t + \phi) \tag{87}$$

Here we have a method of computing manpower requirements associated with a shipping schedule. Let us now compute the labor costs. Let c_n denote the cost of a unit of labor in class n; the cumulative labor cost is given by

$$C_n(t) = \sum_{n} c_n\, H_n(t) \tag{88}$$

Now let us compute material costs. Suppose article A_i is purchased at a cost of $C_i{}^*$. If $X_i(t)$ denotes the purchasing schedule of article A_i, and $C^*(t)$ denotes the cumulative expenditure on this article, then

$$C^*(t) = \Sigma C_i{}^* X_i(t) \tag{89}$$

for those i's which represent purchased parts. Let p_k denote the sale price of article A_k. When we ship A_k, we do not immediately get paid, so we introduce ψ denoting the delay between shipping and payment. Cumulative receivables can be obtained then with the aid of the formula

$$R(t) = \sum_k p_k S_k(t - \psi) \tag{90}$$

With the aid of similar formulae, other important information can also be obtained. For instance, the value of the in-process inventory can be computed. We recognize here the important point that, on the basis of the manufacturing bands, we can compute labor requirements, material costs, and other variables as functions of the shipping schedules. The scheduling system we have developed here associates a unique labor and material schedule with a given shipping schedule. We want to note, finally, that notwithstanding the fact that these variables are uniquely determined, the detailed schedule (within the manufacturing bands) still depends on the decision function to be used. In a certain sense, then, our scheduling model stratifies decision making into two different levels. The basic manufacturing band system establishes overall schedules and specifies labor and material requirements, but it leaves the detailed scheduling open. The detailed schedules are obtained with the aid of decision functions and form a lower level of decision making. Our mathematical model, therefore, incorporates some of the very real aspects of the scheduling problem. First overall schedules are determined with the aid of the manufacturing bands; then day to day schedules are made by the foreman with the aid of predetermined decision functions.

The mathematical model described in this chapter represents the result of limited research work; these models have only been partially tested in actual situations. A great deal of research and empirical work will have to be done before such models can be widely accepted in actual manufacturing situations.

Author index

Ackoff, R. L., 16, 17
Alberts, W. E., 15
Arrow, K. J., 359

Bellman, R., 252
Blackwell, D., 375
Brigham, G., 10
Burrows, G. L., 58

Charnes, A., 72, 76, 132, 139, 145, 200
Churchman, C. W., 17
Cooper, W. W., 72, 76, 132, 139, 145
Crane, R., 14

Dantzig, G. B., 67, 99
Dorfman, R.,

Eddison, R. T., 11
Edie, L. C., 10

Feeney George, 356
Feller, W., 10
Ferguson, A. R., 67
Flood, M. M., 5

Girshick, M. A., 375
Goldberg, E. J., 13
Gozinto, Z., 429

Harris, T., 359
Henderson, A., 4, 132, 139, 145
Hohn, F. E., 87
Holt, C. C., 7, 364

Johnson, S. M., 410

Karush, W., 7

Lavin, M. M., 11
Lemke, C. E., 200
Levinson, H. C., 17
Levinson, N., 352

Magee, J. F., 16
Marschak, J., 359
Mellon, B., 72, 76
Modigliani, F., 7, 87, 364
Molina, E. C., 301

Olcott, E. S., 13

Schiller, D. H., 11
Schlaifer, R., 4
Simon, H. A., 7, 364
Stillson, P., 17
Symonds, G. H., 60, 89

Thornthwaite, C. W., 8
Turner, W. O., 8

Van Voorhis, W. R., 11
Vazsonyi, A., 7, 12, 15, 373, 418, 429,
452

Waugh, F. W., 58
Whitin, T. M., 334
Wiener, Norbert, 352

SUBJECT INDEX

Accounting, 11
Advertising, 15
Agriculture, 8
Air transportation, 5, 67, 161
Aircraft, 67
  carrier, 311, 315
Algorithm, 48
Allocation problems, 4, 5, 20, 53, 58, 61,
  67, 87, 203
Assembly lines, 376
Attrition, 87
Automatic exchange, 8

Ball bearings, 14
Blending, 6, 69, 72
  numbers, 69
British ports, 11
Budgeting, 12, 14
Business loss, 288, 304
Business systems, 19

Calendar, climatic, 8
Capacity limitations, 6, 76
Case Institute of Technology, 11
Catalogues, 16
Clerks required, 10
Commercial Solvents Corporation, 17
Competition, what to produce under, 89

Competitive action, 6
Competitive position, 16
Completion dates, 379
Correlation coefficients, 352
Cost, freight, 5
  inputed, 307
  of hiring, 245
  of ordering, 7
  of shortage, 7, 307, 314
  quadratic, 364
Crude oil, 76
Customer, dissatisfaction, 304
  good will, 16
  relations, 6
Cut and try method, 21, 57

Decision rule, 17, 453
Decision theory, 372, 452
Decisions in business, 3, 5, 9, 12, 45, 88
Defects in quality
Degeneracy, 26, 46, 132, 180
Demand, forecast of, 346
  frequency of, 289
  probability of, 289
Department stores, 6, 16, 287
Distillation, 69
Distribution functions (probability),
  normal, 294

471

Distribution functions (probability),
   Poisson, 300
   rectangular, 302
Dual theorem, 152, 181
   application to transporation, 154

Effort, distribution of, 202
Electronic computers, 12, 428
Employment, steady, 7, 8, 244, 362
Equations, homogeneous, 104
Equipment requirements, 8

Factories, 5, 20
Failures, theory of, 14
Farming enterprize, 8
   allocation of resources in, 6, 58
Flux stock, 70
Forecasting, 12, 346
Frame of reference, 19
Frequency, cumulative, 292
Function, convex, 198
   expressing loss, 309
   expressing profit, 309
   indicator, 290
   inverse, 380
   mathematical concept of, 84
   of completion dates, 380
   of starting dates, 380
   payoff, 93
   quasilinear, 321

Game, geometrical representation, 264,
   273
   two-person zero-sum, 255
Games, rectangular, 279
   theory of, 6, 89
General Electric Co., 16
Gozinto graph, 429
   theorem, 439
Gravity, center of, 172

Heinz, J. H., Co., 4

Idle time, 12
Inequalities, 48
   geometrical representation of, 50, 183
Inventory, in-process, 409
   ordering functions, 345
   ordering rules, 328, 360

Inventory control, 6, 7
   many stages, 328
   rules, 315, 320, 362
   single stage, 320
   system, cyclic, 338
      for large number of parts, 360
      non-S-s type, 358
      S-s type, 326, 356
      two-bin, 330

Labor loading, 465
Lead-time, 7
Learning curves, 384, 390
Linear restrictions, 92
Lot size, economic, 7, 243

Machine shop, 53, 61, 410, 415
Machines, automatic, 10, 61, 87
   breakdowns, 10
   maintenance, 12
   routings in production, 53, 61, 415
Mail order house, 16
Maintenance, 13
Make span, 383, 385, 458
Manpower requirements, 386
Manufacturing band, 383, 454
Manufacturing firm, 20, 65
   management of, 5, 6
Market, conditions, 76, 89
   limitations, 56
   potential, 6
   requirements, 65
Marketing areas, 210
Mathematical argument, 144
Mathematical model, 17
   of assembly line flow production, 345,
      403, 429
   of job shop type production, 418
Matrix, multiplication, 438
   next assembly quantity, 430
   payoff, 256
   setback, 449
   total requirement factor, 431
   triangular, 437
   unit, 435
Mean-value, 293
Measure, 17, 373
Minimax theorem, 266, 283
Model, conceptual, 19
   mathematical, 17

Modification principle, 111
Moment distribution functions, 293, 306
Monte Carlo method, 14, 347, 373
Morra (game), 255
Multistage problems, 252, 328

Naval problem, 315
Night shift operation, 80, 245
Nonlinear restriction, 93
Nut-mix problem, 132
Nutrition problem, 99, 146, 171, 181

Octane number, 6
Oil corporation, study of, 76, 205, 209
Oil industry, scientific programming in, 3, 6
Oil tankers, 5
Operations Research Society of America, 11
Ordering quantity, 7
Overhead, 13
Overtime, 44, 56, 104

Packaging, 17
Partitioning, 197
Parts listing, 429
Planning, financial, 12
Polyhedron, 177
Port of New York Authority, 9, 13
Position-serial numbers, 399
Predictors in inventory control, 345
Price imputations, 146
Probability, cumulative, 292
Production, and inventory control, 6, 79, 213, 238, 313
   bottlenecks, 53
   facilities, allocation of 5, 53, 61, 87
      attrition of, 87, 250
   job shop type, 410
   management, 3
   of assemblies, 377, 395, 439
   on alternate machines, 61
   operations, 410, 458
   plan, 87, 244
   rate, 383
   release, 455
   schedule, 82
   stabilization, 362, 368
   statistical sampling in, 11

Programming, convex, 200
   dynamic, 87, 252
   linear definition of, 95
      fundamental theorem of 101
      geometry of 171
   scientific, 3
Promoting retailers, 16
Promotional campaigns, 16
Protection against loss, 304
Protective stock level, 7, 308
Purchasing, 6, 7, 287

Quality control, 17
Queuing theory, 9

Railroads, 13
Ratio estimates, 11, 12
Raw materials, allocation of, 65, 132
Rayco Manufacturing Co., 13
Recycling, 6
Refineries, programming in, 6, 69, 89
Refining process, 76
Regression analysis, 12, 13, 458
Reid vapor pressure, 6
Reorder point, 326
Reorder quantity, 326
Repairman, 10
Replacements, theory of, 14
Resources, 4
Restrictions, linear, 92
Routings in production, 53, 61

Saddle point, 269
Sales, calls, 16
   due to advertising, 15
   effort, distribution of, 219
   evening, 17
   loss of, 304
   potential
Sampling, 11
Scheduling, 8
   assemblies, 379, 395, 439
   functions, 376
   in a machine shop, 410
   inventories, 464
   operators, 9
   with decision function, 459
Scientific programming, 4
Seasonal variations, 7, 8, 367
Sensitivity analysis, 38, 208

Service, quality of, 9, 10
Setback chart, 457
Settlements, interline, 11
Setup time in production, 7, 12, 56
Shipping, 20, 287, 439
Shop loading, 418
    cost of, 7, 307, 314
Shortage, frequency of, 292
    probability of, 7, 288, 291, 301, 307,
        315, 354
Shutdown, 45
Simplex method, 99, 125
    geometry of, 193
Simplex transformation, 113
Simulation, 14
    retrospective, 347
Single-stage problems, 320
Slack variable, 92, 122
Smoothing production, 368
Solution, alternative optimum, 35
    basic, 36, 38, 102
    family of, 106, 120
    modification of
    optimum, 35
    space, 181
Space, gravity, 188
    requirements, 311, 315
    solution, 181
Standard deviation, 295, 299
    for Poisson distribution 302
Start dates, 379
Statistics, 11, 287
Strategy, concept of, 255
    dominant, 270
    optimum, 281
    pure, 265, 268

Subsidy, 20
Supermarket, 287

Telephones, requirement for, 8
Tetrahedron, 177
Time-reduction curves, 392
Tolerances, 15
Toll booths, 9
Traffic managment, 3, 13
Transportation, allocation, 4, 20
        general method, 29
        mathematical formulation, 47
        two factories and two warehouses,
            22
        two factories and three warehouses,
            26
    and production, combined problem,
        41, 194
    facilities, allocation of, 67
    problem, generalized, 64, 67, 69, 161
        method of solution, 20

Uncertainty in business, 287
United Airlines, 11, 15

Value, imputed, 149
    theory of, 17
Visbreaking, 70
Vitamins, 99, 146, 171, 181

Waiting lines, theory of, 9, 453
Waiting time, 9
Warehouses, location of, 4
Warehousing problem 20, 227, 287
Work stations, 376